DEDICATION

To the Honorable Joseph P. Kennedy and the Kennedy Family, who, through dedicated efforts and wise and generous use of Kennedy Foundation funds, have within the recent past awakened interest, stimulated research, and performed a service of great magnitude to a group heretofore too often forgotten—the mentally retarded.

About the book . . .

"A treasury of information on all aspects of psychiatry, which is readily understandable to the general reader, this new book is modestly called by Dr. Braceland 'A handbook for believers.' It is more than a handbook—it is a thoughtful and balanced study of the vast and complicated world of the human mind and the myriad efforts by psychiatrists to resolve its dilemmas."   *The Hartford Times*

"The chief merit of this book is that it offers a clear exposition of psychoanalytic psychiatry by an eminent Catholic psychiatrist and an informed Dominican priest. It aptly demonstrates that a harmonious synthesis between religious belief and psychiatric practice is not only possible but a reality."   *America*

"There has long been a widely felt need for a book which presents the findings of modern psychiatry in non-technical language, well within the ken of the intelligent layman. This need is admirably met by the present volume in which a psychiatrist and a priest collaborate and show the benefits of closer cooperation between clergy and doctors in the treatment and prevention of mental illness."

Rev. John A. O'Brien, Ph.D.

"In *Modern Psychiatry,* Dr. Braceland and the Rev. Stock have undertaken a difficult and, in some instances, an almost impossible task. They have done well."   *Pastoral Psychology*

"*Modern Psychiatry* offers a history of psychiatry, scholarly in content and popular in form, together with an assessment of the resources it puts at the disposal of the Catholic, without any compromise of his faith. Both dispassionate and incisive, this extremely valuable book has practical, everyday importance."   Msgr. John S. Kennedy
Catholic Transcript

"In reading the balanced and realistic account presented by one of the most distinguished psychiatrists in this country and a psychologically trained priest, one is tempted to feel that the dialogue between religion and psychiatry has come to maturity."   *Theological Studies*

About the authors . . .

Dr. Francis J. Braceland is one of the most distinguished psychiatrists in the United States. He was Psychiatrist-in-Chief at the Institute of Living in Hartford, Connecticut, from 1951 to 1965 and is now Senior Consultant there. He has been a Lecturer on Psychiatry at Harvard University and a Clinical Professor of Psychiatry at Yale University. Dr. Braceland has held many distinguished offices in the field, among them: President of the American Psychiatric Association, President of the Association for Research in Nervous and Mental Disease, Chairman of the American Medical Association Section Nervous and Mental Diseases and President of the American Board of Psychiatry and Neurology. Dr. Braceland was also head of the Section of Psychiatry at the Mayo Clinic, has taught in the Graduate School of the University of Minnesota, and was Dean of Loyola University School of Medicine. Between 1942–44 he served as Special Assistant to the Surgeon General, U. S. Navy, and was Chief of Psychiatry, Navy Department, Bureau of Medicine and Surgery, Washington, D.C. from 1944–46. Dr. Braceland's articles have appeared in over two hundred journals and he is the editor of FAITH, REASON AND MODERN PSYCHIATRY.

Father Michael Stock, O.P. is President of St. Stephen's College, Dover, Massachusetts. He is also Professor of Psychology at the Dominican House of Studies in Dover. Fr. Stock has written for various professional journals, and has supplied articles on psychological topics for the NEW CATHOLIC ENCYCLOPEDIA.

Modern Psychiatry

A HANDBOOK FOR BELIEVERS

FRANCIS J. BRACELAND, *M.D., F.A.C.P.*

MICHAEL STOCK, *O.P., Ph.D.*

IMAGE BOOKS
A DIVISION OF DOUBLEDAY & COMPANY, INC.
GARDEN CITY, NEW YORK

IMAGE BOOKS EDITION 1966
BY SPECIAL ARRANGEMENT WITH DOUBLEDAY & CO., INC.
IMAGE BOOKS EDITION PUBLISHED FEBRUARY, 1966

ACKNOWLEDGMENTS

The sincere thanks of the authors are due to several kind and patient friends, notably to Dr. Rudolf Allers for his advice and direction in the historical aspects of this work; to Miss Mary Ellen Evans, who did her best to get the project under way several years ago; to Mrs. Mary B. Jackson and Mrs. Helen Lansberg, who took infinite pains in checking and assembling data; and to Miss Frances Nagl, who typed and retyped and retyped again.

We are indebted also to the Joseph P. Kennedy Foundation for their generous help and to Mr. John Delaney, whose idea it was to have this task done and who kept up the authors' oft flagging spirits. Finally, the senior author offers this work as an olive branch to his wife, Hope, and his children, John Michael and Mary Faith Braceland, who knew all too well that the writing of the book did nothing toward improving his disposition.

F.J.B.
M.S.

CONTENTS

INTRODUCTION

Pascal, with the insight for which he is famous, once noted that the last thing one discovers in writing a book is what to put at its beginning; so, in order to pretend that this is not true in this instance, we shall hasten to give reasons for adding an additional volume to the rapidly growing store of psychiatric literature.

This book is concerned with the beliefs and practices and the past, present, and future of modern dynamic clinical psychiatry. It is written for physicians, clergymen, seminarians, students, and educated laymen; in fact, for anyone interested in the numerous facets of this rapidly moving medical specialty or the distressed individuals who constitute its particular mission. It is felt that there is a need for a book of this sort, lying somewhere between the highly technical treatises of the medical profession and the anecdotal approach of the popular press, a book which will offer the interested non-psychiatrist a comprehensive and balanced picture of the work of psychiatry with the scientific jargon pruned away. With the problem of mental health assuming the proportions of a national issue, educated people will be looking for a straightforward account of the psychiatric enterprise—what it has done and what it plans to do, the problems it faces and the solutions it is testing. There is, besides, a rapidly growing group of workers in many fields whose areas of interest are such that an appreciative knowledge of psychiatry's contribution would be of definite value—counselors, social workers, personnel officers in industry, clergymen, and teachers. It is hoped that this book will present them with a clear and practical understanding of psychiatry at the layman's level.

The volume is especially directed toward allaying the fears of religious believers who still have doubts about this discipline or those who have been adversely influenced by the misinformation which is abroad concerning it. Psychiatry is still regarded with outright suspicion by some very fine people, and a number of others are still not sure that its practitioners are not preaching irreligious doctrines. Some people believe, erroneously, that if everyone lived "a good life" they would not become mentally ill, and yet others regard psychiatry as a form of occult practice.

Nowhere is it implied, however, that religious believers are the only ones who have exhibited a coolness toward psychiatry, for, in fact, it is known that hostility has been directed at this specialty throughout its history. Although the situation is much improved now, the discipline is still not beloved by some of the older practitioners of medicine. Their professional distrust of psychiatry is a holdover from medical school days and in part is a relic of the severely organic orientation of medical education in the first half of this century. It is a well-known fact now, however, that one cannot be sick physically without one's emotions being involved deeply in the illness. There is general agreement, too, that a number of symptoms, heretofore attributed to nebulous or hidden physical causes, actually have their roots in emotional problems. Emotions may act as noxious agents, as do physical poisons. They are accompanied by physiological changes and, if these persist or are repeated frequently enough, structural or organic changes may supervene in the tissues involved.

As one contemplates the material discussed in the chapter on psychosomatic medicine, it becomes obvious that disease is not a static affair; it is a process, and emotions play an important part in this process, even in those diseases caused by known agents. An individual cannot be separated from his emotions in health or in disease, and it is axiomatic that one does not become ill in a vacuum. Illness is modified and influenced by all of the internal and external factors in and about the person, and feelings loom large among these factors.

The book demonstrates that modern psychiatry has amassed a body of knowledge concerning the actions of individuals under stress, and that this knowledge can be used not only to salvage sick human beings who might otherwise be lost but also to help "normal" individuals who are in danger of becoming ill. Conditions which heretofore have been only names to the lay reader are described in this work in sufficient detail to make them understandable, and the most modern methods of treatment are evaluated.

Some of the reasons for the coolness and mutual suspicion between religion and psychiatry are examined in the first chapter; then a long-section view of the checkered history of mental illness is considered, though necessarily in truncated form.

Freud, whose work is completely misunderstood by some people, is discussed objectively in the third chapter and an effort is made to place this genius in proper perspective. Then, as we discuss some of the illnesses in question, we necessarily become a bit detailed for a few chapters, and this fact prevents the book from becoming mere "hammock reading."

Before prognosticating the future of psychiatry, as nearly as can be done from our present knowledge, the roles of the family doctor and the clergyman in handling the emotionally involved individuals who consult them are considered. The work of both professional groups in this endeavor is exceedingly important and, from all appearances, is destined to become even more so as problems mount in these unsettled times.

Unfortunately, the volume must remain incomplete. A number of omissions will be noted, but these were made necessary because consideration of all things would make the work unreasonably long and in fact change its character. This is anything but a psychiatric "do-it-yourself" manual. Its main interest is, as already outlined, to present psychiatry as it stands today in its major contours, and to give a perspective on it which will remove any lingering hesitancy toward it on the part of those who have thought that, in some way, it infringes upon or quarrels with their religious convictions.

Many ideas are to be found in this book which have been gleaned from diverse places and various authors. Where some of them came from, we know not now. If we do know, due credit is given, but the origin of others is lost, for we absorb things and soon the separation of "mine" from "thine" becomes impossible. Should someone recognize something that he originated, let him feel free to claim it; he is extended due apologies for our omission. We feel about it all, as Robert Burton does in his *Anatomy of Melancholy:* "I have laboriously collected this cento out of divers writers and that without injury. I have wronged no authors but given every man his own. I cite and quote mine authors. I have borrowed, not stolen; and what Varre speaks of bees—they are by no means malicious because they injure nothing they take honey from—I can say of myself: Whom have I injured?"

Finally, as this work goes forth for whatever fate awaits it, we paraphrase St. Thomas Aquinas in regard to the parts of it which are controversial: Truth alone will stand the test of time and, when it is manifested, errors will be quickly abandoned.

F.J.B.

M.S.

Hartford, Conn.
Dover, Mass.

(Note: Terms unfamiliar to lay readers should be found in glossary appended to last chapter.)

I

SURVEY AND CONFLICT

*Mental disease, an illness that stands in the catalogue of
human suffering with a sad preeminence of claim over
all the others upon our commiseration but which, in
truth, has received the smallest share of our assistance.*[1]
Eli Todd, 1824

Clinicians who have thought deeply about the subject have
long believed that, were the content of the minds of men
made known, there would at times be little difference between those who were sick and those who were well. There
would be the same hopes, the same wishes, the same fantasies, and the same extravagances; they would differ only in
time, in intensity, and in the behavior they call forth. The line
between mental health and mental illness would be found
not to be a sharp, impenetrable barrier, but rather a hazy
area, now distinct, and then again barely discernible. The
dreamer would appear the sick man, controlled and quies-
cent; the sick man, the dreamer, uncontrolled and in action.
In the minds of most people, however, the boundaries are
much more clearly delineated; people are either sick or well,
sane or insane, and each should be treated accordingly.

It is because of inflexible reasoning of this type, one distinguished psychiatrist tells us, that people approach panic
when they see some unreason in themselves. Yet, he added:
"If they only could get a better idea of how reason and unreason, controlled thinking and blind emotion, civilized and
savage notions are intertwined in everyone, they could live
more confidently and seek help more easily."[2]

[1] Todd, E. Report of the Superintendent, Hartford Retreat for
the Insane, 1824.
[2] Bond, E. D., *One Mind Common to All* (New York: The
Macmillan Co., 1958).

A great deal of effort has been expended in recent years in an attempt to explain the various degrees of emotional distress and psychiatry's role in alleviating it, but apparently much of the effort has been put forth in vain. Many people still declare themselves for or against psychiatry, as if it were standing in a docket to be judged. Even some educated people who should know better let it be known that they "have no time for psychiatrists," or that they "do not believe in psychiatry." The first reaction is understandable and acceptable, but the latter is not. One might as well not believe in thermometers because they sometimes register hotter or colder than one would like. This statement, in fact, is faintly reminiscent of a declaration once made by Margaret Fuller. This famous New England lady on one occasion let it be known publicly that finally she had decided to accept the Copernican theory, whereupon Carlyle, in London, reading about it, observed that she "jolly well better had accept it." Well, people jolly well better had accept psychiatry, too, for as a part of its function it cares for patients who occupy half of the hospital beds in the nation.

SURVEY OF PSYCHIATRY'S ROLE

Psychiatry, though it is a branch of medicine of fairly recent vintage, has as its important mission the care and treatment of individuals who suffer from one of the oldest and most distressing of man's afflictions—his "loss of reason." This mission has grown steadily in importance, as more and more illnesses have been recognized as having emotional components. Today its field of operations—the care of the emotionally distressed and the mentally ill—covers the area of one of the nation's greatest health problems.

Psychiatrists are physicians who have undertaken special training in the field of mental disorder, so that basically they are medical practitioners. By reason of their work and by knowledge of the way distressed human beings with mental diseases have been regarded and rejected down through the ages, they are not particularly bothered by prejudice, criticism, or misunderstanding of their field or their function. They do feel badly, however, that some distressed individuals, who might benefit from their ministrations, are warned away from them through prejudice or ignorance of their mission, because sometimes this shortsightedness results in tragedy.

Whatever the remote causes of the various mental diseases may be—and many of them are as yet unknown—one thing is certain: they are not respectful of persons, and no one is entirely immune to them. One has only to look at his own family history or the histories of the families of his friends and neighbors, and it is reasonably certain that the survey will turn up someone who is, or has been, emotionally distressed, no matter what form of circumlocution has been used to conceal it, or what quasi-"respectable" diagnosis has been placed upon it in order to save the family feelings.

Mental disease affects young and old, rich and poor, religious and irreligious alike. It is generally agreed by hospital psychiatrists that Catholics, Protestants, and Jews are afflicted in almost direct proportion to their numbers in the community.[3] All too often, when the illness is encountered, it is accompanied by overtones of unutterable tragedy, not because of the illness itself, for it is now known that much of it can be remedied, but rather because of the way it is looked upon by the population in general. Instead of being recognized for what it is—an illness—it is still thought of by some as a chastisement or as something shameful, and efforts are made to deny or conceal it, lest someone think ill of the family. This unwillingness to face the reality of the situation often reacts to the detriment of the sick person, and precious time is lost

[3] "Two questions are often asked: Whether one religious group shows higher mental illness rates than another; and whether any differences exist as to symptom choice, i.e. does one religious group show, for example, high suicide rates while another high alcoholism rates? Rates of illness and types of illness have a great deal to do with factors other than religious affiliation. Education, income, occupation, ethnicity, place of residence, and age distributions are some of the factors that would have to be controlled and their influences understood for each religious group before a meaningful answer could be obtained." Richard V. McCann, *The Churches and Mental Health*, Monograph No. 8. Joint Commission on Mental Illness and Health (New York: Basic Books, 1962), p. 219.

as he is carted back and forth, from doctor to doctor, in an effort to obtain a diagnosis of a physical illness which is more "respectable" and acceptable. Tuberculosis and cancer used to call forth this type of reaction but, fortunately for the sufferers, the stigma has been largely removed.

Happily, within the last few years there has been an arrest in the upward trend in mental hospital "populations," due to new knowledge, to a broader viewpoint in caring for patients, and to new, potent therapeutic agents. Since 1955–56 a decrease of more than 1 per cent occurred for the first time in the year-end resident patient population of the nation's public mental hospitals, from 541,883 at the end of 1959 to 532,-328 at the end of 1961, not a startling reduction, but a move in the right direction.[4] The most reliable estimate, made in July 1962, indicates that this patient load will drop to 515,-000, although it will be a year or more before these figures can be validated.[5]

Various estimates have been projected from local surveys to indicate that as many as seventeen million persons, or about one in ten, suffer from some form of emotional illness, and that one in a hundred suffers from a more obviously disabling illness in the intensity of a psychosis. The designation "the nation's number one health problem," sometimes applied to this illness, while it cannot be proven, is obviously not just a figure of speech. As further indices of the size of the problem, several facts should be borne in mind: First, that more than one and one quarter million people were on the books of the public mental hospitals for the calendar year 1960; secondly, that, though first admissions to mental hospitals decreased slightly in 1960, the number of readmissions of patients rose markedly and the overall trend of mental hospital admission has been moving steadily upward since the mid-1950s; thirdly, that these statistics do not include the large number of patients admitted to private mental hospitals, nursing homes, or the psychiatric wards of general hospitals.

[4] Kramer, David, *1960 Special Survey of Public Mental Hospitals* (Washington, D.C.: Department of Biostatistics, National Institute of Mental Health).
[5] Personal communication from David Kramer.

The combined admissions to the latter three categories of institutions equal or exceed the admission statistics of the 277 public mental hospitals—state, county, and community psychopathic. While these figures are cold and perhaps, in the way of statistics, unimpressive, the fact remains that the public mental hospital population quadrupled in the last half-century, whereas the general population only doubled.

There is little that is dramatic about mental disease; it is rarely thought of as fatal, as are heart disease and cancer, but it is known to be a wrecker and waster of useful, satisfying human life. It is commonly overlooked, too, that more than 50,000 persons die annually in mental hospitals. These, plus the daily tragedies not generally thought of as coming under the cognomen of mental illness, all contribute to the misery of patients and families alike. Suicides, narcotics addiction, divorce rates, all are now higher than ever, and all of these are related to some form of emotional instability. There are well over four million alcoholics in the United States and there are at least four million others apparently intent upon earning that appellation. Besides these, there are countless other people in need of assistance—the anxious, the fearful, and the depressed. Children's lives are blighted; families are broken up; hopes are dashed by the illness of loved ones; and, sadly also, countless old folks, many of whom have lived good and useful lives, are destined to enter mental hospitals and to end ingloriously with senile psychoses. These facts and figures roll easily off the tongue, but rarely is there a hint conveyed of the depth of personal sorrow which frequently accompanies each individual illness.

As the psychiatrist surveys these statistics, which indicate the enormity of the problem, he does so with a certain amount of trepidation, for he is aware of his limitations and those of his specialty in the face of all this suffering. Though the number of psychiatrists in the United States has tripled since World War II, from 4,000 in 1946 to nearly 13,000 at present, only one third of this number is engaged in full-time mental hospital practice. The remainder are either in private practice or divide their time between private practice and salaried positions. Thus, in view of the seriousness of the illnesses in question, it appears that the number of psychiatrists engaged in broad, therapeutic endeavor in mental hospitals is pitifully small.

While the individual psychiatrist knows his limitations in the face of these ubiquitous and varied disorders, he knows also that his specialty now has acquired a fund of information and knowledge about man's emotional reactions which was gained by laborious effort in hospitals, in laboratories, and even in the asylums of old. Mental disease, in the past, has been a disabler of human life, a disrupter of family and social life, and a wrecker of human happiness. We hope to be able to demonstrate, however, that in the light of our modern attack upon it, the results do not need to be so grim. The discipline does have a valuable contribution to make toward the alleviation of emotional distress, particularly if it can be treated early, before it "jells." Because of these contributions and these potentialities, psychiatry merits an important place in the medical firmament.

The Discipline

What is there to say regarding this fledgling specialty which arouses such mixed emotions and which has suddenly sprung into prominence? What is it? Where did it come from? Why is it to the fore at the present time, perhaps more in the public eye than any other medical specialty? It is a *medical* specialty—of that we are sure. It is both a science and an art, and it deals with the origin, diagnosis, treatment, and prevention of mental disease, emotional ills, and asocial behavior. Like psychology, it can be said to have a long past and a short history. Its study requires investigation into the development of culture and some aspects of jurisprudence, theology, and philosophy, because for a number of centuries these disciplines had a great deal to do with the mentally ill and are, after a fashion, psychiatry's remote forebears.

It was only belatedly that the medical man really came into his own in the actual treatment of the mentally sick, and it must be admitted that, with some notable exceptions, he seems not to have been in too much of a hurry to assume the task. He too was a creature of his age, and he was content to leave these strange individuals, whose illnesses were all bound up with spirits, evil and benign, to anyone who held himself able to care for them. Actually, psychiatry had an exceedingly difficult time in getting started, for, unlike other medical disciplines, it had no technological advances to depend upon. The term "psychiatry" itself first appeared in Europe circa 1817 and did not come into common use in this country until the early part of this century.

As to the reasons for the present-day widespread interest in mental health and in mental disorders, they are many and varied. Among them are to be numbered the unprecedented progress in medical science resulting in the control of infectious and epidemic diseases, leading to a longer average life span. With acute infections largely under control, much of the doctor's practice now concerns chronic diseases, emotional illnesses, and the disorders of old age. In other words, more people now live long enough to acquire some of the emotional disorders of middle and old age, in contrast to the usual situation a half-century ago. Also, the marked economic and cultural changes in a greatly expanding population produce their own emotional pressures.

It was World War II, however, which really focused national interest on the size of the psychiatric problem in the nation. When it became apparent that more men had to be rejected at induction stations and more had to be discharged from military service for psychiatric reasons than for any other single cause, it was realized then that some attention would have to be given to this unwelcome problem. Also, when it was realized that men in the field, who were psychiatric casualties, were just as truly lost to the service as if they had been wounded, then the deficiencies in the knowledge and handling of this problem became evident, and the psychiatrist, somewhat grudgingly, came to be recognized as an important member of the medical team.

We noted earlier that psychiatry is both a science and an art. By "science" we mean here, not mathematical science in the narrow sense of the term, but rather in the meaning which it had of old, an encompassing and well-ordered knowledge; not simply instruments and complicated equipment, therefore, but inquiry and a search for knowledge. It is a science because it aims at the establishment of generally true statements on the origin, nature, and differentiating features of the conditions of which it treats. But it is also an art because, while it utilizes the scientific knowledge at its command, it is concerned with healing and with prevention, and most of all, because it necessitates a comprehensive understanding of the individual. Though it is true that understanding of the person is required in all branches of medicine, in no other branch is it as important as it is in psychiatry. Here one deals not only with the affliction itself, but, more importantly, with the person who is afflicted. Here, then, is the exemplification of the medical art in its highest degree, for it focuses upon the unique in the individual, while science is more prone to deal in generalities.

Finally, psychiatry is an important part of the science of man; it has a place in it; it is dependent upon it and is a contributor to it. It is a part of this science because it deals with certain basic and historic problems of man and his society, with thought, emotion, behavior, and human relatedness gone wrong. It is dependent upon it inasmuch as appraisal of the abnormal is necessarily based upon knowledge of the normal, on man's intrinsic nature and what makes him function and behave as he does. It contributes to it by demonstrating certain basic features of the human psyche and their universality.

The Mental Hospital

That psychiatry has attained its present status is due to a number of things. Important among them is the fact that modern medicine points toward a comprehensive rather than a segmented approach to the problems of health and disease. This, in turn, calls for more attention to the specifically human and intimate personal problems of man, which have been and are the main interests of modern dynamic psychiatry.

Unfortunately, though this medical specialty has emerged

and has made great strides, the mental hospital, which nurtured it, has not shared in its emancipation. For the most part the latter still stands remote and alone and all too frequently outside the pale of medical advance and psychiatric progress. The mental hospital has been aptly called "an historic accident." It reflects the mores of the past much more than those of the present. More often than not it has failed to reflect or has reflected poorly the current knowledge of psychiatric disorders. Although the situation has changed markedly for the better within the past decade, one should not forget the unconscionably low base line from which this upward trend began. Our state mental hospitals are, and have been for decades, the first public health institutions to suffer in bad times and the last to benefit in good times. True enough, there were and are islands of greater respectability and humanitarian effort in state hospitals in some parts of the country, but, in general, the overall picture has been unbelievably grim. "Our state hospitals began a downward trend during the great economic depression of the early 1930s and they had not recovered from setbacks in financial support during this period, when they were struck by another severe blow. World War II bled them of their never plentiful professional and other personnel, their financial resources and their institutional morale. . . . War, of course, demands sacrifice of non-essentials; in the minds of many the incarcerated mentally ill are non-essential and they were sacrificed."[6]

No part of the picture is pretty; the story is basically that of man's inhumanity to man. Often a harassed and beleaguered hospital superintendent and his small staff did what they could to care for their pitiful charges and, just as often, they were made scapegoats and pilloried because of the deficiencies of their institutions, even though the legislatures had failed to give them the funds needed to care for their patients properly and with dignity. In the minds of many legislators, precedent dictated that mental patients should be treated and cared for as cheaply as possible. A breakdown of statistics and

[6] *Final Report of The Joint Commission on Mental Health and Mental Illness,* ed. Jack Ewalt. In MS.

budgets shows that this requirement was usually met, and often it was the only one. Yet the *total* amount spent was enormous. This paradox of parsimony and extravagance was produced in part by the magnitude of the problem of mental illness, the recalcitrance of the symptoms to ordinary treatment methods, the crowding of all facilities, and the necessity of expanding mental hospitals constantly without ever being in a good position to attack the problem at its source. The treadmill accelerated; more people were on it, while those who were responsible could do nothing to stop it.

Most existing psychiatric institutions are obsolete. Many of them were built at a time when psychiatry was in its infancy, groping for clues to the understanding of mental illness and its treatment. They were built to get the mentally ill out of prisons and poorhouses, garrets, and cellars, and into places in which there would be some semblance of humane consideration and in which patients would be protected during their illnesses. They were built big, solidly, and for good, because it was assumed to be cheaper and more efficient that way. The architectural design became frozen and was imitated, with few variations, through succeeding generations. Today we are still handicapped immeasurably by those bleak, forbidding, dysfunctional structures that served well enough for incarceration purposes, but lend themselves poorly to modern therapeutic work. Under the best of circumstances it is difficult to make them into therapeutic communities in which the march of patients toward regression can be arrested or reversed.

There is little to be gained by dwelling for long upon the sickening neglect, the beatings, the overcrowding, and lack of privacy to which the mentally ill were subjected down through the ages. It recurred constantly, no matter what the creed or what the form of government in power. Our own nation, even in its earliest beginnings in the first hospital, established by Quakers, placed its patients half way under ground and fastened them with irons if they became obstreperous. Restraint was freely used, as an account of March 7, 1752, to the Pennsylvania Hospital shows:

John Cresson, blacksmith, against ye hospital 1 pr. hand-cuffs, 2 legg locks, 2 large rings and 2 swiffels for legg chains. . . . Paid for 7 yds. of Ticken for Mad Shirts, etc.[7]

The records of the hospital indicate, too, that the "cells of the insane were without adequate heat for almost eighty years until 1833"; also, that the great crowds that invaded the hospital on Sundays to gape at these unfortunates sometimes gave trouble. On May 10, 1762, they created such disturbance that a workman was employed "to make a suitable hatch door and get an inscription thereon notifying that such persons who came out of curiosity . . . should pay a sum of money, a groat at least, for admittance."[8]

Then, later, as one author notes:

In the 1830s the main trouble was overcrowding, which was to dog and retard every step for the improvement of mental hospitals for the next hundred years. Men and women in all sorts and conditions of mental disease were placed too closely together on a basement floor. The building occupied less than three-fourths of an acre including the airing ground. Patients whose illnesses had begun only a few weeks before their admission were placed with those who had been in the hospital from 25 to 42 years.[9]

This was in the 1830s in this fair land of ours. Now, let us examine the advances which were made in the humane and scientific treatment of patients in the next hundred years. During 1946 and 1947, Mr. Albert Deutsch, a writer and medical historian, visited more than two dozen state mental hospitals:

Most of them were located in or near the great centers of culture . . . in some of the wards there were scenes which revealed the horrors of Nazi concentration camps

[7] Strecker, E. A., M.D., "Reminiscences from the Early Days of The Pennsylvania Hospital," *Annals of Medical History* (New York: Hoeber), Vol. I, No. 4.

[8] *Ibid.*

[9] Bond, E. D., *Dr. Kirkbride and His Mental Hospital* (Philadelphia: Lippincott, 1947).

. . . hundreds of mental patients herded into huge, barn-like, filth infested wards in all degrees of deterioration, untended and untreated, stripped of every vestige of human decency, many in states of severe starvation . . . the writer heard state hospital doctors freely admit that the animals in nearby piggeries were better fed, housed, and treated than many of the patients in their wards.

. . . The writer saw black eyes and bruises, saw court records and hospital accident lists showing that brutality against patients, while not as common as occasional newspaper exposés might suggest, was of shocking frequency. Personal accounts of fatal beatings of mental patients attested the end results of some of this treatment.[10]

It is difficult to believe that all of this was taking place a little more than a decade ago in this nation, with its Christian background and its humanitarian concerns. The blind spots which tolerate this kind of treatment of human beings are difficult to fathom. American people generally are indignant about any cruelty or unfairness in the treatment of anyone or anything, but this has not seemed to hold true in the case of the mentally ill. Humane societies and anti-vivisectionists collected names for their numerous petitions to protect laboratory animals, which were treated much better than some of the patients in question, but there were few voices raised for the mentally ill, even among those in the professions charged with the care of men's bodies and souls.

Rejection

As one looks for an answer to explain these phenomena, several suggestions as to the cause present themselves. One of the most likely holds that:

The mentally ill lack appeal, rather that they eventually disturb and offend people and, when they do, people generally treat them as offenders and disturbers. People do feel sorry for them, it would appear, but in the balance they do not feel as sorry as they do relieved to have

[10] Deutsch, A., *The Shame of the States* (New York: Harcourt, Brace & Co., 1948).

out of the way persons whose behavior disturbs and offends them.[11]

Another difficult thing to understand is why a nation that will expend billions of dollars upon the education of the young will reject them out of hand if they falter emotionally and require treatment in a mental hospital. Upon discharge from the hospital, employment is often denied these individuals; the military services reject them; and their lot in general is not a pleasant or encouraging one. It is not hard to understand, in view of this, that the only place in which some of these hapless individuals feel at home is a mental hospital, and all too many of them gravitate back to one.

While things are still far from perfect, there have been remarkable improvements made recently. In fact, the mental hospitals have advanced further in the past decade than they had for hundreds of years before. Present-day improvements are due to: 1) the interest of the United States Congress,[12] which has appropriated funds for the training of physicians and personnel through grants from the U. S. Public Health Service; 2) the dedication of a small group of hospital physicians who have espoused the cause of their patients, stood by them, and fought for them despite great odds; 3) the advent of new drugs which have made the patients more amenable to therapy and the hospitals much more habitable; 4) the new concept of the "open hospital." As a result of these advances 80 per cent of those not organically ill who enter mental hospitals today are discharged or improved within a year.

CONFLICT

In view of the things we have discussed and in view of the great need of mental patients for understanding and assistance, any misunderstanding or separation between psychiatry and religious groups becomes particularly regrettable.

[11] *Report of The Joint Commission on Mental Health and Mental Illness,* ed. Jack Ewalt. In MS.
[12] Especially the committees headed by Representative John Fogarty (Rhode Island) and Senator Lister Hill (Alabama).

Christianity has historically identified itself with the needy and suffering, and the greater the need, the more urgent is the plea for succor. It would seem then that religion and psychiatry have a mutual interest. That all is not harmonious between them, however, is common knowledge. While the situation is much better now than ever before, due to numerous conferences, seminars, closer associations, etc., there are still evidences of mutual suspicion in a number of places. That any of it exists at all is unfortunate, for the pursuit of mental health, which is psychiatry's main goal, is neither a destructive nor an irreligious pursuit. It is the same man who needs the dedicated ministrations of religion who needs, at times, the help of psychiatry. We shall attempt here to get at some of the reasons behind this coolness and mild suspicion.

As a relic of ancient times there still lurks in the minds of some people the idea that psychiatric illnesses have moral connotations. Somehow an unfortunate connection has been made and mental health has become equated with happiness and virtuousness. Père Noël Mailloux, a Canadian Dominican psychologist, points out that this tendency is evident even among some moral theologians, although it is not explicitly stated. The opinion is often held widely but covertly that, if a patient is virtuous, he should be immune to emotional distress and mental upset. This, of course, does not hold true. That virtuous people may fall prey to mental illness is just as certain as is the fact that people who are not mentally ill may not necessarily be virtuous.

A more serious factor, however, which has prevented an easy understanding between psychiatry and religion, has been the encroachments and sometimes apparent encroachments of one on what the other has considered its own special preserve. As is usual when major disagreements between disciplines occur, the fault never rests on one side, and most certainly is this true in this instance. Much of the trouble today resides in the lingering mistrust of science in the minds of believers and the even greater mistrust of religion, as they conceive or remember it, in the minds of the scientists. Here are remnants of the old quarrel between religion and science which has plagued man for centuries and which usually erupts anew when some startling or revolutionary concept has been promulgated.

Actually, these quarrels are usually not between religion and science so much as between adherents of both who do not understand one another. "Conflicts between what man wants to do with science and what he wants to do with religion . . . make either of them purely utilitarian, power seeking, or an instrument for man's self-assertion and acting in his own behalf, and the conflict becomes not only inevitable but intolerant and intolerable."[13] Unfortunately, too, we are reminded that: "The underlying attitude of the average Catholic toward the whole enterprise of a theoretic science is usually assumed to be one of hostility. He is the inheritor of a sad tradition of misunderstanding which goes back more than three centuries to where physical science was taking shape."[14]

It is unfortunate that it is only by hindsight that we gain proper perspective on many of the quarrels which disturbed religious and scientific men in the past. Usually there was sufficient information available at the time which, if utilized, would have obviated the necessity of these bickerings, just as there is sufficient information at hand now to encourage a fruitful and satisfactory relationship between religion and psychiatry. Strangely, however, when proponents take sides and gird for battle, various extraneous factors seem to become involved, and then these become more important than the problem at hand. Scientists who espouse one cause simply assume that theologians and philosophers have closed minds, while the latter assume that scientists are by nature and by calling irreligious and that, as an accompaniment of their theories, they will adversely influence the religious beliefs of those whom they encounter. In addition, at times, when the quarrels become tangential and involved, the question of status enters and each proponent feels that he is upholding

[13] Zilboorg, Gregory. Address, St. John's Workshop, Collegeville, Minn., 1956.

[14] Braceland, F. J., "The Philosophy of Psychiatry," *Digest of Neurology and Psychiatry* (1950).

the honor of his discipline and remains determined not to be proven wrong.

There is frequently evident in religious, as in other, circles that all too human tendency to regard old ideas as best, particularly when new truths require a complete readjustment of thought processes that have become pretty well settled. For some reason the older sciences gradually became tied up with basic issues in Christian cosmology, so that, when these are attacked, it seems, as it did in the case of Copernicus, that Christianity itself is being undermined. Until very recently every new idea was regarded in some quarters as a threat to religious belief, and immediately a state-of-siege mentality supervened. Then, as wiser heads prevailed, the new concepts were seen simply as a part of the unfolding of God's plan and as further manifestations of His wisdom. Later, after the scholars have carefully surveyed the situation and the concepts have been cleansed of their broad overtones, they may write of the new ideas, as does Father Walter Ong, S.J., about one problem of vexatious nature:

> There can be no doubt that the discovery of the process of evolution, cosmic and organic, has been one of the greatest achievements of the human mind. In a sense, this is the central discovery in the Western World since Renaissance times, and in a still further sense it is the central corporate discovery of all mankind.[15]

Perhaps soon the basic concepts of psychiatry will be similarly freed from shadows of suspicion.

The Special Case of Psychiatry

The psychiatry which was practiced in Europe and America at the turn of the century was solely hospital psychiatry. While the related fields of medicine and surgery were advancing rapidly with the progress in general knowledge and with the developments of adequate technology, this discipline was still bumbling along in its descriptive phase, hopelessly

---

[15] Ong, Walter, S.J., Ph.D., "Evolution and Cyclism in Our Time," *Darwin's Vision and Christian Perspectives* (New York: The Macmillan Co., 1960), pp. 125–48.

behind its sister specialties and with no technological advances at all to lean upon. It had little contact with the world of medicine—little concerning it was taught in medical schools —and no contact at all with the world of ideas. It was not in trouble with religion, nor with any discipline in fact, for no one paid any attention to it. The specialty was practiced by "alienists," and alien they were to their medical colleagues and to the world at large. Then the situation changed dramatically. Psychoanalysis made its appearance in the field of emotional and mental illness, and the world perforce took notice, and with mixed feelings.

There is now general agreement with the statement that no single individual ever contributed so much to the knowledge of psychiatry as did the founder of psychoanalysis, Sigmund Freud. As we shall see in Chapter III, when he began his studies in the last two decades of the nineteenth century he soon became dissatisfied with the "anatomical diagnoses" then in vogue and came to believe that there were other causes for some of the physical and mental symptoms which he saw in abundance in the clinics. Briefly, his idea was to discover whether anything could be learned from the patient's own buried memories, and, eventually, as a consequence, a whole new world was opened to our view. As Karl Stern observes:

> This dynamic approach, which rose out of the depths of 19th-century materialism, represents a new era no less significant than the Galilean era in physics, and as a result of what we have learned from psychoanalysis, our image of the interior world of man can never be the same as it was previous to 1894.[16]

Though we shall consider later the details of the differences which arose between religion and psychoanalysis, we shall only mention here that once again the Christian cosmos was thought by some to be in jeopardy. Once more the old fires of conflict were to be rekindled and once more churchmen were to be maneuvered into a position of seeming to oppose scientific advance. Extravagant statements were again the order

---

[16] Stern, K. *The Commonweal* (October 22, 1948).

of the day, and again God was dismissed and, of course, there was to be no further use for religion.

There is no question about the major proportions of this quarrel. Here, supposedly, was scientific fact on one side and religious truth on the other, once more locked in mortal combat. Proponents of the new belief saw religion at the base of some of the illnesses it encountered. Religious men, on their side, were repelled by the reduction of the God of the Judaeo-Christian belief to the role of "nothing but a father image." Heretofore, in his search for first causes man had seen God as the center of the universe; now His role was to be usurped by the "oedipal situation." Now, with these changes, God was to be created in man's image, rather than the reverse of this. It is obvious, of course, that none of these concepts would gain the confidence of religious people, and then, when Freud spoke of religion as an illusion and characterized its ritual as obsessive phenomena, the battle lines were drawn and the war was on. Here once again was a new battleground—science vs. religion—with a difference, and it would take a long time until the various aspects of the problem could be seen in proper perspective.

More fuel was added to the flame which separated psychiatry from philosophy, religion, and even from medicine by the popularizers of psychiatry who took up the new ideas with a vengeance. Seemingly, here was scientific justification now for iconoclastic ideas which had been previously cherished but had little to tie to. Psychiatry became popular in Sunday supplements and on the stage and screen, as well as in current fiction. Although a number of "psychological novels" and works which dealt rather directly with sexual themes had appeared without benefit of Freud, the stage was set for something new and analysis filled the bill admirably. The new jargon spread quickly by word of mouth and devotees of various "sets" felt entitled to talk about it freely, even though they knew little about it; it gave them an apparently scientific reason for scoffing at old beliefs and standards.

Certainly psychiatry, like every other activity in which human beings are involved, has its adherents and practitioners of whom it is proud, and in the same fashion it has those of whom it is not proud. Undoubtedly, too, there are psychiatrists who have disregarded or compromised the ideals and the standards which their profession requires of them. But this is not the fault of psychiatry, and psychiatry, as a discipline, should not be condemned because of them. It is a chastening thought that, judged on the same *ad hominem* ground, religion would be even more vulnerable to condemnation because of the action of its adherents, if only because it is much older and has had many more constituents. Religious men understand, as does every impartial historian, that, whatever scandals smudge the record of any profession—clerical or lay—are due to the human element, the failure of individual human beings.

Fortunately, some of the disagreements between religion and psychiatry, which earlier seemed insurmountable, are now seen as capable of solution and a *modus vivendi* is slowly being developed. One author can happily write:

> The old war is over. Pastors and psychiatrists now are friends, priests talk in the meetings of psychoanalysts, and psychiatrists lecture in seminaries. There are many excellent sanitoria which are run under religious auspices following the methods of the new psychiatry, Freud's included, with all rigor.[17]

Numerous reasons are ascribed for this delayed but welcome movement of psychiatry and religion toward collaborative ventures for the good of man. At one level, there is the undoubted deepening of understanding on the part of churchmen for what psychiatry really is and what it can legitimately claim to do. There is a clearing of the air; the psychological insights provided by psychiatry are recognized for what they contribute to the understanding of human nature and for the value they have in alleviating human suffering. The philosophical overtones, the speculations about God and the human spirit and religion and the like are recognized more

[17] Weigel, G., S.J., "The Challenge of Peace," *Pastoral Psychiatry*, Vol. 10, No. 81 (February 1959).

clearly for what they are—excursions into philosophy essentially unconnected with the facts of psychiatry. Meetings and seminars have served to spread a clearer understanding of psychiatric pursuits and goals among non-professionals, and have been a potent force for good. On the other side, the more mature of the psychiatrists realize that there are some human problems which must be forever beyond the reach of scientific grasp and beyond their therapeutic abilities. In this the specialty has changed markedly within the past decade or two, and no longer is it quite so brash.

But all is not yet clear sailing. One French Dominican, who had broad experience in these efforts, makes this comment:

> What could be more disappointing than the innumerable conferences and meetings at which Christian psychiatrists and psychologists put questions to the theologians. Despite the good will and common belief of those taking part, one gets the impression of a conversation between deaf persons. Everyone states his own case, but nothing results. This failure cannot be attributed solely to unavoidable difficulties in vocabulary, methods, or "formal" points of view. There is something more to it; we seem to be confronted with a "pattern of civilization."[18]

The work of approaching a mutual understanding still requires genuine effort, and the clergyman should be perhaps the one to try hardest. The same author adds:

> A theologian can return no real answer to the question posed by depth psychology, unless he effects a complete change in his conception of man and of the moral life. We must get rid of the attitude of mind which has characterized the last six centuries and recover, without falling into undue anachronism, that rich and balanced conception of man possessed by the first centuries of the Church by the Fathers and by St. Thomas Aquinas.[19]

[18] Plé, A., O.P., "St. Thomas and the Psychology of Freud," *Cross Currents,* Vol. 4, No. 4 (1954).
[19] *Ibid.*

The need becomes urgent as the magnitude of the problem is considered. What is needed now is continuous enlightened discussion, seminars, study, and, wherever possible, collaboration on the part of all concerned. Pinpoints of dialectic or doctrinal hairsplitting, or standing off and railing at, or shooting verbal darts at, adversaries is out of place in a field which takes care of the needs of sick people. Also, it is most important to remember that, no matter what form the disagreement may take, it is always wise to be sure of what one is fighting against before rushing to battle stations. Newman's impressive advice is the order of the day: "What I would urge upon men of science, what I would venture to recommend to theologians when their attention is drawn to the subject of scientific investigation, is a great and firm belief in the sovereignty of truth."

It is probable that, had the admonition of St. Augustine, quoted below, been heeded down through the ages, we would have avoided many of the interminable quarrels which have helped to drive men from the Church. In addition, we would have avoided the ridicule of unbelievers when they replied to some of the more rash statements of men not quite equipped to challenge various scientific tenets. St. Augustine's admonition, as quoted by St. Thomas, himself an expert in this department, is as follows:

Often in connection with the earth and the heavens or other elements of this world—and many similar things —it happens that a man who is not a Christian possesses a knowledge which is so profound that it is guaranteed by certain calculations or even by experience. Now here is a thing which is too disgraceful, too disastrous, and from which we must above all guard ourselves. A Christian speaks of all these subjects; he thinks that he speaks of them according to our Holy Scripture; yet, every unbeliever may hear him rambling so much that in the presence of such great errors the unbeliever cannot help laughing and the real evil is not that a man is subjected to derision because of his error, but it is that to profane eyes our authors (i.e. the sacred

authors) are regarded as having had such thoughts and
are also exposed to blame on the score of ignorance to
the greatest possible misfortune of people whom we
wish to save.[20]

The time for collaboration between religion and science is
most opportune. Pope Pius XII, in one of his last allocutions,
foresaw great advances in science, which will bring about a
beautiful springtime for humanity in general. Man is not only
expanding his knowledge of outer space, but also advancing
his knowledge of living substances, earth, and oceans.
Weather satellites, bathyspheres, telstars, and numerous instruments heretofore undreamed of are increasing our knowledge of the physical world at a dizzy pace. It is now suggested that we may soon be able to exert a considerable
measure of control on climate.

It is easy to imagine the kind of disquiet that a hint of present-day actualities would have caused a generation ago, and
yet all sorts of discoveries of equal magnitude are in the
offing. Some will stagger the minds of men as they appear
in diverse fields. Moreover, some of the discoverers will be
believers; some will be unbelievers; but what they are matters little to science. What they say and what they discover
are the important matters. Are they true or are they false? If
they are true, they belong to us, no matter how badly they
offend our rigid, narrow, protective attitudes.

Speaking in this same vein, Father Henri de Lubac, S.J.,
says:

There will always be some individuals who perfectly
identify their own cause with that of the Church and
end by subordinating in good faith the Church's cause
to their own. In their desire to serve the Church they
actually put her to work for themselves, a dialectical
turnabout which changes friend into foe and takes
place with much ease and subtlety. For them the
Church is in fact a certain familiar social order to which
they belong. . . . Whatever disturbs this order or en-
dangers this equilibrium, whatever upsets or merely

[20] *De Genesi, ad Litteram, Liber I,* Cap. XIX

startles these men, appears to them as an attack on a divine institution.[21]

And now, before we examine briefly the background and the remote ancestors of modern medicine and psychiatry, in order to be better able to fix them in space, one further observation from the same wise author seems to be in order, as he warns us that a certain confidence and a certain detachment are part and parcel of a Christian outlook. We will need to keep this in mind as we discuss psychiatry and try to evaluate its contribution to our Christian heritage:

A Christianity that deliberately and completely shelters itself behind barricades, disclaiming all advance and assimilation, would no longer be Christianity. . . . A sincere attachment to the Church cannot serve to canonize our prejudices nor make our personal bias share in the absolute of a faith which is universal.[22]

[21] Lubac, H. de, S.J., *The Christian Vision* (London: Blackfriars, 1955), p. 151.
[22] *Ibid.*, p. 152.

II

HISTORICAL PERSPECTIVE

Nothing under the sun is new, neither is any man able to say: Behold, this is new, for it hath already been done before in the ages that were before us.

Ecclesiastes 1:10

In order to understand a medical discipline it is necessary to know something of its antecedents and its directions. This is particularly true of psychiatry, which has reached its present status only after a long and trying ordeal. Psychiatric history confirms the thought in the above quotation from Ecclesiastes. Time after time concepts have appeared and disappeared, only to reappear at a later date embellished with ideas peculiar to the day and perhaps a round higher on the spiral of scientific progress.

Unlike Athene, who sprang fully armed from the brow of Zeus, psychiatry in its developmental period was completely weaponless. All it had was a forlorn hope and a humane purpose—that people be treated decently while they were in the throes of mental illness. Gradually, with numerous detours and against many obstacles, psychiatry moved forward, slowly acquiring a body of basic knowledge, yet remaining outside the pale of scientific respectability. As noted previously, it was not until this century that the extent of the psychiatric problem became recognized, and it is only within the past two decades that psychiatry developed really potent therapeutic weapons for use in the massive task that confronts it.

Early Cultures[1]

Man at all times and in all phases of his history has had to

[1] This historical account is of necessity brief and incomplete. For a more complete historical survey of the entire panorama up to 1940 see Gregory Zilboorg's *A History of Medical Psychology* (New York: W. W. Norton Co., 1941).

cope with disease, suffering, and death. If we define medicine as the effort to assist him at the time of these calamities, then we can say that medicine is as old as civilization, even as old as mankind. Primitive men, ancient and contemporary, have tended to see evidences of supernatural beings and supernatural influences all around them. Some of the spirits are visible; many are invisible. Some are dark and evil; others are helpful and good. The less man knows of the world about him, the more potent these influences appear to be. Any of the spirits might become angry with mortal man and, when they do, they have to be propitiated. This is the task of the primitive medicine man. To the superstitious mind, disease is immersed in magic of a malevolent or punitive sort. This concept was held, for instance, by all people belonging to the higher primitive cultures. The rather advanced Assyrians reasoned that the victim of disease must have brought the trouble upon himself. Disease was primarily punishment for transgression. Though man was free to do as he chose, he existed at the discretion of the gods. To flout their laws was to invite the appropriate penalty: pain, disease, death.

The civilization of ancient Greece is more nearly related to our own. There the science and art of medicine developed early and more or less independently of other disciplines. Though influenced by philosophical ideas, Greek medicine was largely empirical, founded upon observation and experience. The texts assembled under the name of Hippocrates offer eloquent testimony to this. Among the best known is the text devoted to epilepsy, which repudiates the popular notion of the supernatural origin of this disorder and proclaims it to be a disease like any other.[2]

The Greeks tended to regard mental (and moral) deviations as consequences of physical disorder and a lack of harmony in the combination of humors. Hence in the treatment of the mentally afflicted the physiological approach was not neglected, and hellebore, purging, and cold baths were ac-

[2] *The Genuine Works of Hippocrates,* translated from the Greek by Francis Adams (New York: William Wood & Company, 1886), Vol. 2, pp. 327–46.

cepted procedures. Hippocrates recognized and, after a fashion, described a number of mental conditions—confused states after serious hemorrhage, delirium accompanying feverish disease, postpartum psychoses (mental breakdown following childbirth), and hysteria. Although his clinical observations and differentiation of symptoms were imprecise, it is apparent that he recognized the relation between elation and depression.

Even in the period when it was believed that madness was caused by malign influences, there were those who had other ideas. This is quite evident in Greek literature, in which mental aberrations in the wake of excessive emotion are described. Poets, novelists, and dramatists in later periods, like those of ancient Greece, have often possessed psychological insight far in advance of the insight of physicians, who have tended to seek more tangible causes of illness. Even a casual search among the works of novelists and dramatists will reveal innumerable instances of knowledge of man's hidden emotional life, the meaning of his dreams, and the effect of his emotional states upon his bodily system.

Decline of Classical Medicine

The three main ideas on the origin and nature of mental illness prevalent in antiquity persisted for many centuries. Sometimes the role of malign supernatural powers was emphasized; this was later conceived as demonic possession, and often the difference between possession and insanity was hardly recognized. Sometimes the role of intense emotion—the so-called psychogenic origin of mental disorders—was more clearly seen. And sometimes the role of physical factors was stressed, when the unbalance of bodily humors was cited as the cause of mental disease.

The Romans failed to nurture the legacy received from the Greeks, and the brilliant medical principles enunciated by Hippocrates were allowed to deteriorate as magic and superstition again carried the day. There were a few glimmers of hope, but they did not last long, and the lights of medical progress were destined to go out after the death of Galen in 200 A.D. Galen, a Mysian physician who practiced in Rome, wrote on all sorts of medical subjects, collecting all the medical knowledge accumulated by his predecessors and supplementing it with his own observations. Like others before him, Galen was convinced of the influence of the humors in disease processes. His approach to mental disease was physiological. He described the brain and its coverings, the meninges, the ventricles, and the cranial nerves, and suggested that psychic functions are contained in the brain. His reputation as the greatest of medical authorities continued for nearly 1,500 years. Time brought many distortions, however, and the whole field of mental diseases became separated from medicine.

The Middle Ages

That evil spirits may take possession of a human being was then and is now a doctrine of the Church, resting upon the Gospel. At no time, however, was it implied that "possession" was the only cause of mental illness. In fact, early Christian medicine showed much promise. Though none of the early Christian medical texts have come down to us, there are evidences that the Christian physicians accepted Greek pathology, while rejecting the excessive Hellenic naturalism associated with it. They also rejected the belief that it was futile to treat patients with incurable diseases. To love one's needy and suffering neighbor was a Christian obligation. There were some among the early Christians who disparaged the use of herbs and medicaments and thought disease should be treated by exorcism and prayer, but this was not the general orientation. Christianity recognized, however, the limitations of the medical art and had faith in the possibility of divine intervention. The early Christians also inaugurated regular medical, nursing, and social assistance through their hospitals, and there came to the fore a religious form of psychotherapy which was both therapeutic and consoling. Had Christianity been able to maintain the equilibrium of its early outlook, the history of Western medicine might have been quite different. Instead, medicine in general went downhill and the mentally ill were excluded from its province.

The decline of medicine was part and parcel, of course, of the universal decline of civilization in Europe, when the barbarian hordes swept over the disintegrating Roman Empire. As the political and social structure of the Empire collapsed, and the populations declined under the ravages of war, famine, and disease, the schools, academies, and libraries disappeared, the arts and crafts were forgotten. Along with most other civilized achievements, medicine succumbed in the turmoil and confusion of the Dark Ages.

When eventually the tide began to turn, and European civilization began to re-form its bases, medicine was one of the earliest arts to enjoy a revival. It was, indeed, then far behind the best levels attained in the ancient world, but a new scientific spirit was stirring. One of the most famous centers of the revival was the school at Salerno, whose physicians were far advanced for their day. Among other things, they knew of the relation of the cerebral hemisphere to the opposite side of the body, and paid particular attention to the brain. From Salerno, in all probability, came the ideas which proved to be of the greatest importance to philosophers and theologians.

The ideas of comprehensive thinkers, philosophers, and theologians exert considerable influence on all the arts and sciences, just as they are in turn influenced by them. Before the time of St. Augustine, thinkers were disposed to view body and soul as two independent substances, as though the soul were some kind of spiritual being somehow caught and imprisoned, against its best interests, in the shell of the body. St. Augustine's writings presented a more integrated view of human nature, with the soul and body in intimate union and harmony, each contributing to the benefit of the other. But it was after the Dark Ages, when interest in the philosophy of Aristotle was revived, toward the end of the twelfth century, and incorporated into the Christian speculation of St. Albert the Great and St. Thomas Aquinas, that a new conception of human nature appeared. The unity of mind and body was stressed more than ever before in Christian thought. Man was a *per se* unity. The soul was not a pure spirit but a corporeal form, giving shape, substance, dimensions, and animal vitality to the whole, individual man. Granting that the soul was also the seat of spiritual powers—reason and free will—it did not and could not operate even spiritually except under the conditions of physical and sentient life. Granting also that the soul would exist after the corruption of the body, it would only exist as a violated half-being, torn from its natural element.

In man there was discerned a broad hierarchy of natural powers, ranging from the power to nourish himself, grow, and reproduce, to the powers of sensation, memory, imagination, and instinct, through passions and affects, up to the rational and free operations of the mind. All of these capacities except reason and free will were shown to function in physical organs of the body, and so knit was the unity of man that whatever affected one part of him affected all the rest. His digestion could affect his loftiest speculations and his speculations could affect his digestion. His mind was not free from the surge of his passions, and his passions could be roused by mental activities. St. Thomas frequently referred to psychosomatic interactions: the excesses of passion which sicken the body and disorder the mind, the vehement perceptions of the mind which stir the emotions and alter the body's functions, the diseases of the body which influence mind, spirit, imagination, and feelings. These concepts would naturally indicate that mental ills belong in the domain of the physician.[3]

[3] St. Thomas, of course, had no knowledge of the Freudian unconscious. He did not, however, close off his psychology from the possibility. He recognized the fact that men think while they are asleep, and suggested that they sometimes syllogize better then than when they are awake. He noted that perceptions are often more acute when we are asleep, and that our dreams are often products of physical states and conditions. In one place he makes the remarkably modern observation that doctors like to know their patients' dreams because often they can tell a great deal from the dreams about the patients' internal dispositions! He noted that men often have intentions or purposes of which they are unconscious, and that thought and judgment can be so affected by feeling and passion that men become incapable of seeing the plainest truths, and that this can become a permanent condition.

Unfortunately, the many germinal insights shown at various times failed to take hold. While not all mental illnesses were viewed as evidence of demoniacal possession, a number of them were so considered. Ironically enough, this belief and the belief in witchcraft, black magic, collusion with evil spirits, and other ideas of this nature did not reach their height in the Middle Ages, but rather at a time when the Middle Ages were already waning and the age of the Renaissance had already gained considerable strength.

These were troublesome times and times of the greatest contradiction. The contrasts are apparent in certain events recorded in large letters in the pages of psychiatry. On the one hand, patients were treated humanely and with insight, as in Gheel, Belgium, where, under the aegis of the Church, mental patients were cared for in the townspeople's homes and made participants in their family life. That tradition persists to this day. Furthermore, mental patients were admitted to the general hospitals which had been set up by Innocent III, and at the Monastery of Monte Cassino the Order of St. John of Jerusalem bestowed benign care upon the mentally afflicted. But in the fourteenth and fifteenth centuries, there were fresh outbursts of witch hunts and demon scares. Even the most educated people were not immune to the hysteria. About 1487, two friars, James Sprenger and Heinrich Kraemer, published their *Malleus Maleficarum* (Hammer of the Witches), which presented evidence for the existence of witches, clinical reports showing how to identify them, and legal forms for examining and sentencing a witch. The writers of the *Malleus* had political and medical, as well as theological, support. Their book became the standard reference at all witchcraft trials. The degree to which insanity was confused with witchcraft during these times is hard to tell; the difference was understood in principle but not always in prac-

He did not formulate a concept like the Freudian id, but he noted that sensuality in its roots is an undifferentiated power or drive, chaotic, not controllable by reason, and not susceptible to the formation of moral habits. Cf. Michael Stock, O.P., "Thomistic Psychology and Freud's Psychoanalysis," *The Thomist,* Vol. XXI, No. 2 (April 1958).

tice.[4] The picture was further confused when unscrupulous charlatans, pretending to preternatural powers, played on the fears and superstitions of the times for personal profit. All this was symptomatic of the unrest and insecurity attending the restructuring of the social forces of the time. It was, as historians have pointed out, a reaction against the disquieting signs of growing instability in the established order.

Renaissance

Shortly after publication of the *Malleus* a man was born in Valencia who was to be known later as the father of modern empirical psychology and a forerunner of modern dynamic psychiatry. He was Juan Luis Vives (1492–1540), a friend of Sir Thomas More and a broadly educated man from a religious family setting. He stressed the importance of psychological associations and the emotional influences bearing upon them, and was aware also of the relation of psychological associations to memory. He espoused the cause of the mentally ill and advocated gentleness in all dealings with them. Of the mind he had this to say: "Since there is nothing in the world more excellent than man, nor in man than his mind, particular attention should be given to the welfare of the mind."[5]

Other voices were also heard. Paracelsus (1493–1541) conceived of man as a psychobiological entity, a well-knit organism, and criticized the belief in witchcraft and the prejudices of contemporary medical practice. Cornelius Agrippa of Nettesheim (1486–1535) was also scornful of the prejudices of his time, and it was probably then that the foundations were laid for a scientific understanding of mental disease, particularly through the work of Johann Weyer

[4] The authors of the *Malleus*, for instance, were influenced by St. Thomas Aquinas' opinion on natural impotency and impotency due to witchcraft. If a man were impotent in relation to all women, it was from a natural cause; if in relation to only one and not to others, he was bewitched.

[5] From Sir Thomas More's *De Subventione Pauperum* (1516). Quoted by Gregory Zilboorg in *A History of Medical Psychology*, p. 187.

(1515–88), a student of Agrippa. In his book *De Praestigiis Daemonum* (1563) Weyer made a vigorous attack on the thesis used to justify proceedings against witches, declaring that the witches were mentally ill. Zilboorg credits Weyer with the discovery of the power of imagination and the role of fantasy in the formation of the symptoms of mental disease.

In the beginning of the sixteenth century, philosophy took a new direction, and in doing so, the recognition of the unity of the human individual was badly damaged. The brilliant mathematician and founder of modern philosophy, René Descartes, taught that everything in the universe could be reduced to two separate and distinct substances—mind and matter. The essence of mind was thought to be conscious activity, and the essence of matter, extension. In the process of reasoning, he found what he conceived as the fundamental proof of spiritual life and existence: *Je pense, donc je suis.* In man's body, as well as in the rest of the world, he saw only mechanical laws operating. His psychology was purely mechanistic, and he spoke in terms of *l'homme machine.* As far as psychiatry is concerned, the influence of Cartesianism, with its exaggerated emphasis on dualism, was unfortunate. If man's body is a machine following the laws of mechanics, and his mind is a spark of intellect following laws of the spirit, the unity of the individual is lost and research into the relationships between the mental and the physical is futile.

The Transition Period—The Antecedents of Modern Psychiatry.

By the eighteenth century medicine had made strides in anatomy and, to some extent, in physiology. Albrecht von Haller (1708–77) established physiology as a special branch of science and laid the groundwork for experimental medicine. Finally, in the latter half of the century, medicine came to grips with pathology and began developing useful aids to physical diagnosis. These advances in general medicine were not duplicated in the area of psychiatry. Knowledge of brain pathology and of the physiology of the nervous system continued to be rudimentary. This dearth of knowledge, however, did not prevent many observers from proclaiming that some forms of mental disease are related to cerebral alterations.

By the mid-nineteenth century two viewpoints regarding the genesis of mental disease were clearly discernible—one somatic and the other mentalistic. The idea that complex cerebral performances could be separated into simple functions, to which definite parts of the brain could be related, dated back to the days of John Locke (1632–1704), David Hartley (1705–57), and David Hume (1711–76). It was a basic concept that complex mental phenomena were composed of simple elements, labeled sensations or impressions. Gustav Theodor Fechner, a German experimental psychologist (1801–87), felt that in the study of mental life, as in other scientific research, it should be possible to break down the phenomena of immediate observation into elements which can then be studied separately. A very important development was the demonstration by the French surgeon Paul Broca (1824–80) of lesions of the temporal lobe of the brain which resulted in "pure lack of speech," that is motor aphasia. Here, for the first time, a circumscribed area of brain cortex was related to a well-characterized clinical picture. With this the theory of cerebral localization began, and interest in it spread rapidly.

To the degree that clinical observation revealed the presence of neurological symptoms in some cases of mental disease, psychiatry became influenced by neuropathology and neurophysiology. As this influence progressed and as scientific trends grew increasingly naturalistic and materialistic, the notion that mental diseases are brain diseases grew more and more plausible. It was tacitly understood that it was only a question of time until anatomical lesions would be found to explain all mental ills. The search was on, therefore, to establish causal factors and to devise criteria by which mental diseases could be defined. All these efforts culminated in the work of Emil Kraepelin, as we shall presently see.

The course of science is never uniform nor smooth. Because of the overlapping of generations, ideas which younger men are ready to abandon are still maintained by their elders.

Moreover, apart from science itself, contradictory concepts always coexist to produce what Rudolf Allers calls "neophenomena," i.e. an upsurge of ideas which have existed before and now become revitalized, changed in some ways, but nevertheless fundamentally related to previous stages. For, even when rejected by the majority as obsolete, ideas persist, however unnoticeably, to affect the thinking of some. Thus, in the period under consideration, psychiatry as a whole moved more and more toward a medical approach; yet the idea of a strictly mental causation of psychiatric disorders continued to influence workers in the field.

As noted earlier, the popular opinion that strong emotions, especially those of a depressive nature, are at the root of mental illness is ages old. The same is true of the belief that guilt, sin, and moral defect can be expressed in mental illness, and that continual stress and strain can produce emotional difficulties. This last idea finds expression in the so-called mental "breakdown," a phrase implying that the "burden" of life gradually becomes too heavy and the individual "breaks" under the strain. However farfetched or oversimplified these popular ideas may be, they are worthy of consideration, for they convey the feeling that the individual is responsible for his own illness or, at least, that his illness results from his own conduct. The conclusion follows that to avoid mental disease one must live circumspectly, control one's self, and comply with the demands of faith, morals, and society. This desirable philosophy of life, however, does not necessarily protect against mental illness.

In a small book published in 1840 under the title *Zur Diatetik der Seele* (Hygiene of the Mind),[6] the psychiatrist Ernst von Feuchtersleben (1806–49) made a masterful presentation of the value of virtuous conduct in the promotion of mental health. He could find no sharp distinction between normal and abnormal mental states and felt that the treatment of mental patients should be in line with measures ordinarily indicated for the correction of inappropriate con-

[6] English translation, from the 3rd edition of 1910, by F. C. Sumner (New York: The Macmillan Co., 1933).

duct. His thinking was molded by the Christian tradition. Thus, frustration is a necessary and a healthy factor in human development and conduct; it is often the indulgence of every whim, the unwillingness to support hardship, and the refusal to sacrifice that contribute to mental illness. Therefore, the essence of psychotherapy would be re-education. This oversimplification of the problem did not conceal from Von Feuchtersleben some important aspects of mental life to which modern psychiatry addresses itself. He had a rather clear notion of "total personality," and was impressed with the contribution of imagination to disease or to the symptoms of disease. "Fantasy," he stated, "is the atmosphere of the mind. In it alone the real diseases of the mind have their root and their seat." Fantasy always increases the capacity for the unreal. In fantasy, sensation and imagination fuse. If fantasy grows out of bounds, "it makes us dream while awake and we stand at the first step of insanity."

Our present concept of the psychogenesis of symptoms, while not known by that term, was widely accepted in the first four decades of the nineteenth century. However fanciful and incomplete the case histories of the time now appear, it is certain that much of today's psychosomatic medicine was known, or at least glimpsed, in certain German schools of medicine. There were other anticipations of modern ideas. Johann Christian Heinroth (1773–1843) gave excellent descriptions of melancholia, self-centeredness, and withdrawal from reality, and was impressed by the significance of guilt feelings. He also showed some awareness of the unconscious, for he found that the "real guilt" which underlies the symptoms is often unknown to the patient, who accuses himself of all sorts of imaginary misdeeds. The German philosopher, K. L. Michelet (1801–93), interpreted mental disease as a state in which two personalities—the personality of the dream and the personality of awareness—appear in the state of awareness as equally justified and equally real. He also spoke of "the extreme of melancholic temperament, a state in which the individual is closed to the external world and has lost all practical, but not necessarily all theoretical, interest." What he had in mind, probably, is a form of schizophrenic withdrawal. Implicit in these allusions is the idea of an unconscious.

As a matter of fact, the literature of the first half of the nineteenth century contains numerous explicit references to the "unconscious." The unconscious was mentioned by Karl Gustav Carus (1789–1869),[7] director of the Medico-Chirurgical Academy at Dresden and personal physician to the King of Saxony. For Carus the soul is the life-giving and formative principle of the organism, but its operations are unconscious. The unconscious performances, in fact, underlie all others. The key to the knowledge of the conscious life of the soul, he said, lies in the region of the unconscious. Carus shared with the Romantics the idea of a universal symbolism and also their interest in hypnotism. This he regarded as a potent therapeutic measure, though not to be used indiscriminately.[8]

The rise of the Romantic movement in the nineteenth century created an atmosphere favorable to the emergence of ideas which would prove compatible with modern psychiatry. In rebellion against the rationalism, formalism, and classicism of the preceding century, the Romantics sought naturalness, spontaneity, and movement, the feeling and mystery of life. Wordsworth, Coleridge, and Carlyle in England, Rousseau and Balzac in France, Goethe and Schelling in Germany, and a host of other famous names attest to the strength and depth of this movement. The Romantics were intensely aware of the "nocturnal sides of the soul." Dreams, hypnotic phenomena, and somnambulism figure prominently in their writings—literary, philosophical, and medical. The Romantics preferred to consider these phenomena not in abstract generalizations but in terms of the feelings and emotions

[7] Carus, K., *Psyche*, ed. Ludwig Kalges (Jena: Diederich, 1926). Quoted by Ellenberger, H., "The Unconscious Before Freud," *Bulletin of the Menninger Clinic*, 21:3–15 (1957).

[8] The origins of hypnotism go back to the latter part of the eighteenth century, when the Viennese physician, Friedrich Anton Mesmer (1734–1815), discovered "animal magnetism." We shall discuss this phenomenon in Chapter VII.

proper to the individual alone. They were interested in hypnotic phenomena from the point of view of the individual, unlike Mesmer, for instance, who attributed these phenomena to some agent ("magnetic fluid") supposedly possessed by the hypnotizer. What is of importance for our purposes is that the magnetic "cures" entailed a personal relation between physician and patient. The psychiatrist today realizes the great importance of the physician-patient relationship. Thus, by recognizing the role of irrational factors in human conduct and experience, and by centering interest on the individual, the Romantics brought more attention to the history and personality of the patient and to the circumstances of his personal life. All these came to be regarded as most important aspects of a "case." The logic of this point of view is confirmed by modern psychiatry.

The anti-mechanistic trend in Romanticism and its rejection of pure reason as sufficient for understanding nature, plus the idea of a progressive complexity of life, as stressed by Jean Jacques Rousseau (1712–78), led to an idealization of the past as a time of a simpler, more natural, life for man. Apparently the Romantics saw the immediate and spontaneous expression or realization of man's being as threatened by the new forms of existence. There was a feeling, too, that the practice of medicine was no longer adequate, that the medical art needed to penetrate more deeply into the interior of life.

The ideas of those who related mental disease to the personal antecedents of the patient (sin, guilt), as well as Romantic notions of the "irrational" elements in man, of the influence of mind over body, of "depths" and "nocturnal sides" in human nature, led to a more personalistic interpretation of mental disease. Unfortunately, these valuable insights were not supported by sufficient empirical data. Just as the proponents of rationalism had had an exaggerated confidence in the power of reason, the Romantics in their revolt against this relied too much on intuition and on imaginative explanation and construction. Nor could their opposition to the growing mechanization of life change the course of events. The Romantic movement was doomed to an early eclipse. From the middle of the nineteenth century empiricism and science predominated. "Romantic" became a derogatory term, synonymous with "fantastic," "unscientific," and "unrealistic." There reigned a new spirit, increasingly inclined toward the principles effective in other disciplines: objective observation of phenomena, experimentation, the conversion of observations into measurable data, and the induction of physical laws which seemed to determine such data.

Institutional Reforms

It is necessary to return at this point to the time at which reforms in the care of the mentally ill became of interest to the medical profession. From the eighteenth century on, as science made rapid advances, medical practitioners were returning to the neglected territory of mental disease. At first they devoted their efforts to clinical observations and to the construction of theory, but near the close of the century they became increasingly concerned with the humanitarian aspects of the problem. Anton Mueller (1755–1827) in Germany, Vincenzo Chiarugi (1759–1820) in Italy, Philippe Pinel (1745–1826) in France, and William Tuke (1732–1822) in England pioneered the revolution in the care of the insane that foreshadowed a new era.

Until the end of the eighteenth century, there were no properly organized mental hospitals. Psychotic patients were usually incarcerated in dismal places, along with the criminals and derelicts of the time. In 1793 Pinel was made physician-in-chief of the old *Grange aux Gueux* (*La Bicêtre*) in Paris. He immediately had forty-nine inmates released from their chains, prescribed walks, outdoor work, and humane consideration in their treatment, and censored the injudicious bloodletting prevalent at the time, along with the indiscriminate use of drugs. He studied his patients carefully, talked to them frequently, and kept detailed case records of their illnesses. He also produced a three-volume work, *Nosographie Philosophique* (1798)[9] in an effort to bring some order out of the chaos of nosology, for without this kind of systematic classifi-

[9] 3e ed.; Paris: Brosson, 1808.

cation of diseases, medical science can hardly begin. With justification this humanitarian physician really could be called the father of modern psychiatry.

In Britain a similar revolution was under way, initiated this time by a layman, William Tuke. For long periods the mentally ill in the British Isles had shared the tragic fate of their fellow sufferers in other lands. In the days of the Saxons they lived in an atmosphere of superstition and castigation, with a rather weird polypharmacy thrown in for good measure. In his *Chapters in the History of the Insane in the British Isles* (1882)[10] Daniel Hack Tuke cites a tenth-century work of unknown authority, *Leechdoms, Wortcunning and Starcraft of Early England,* of which the title alone establishes the level of scientific understanding. The various prescriptions cited by Tuke show that a distinction was made between devil-sickness and lunacy, or witlessness. All, however, contained a dash of magic. One prescription for the lunatic reads as follows: "Take clove wort and wreathe it with a red thread about a man's swere (neck) when the moon is on the wane, in the month which is called April, in the early part of October; soon he will be healed."

In Ireland there was the Valley of the Lunatics in Kerry to which all "lunatics" would find their way on their own. In the valley there were two wells edged by cresses. He who drank from these wells and ate of the cresses would be restored to mental health. This ancient tradition still reigned a century ago. It is of interest that the Valley of the Lunatics was not the gloomy place the name might imply. A visitor in the year 1845 wrote of it: "Lo we turned a hill and there before us lay a lovely valley . . . so varied and so beautiful was the Madman's Glen. If any aspect of nature could work such a blessed change, the repose, peace, and plenty of this charming valley would restore the unsettled brain of a poor unfortunate."[11]

In London, around the fourteenth century, Bethlehem Hospital, originally a priory, came to be used for the insane,

10 Kegan Paul, London: Trench & Co., 1882.
11 *Op. cit.,* pp. 23–26.

as well as for criminals of many types. At an early period it was styled Bethlem Prison House; later it was called Bedlam. Half a century after the death of Henry VIII the name carried hideous implications. In 1674 the premises were so unfit that it was decided to build another hospital. Under the same name and accommodating 120–150 patients, this hospital opened in 1676—the first large asylum in England. It also became one of the sights of the metropolis; an admission fee of one shilling was charged for the privilege of witnessing the antics of the lunatics. This practice continued until 1770. Hogarth's portrayal of "The Rake's Progress," which shows the latter's fall to complete degradation in Bedlam, reflected the attitudes of society toward the insane.[12] Like the criminal, the deranged person in that attitude was not like other humans but one whose fate was determined by his own depravity.

By the beginning of the eighteenth century the social problem of mental illness forced governing bodies to place paupers under the control of lay overseers. The change was not altogether commendable. Management concerned itself largely with the control or prevention of unruliness, by punishment if necessary. The wardens chained, beat, and bled the patients, usually in clear conscience, since these practices had the endorsement of the medical profession. Thus, William Cullen (1710–90) advocated restraint as a means of controlling excitement and also of ensuring the safety of the patient. It was essential, he held, that patients be afraid of their keepers. Beatings were therefore justified, unless it was clear that the patient did not understand the reasons for the punishment. John Battie, a private-hospital physician, also recommended punishment if excitement could not be controlled by medication (use of the poppy). In addition to beating, he prescribed "blisters, caustics, and rough cathartics."[13] Some doctors were indignant at the ignorance of others. Dr. John Munro, then medical superintendent of Bethlehem Hospital, attacked

[12] See Bromberg, W., *Man Above Humanity* (Philadelphia: J. B. Lippincott Co., 1954), p. 77.

[13] Battie, W., *A Treatise on Madness* (London: Whiston and White, 1758).

Battie's use of bleeding, blisters, and other brutal methods. "If these general methods are applied without judgment or discretion," he declared, "common sense will at once join with madness and reject them too."[14] An outstanding advocate of humanization of treatment was W. Perfect (1740–89), whose book *Select Cases in the Different Species of Insanity or Madness*[15] was a landmark in eighteenth-century psychiatry. Dr. Battie was eventually brought before the House of Commons during an investigation of madhouses by this body, which led to the 1774 bill bringing private mental institutions under state regulation.

The stage was now almost set for the extension of the reforms inaugurated in 1796 by William Tuke at the York Retreat. However, one event was required to bring the lessons home to all. This event was the insanity of George III, who suffered a number of attacks of manic-depressive psychosis and spent his last years, before his death in 1820, in an intractable psychotic state. In one of his early attacks (1788–89) he was confined in a straitjacket. Numerous consultants were called and there was a fierce difference of opinion between two of them as to the need for force in subduing the King in his delirium. Hearings were held before the House of Commons. The psychiatric controversy occasioned by the use of restraints on the King raged for years. This, together with the sad fate of George III, brought salutary changes in attitudes toward mental illness.

William Tuke shared the belief of humanitarians of his day that the mentally ill were innocent sufferers who were entitled to compassionate understanding, that they had been deprived of reason because of stresses which could be psychological as well as physical. William Tuke was 60 years old when he set the example of moral treatment for the insane in England. Opposed in principle and spirit to the system of restraint treatment, moral treatment acknowledges the human dignity of the patient, and advocates that he be given as much

[14] Munro, J., *Remarks on Dr. Battie's Treatise on Madness* (London: John Clarke, 1758).

[15] (Rochester: J. Murray, 1787).

freedom and responsibility as he is capable of assuming, in surroundings peaceful and conducive to relaxation. In itself, moral treatment is therapeutic, and it provides the atmosphere within which any other kind of therapy can most effectively produce its benefits. Tuke's work made a great impression throughout Europe and America, and he inspired his own family for generations to fight for the cause of the mentally ill.

While the York Retreat became the example of enlightened care and treatment, the York Asylum became the horrible example of the madhouse environment. In response to public pressure after the death and disappearance of several patients, whose relatives had been denied visitation privileges, and then the destruction by fire of the records of the establishment, an investigation was launched. The revelations were more than enough to arouse general indignation, and in 1815 a select committee was appointed to consider the question of providing for the "better regulation of madhouses in England." The committee found shocking things going on, not only at York Asylum, but also in private hospitals operated under license and even in the Admiralty establishment for naval "maniacs." In all, there was a similar reliance on chains, the use of straw or bare boards for beds, filthy conditions, and overcrowding and underventilation that endangered life. The public indignation created by these exposures forced salutary changes, but not all the abuses were rooted out or permanently corrected.

In the second quarter of the nineteenth century new county asylums were provided in which the enlightened treatment of the mentally ill was further advanced. Here the non-restraint movement really began. Pinel and Tuke had abolished chains. Robert Gardener Hill pioneered in non-restraint methods in the mid-1830s.[16] John Conolly (1794–1866) insisted that all forms of mechanical restraint be abolished, and when in 1839 he became physician-in-chief of the Hanwell county asylum, the largest in the country, he carried out his policy

[16] Hill, R. G., *Total Abolition of Personal Restraint in the Treatment of the Insane* (London: Simpkin, Marshall & Co., 1839).

almost immediately. The movement spread widely against vigorous opposition.[17]

During the nineteenth century the term "madhouse" was supplanted by the term "asylum," in recognition of the new therapeutic attitude toward the insane. Unfortunately, the emancipation of patients did not last. With the rise in population and the accumulation of chronic cases in the asylums, moral treatment vanished except in the private hospitals. Mechanical restraint reappeared, now under legal supervision. To the general population the word "asylum" became almost as frightening as "madhouse" had been before it. Yet the record of the hospital movement in Britain is a moving document in the history of psychiatry, and it can be said that British psychiatrists never lost their interest in model hospitals.

The birth and growth of psychiatry in America coincided with the birth and growth of hospitals. Zilboorg has said, with considerable justification, that the nineteenth century seems to have assigned English-speaking peoples the task of building mental hospitals, of improving the lot of the mentally ill, and of passing major legislation to see that enlightened care would be ensured to as great a degree as possible. This does not mean that efforts in this direction were absent in France, Germany, and elsewhere. Under the dominating influence of Pinel and Jean Etienne Dominique Esquirol, psychiatry became a recognized medical discipline in France. All the outstanding early French psychiatrists were medical directors of large institutions. However, through most of the nineteenth century there was a separation of administrative and medical powers which had unfavorable repercussions on mental institutions. In Germany little was done in the way of hospital reform during the first half of the century. There was no lack of interest in matters psychiatric, but it was of a speculative sort. Those who were doing all the writing had

[17] Conolly, J., *An Enquiry Concerning the Indication of Insanity* (London: J. Taylor, 1830). See also his *The Treatment of the Insane Without Mechanical Restraints* (London: Smith Elder, 1856).

little, if any, practical experience with patients. Asylums were not reformed until the second half of the century under the influence of Wilhelm Griesinger (1817–69), an advocate of non-restraint. Then they made rapid strides. However, the dominant interest of German psychiatry in this period was the organic substrate of mental disease.

American Psychiatry

With the exception of Benjamin Rush (1745–90), early American psychiatrists were all directors of mental hospitals. Rush, the father of American psychiatry, studied in Edinburgh under Cullen, acquiring from the latter a special interest in the nervous system and in phenomena of behavior. His book *Medical Inquiries and Observations Upon Diseases of the Mind*[18] was the only American book in the field for many decades. Rush used purgatives and emetics in profusion to treat patients, advocated bloodletting, and devised instruments which subjected patients to a rather primitive shock therapy. Psychiatry was but one of his medical preoccupations, and medicine but one of his humanitarian interests, as his signature to the Declaration of Independence eloquently attests.

In the city of Philadelphia the Pennsylvania Hospital received insane patients as early as 1752, but the first public hospital exclusively set up for them originated in Williamsburg, Virginia, in the year 1773. Moral treatment[19] was introduced in America in the first two decades of the nineteenth century during the pioneer period of private hospitals. One of the early asylums was Bloomingdale, opened in 1821 as a separately managed hospital after thirty years of activity within the New York Hospital. Friends Hospital in Philadelphia opened in 1817, McLean in Belmont, Massachusetts, in 1818, and the Hartford Retreat in 1822. The remarkable

---

[18] (Philadelphia: Kimber and Richardson, 1812).

[19] So-called moral treatment was never clearly defined. As used in the early part of the last century, it meant that the patient was made comfortable, treated kindly, and taught some useful form of handiwork. This was in contradistinction to the stripes and abuses to which mental patients were often subjected.

work of Eli Todd (1769–1833) at the Hartford Retreat was an inspiration to a number of New England physicians to devote themselves to the cause of the mentally ill. It did much to persuade influential citizens that mental disease was curable, given adequate facilities, medical direction, and humane treatment. Actually, a cult of curability soon grew up, but its claims became extravagant and it terminated, as most cults do, in disillusionment.

The thirties and forties of the nineteenth century were marked by the rise of state mental hospitals headed by extremely able medical men. Of the thirteen founders of the American Psychiatric Association, six were in charge of state institutions, five of incorporated hospitals, and two of private hospitals. Founded simultaneously by these men was the *American Journal of Insanity* (now the *American Journal of Psychiatry*) under the editorship of Amariah Brigham (1798–1849), superintendent of New York's first state hospital, in Utica. Presented in the *Journal*, usually in Brigham's elegant style, was a worldwide coverage of psychiatric experience and thought, together with original contributions and eloquent statements for the cause of psychiatry.

These superintendents and their example affected attitudes in psychiatry for years to come, and their influence abides. The roster of distinguished names includes the first president of the Association, Samuel B. Woodward (1787–1850); Isaac Ray (1807–81), eminent authority in forensic psychiatry; and Thomas Kirkbride (1809–83), unrivaled authority in hospital construction. The original founders the American Psychiatric Association were advocates of relatively small hospitals. Later in the century, as mental hospitals became monolithic and deteriorated to the status of custodial institutions, the wisdom of their recommendations found tragic confirmation. Only now, more than a century later, are we witnessing a movement in the direction of the smaller hospital favorable to the therapeutic community envisaged by our predecessors.

Another important force in the history of American psychiatry was Dorothea Dix (1802–87), tireless crusader, who was responsible for the creation or expansion of mental hospitals in twenty states and in practically as many nations abroad. Her work, which started in 1841, went on for years. By bringing the issues before the public and their representatives in the legislatures, she helped to get the mentally ill out of prisons, almshouses, cellars, and dungeons and into a humane and promising environment. She would not have been pleased, however, by the ultimate result, for the mental hospital was set apart from the community in a way that led to the isolation of patients, administrators, and personnel alike, thus ensuring their eventual separation from the main body of medical practice.

As victims of mental illness multiplied, it became impossible to continue moral treatment with such a vast case load. The difficulties of the hospital staffs were compounded by the fact that so many immigrants were landing in state hospitals. This, we know today, can only be expected when people are placed under the stress of adapting themselves to a strange country, new customs, and at the same time, in many instances, a strange language. The problem rapidly outgrew the capacity of hospital psychiatry, particularly with shortage of funds added to shortage of available personnel. The moral therapist thus disappeared and the watchful, custodial, mishap-avoiding psychiatrist took his place. Many families would keep patients at home, rather than send them to the bulging, increasingly shabby, increasingly hopeless institutions, which soon did little but house their failures. A new spirit was needed badly. That spirit, as we shall see, gained impetus through the work of Adolf Meyer (1866–1950), a young physician who arrived from Switzerland in the nineties.

Other Preludes to the Modern Era

French psychiatry of the nineteenth century showed a spirit of marked ambiguity, incessantly emphasizing organic, degenerative approaches to mental disease, but on the other hand manifesting a deep interest in its psychological aspects. The latter emphasis was symbolized in the foundation of the Société Médico-Psychologique in 1847. The famed clinician Esquirol (1772–1840) had a healthy respect for the emotions as a source of psychological illness. There is a long list of French workers throughout the nineteenth century, and beyond, who specialized in psychological research, among them Jean Pierre Falret (1794–1870), Jules Gabriel François Baillarger (1809–90), Benedict Augustin Morel (1809–73), Valentin Jacques Joseph Magnan (1835–1916), and Pierre Janet (1859–1947). The great Jean Martin Charcot (1825–93) also displayed admirable psychological intuition, though his interests were largely neurological.

In contrast to German psychiatrists, who remained antagonistic to hypnosis, many French authorities made a serious study of it. From Charcot's renowned clinic in Paris and from the work of Ambroise-August Liébault (1823–1904) and Hippolyte Bernheim (1840–1919) in Nancy came evidence that certain bodily symptoms could be produced by hypnotic suggestion—paralyses of the limbs, anesthesias, blindness, and other sensorimotor symptoms. It was demonstrated that purely mental influences could evoke somatic disturbances, and the inference was plain that bodily symptoms could be made to disappear in the same manner. It was shown that loss of memory and various pathological ideas and motivations could be caused by purely mental factors. Now the scene was set for the arrival of Sigmund Freud, an event of such importance that a separate chapter will be devoted to it.

Emil Kraepelin

From Pinel on, efforts to produce a useful classification of mental diseases continued unabated. Some good leads came out of these efforts, but in the main, classification continued to be naïve and chaotic for most of the nineteenth century. It took the splendid systematizing mind of Kraepelin (1855–1925) to break through the impasse.

An objective observer with a broad biological approach, Emil Kraepelin wished to pattern psychiatry according to the perspectives and methods of internal medicine. Thus, illness is a process engendered by a definite cause, with a mode of development and a course obedient to certain intrinsic laws. The inadequacy of psychiatry in this respect was distressing to Kraepelin. In 1883 he brought out a small textbook of psychiatry, which he called Kompendium, the first version of his famous Lehrbuch. While writing this, he became more clearly conscious of the dearth of psychiatric knowledge and guiding principles. Only a few useful concepts had been worked out before, to guide psychiatric research and therapy —a concept of dementia praecox, of mania and melancholia, and of some forms of schizophrenia—but when Kraepelin entered the field, even these were in eclipse, and workers were floundering around in a morass of symptoms. The best they could do was to classify on the basis of "congenital" or "acquired" disorders. Dealing with masses of clinical observations, Kraepelin reduced these to basic symptoms, modes of onset and evolution, and terminal states. In this way he succeeded in identifying major clinical types, some of which are still accepted. With the fifth edition of the *Lehrbuch* (1896)[20] the Kraepelinian system came to its full expression.

A fundamental part of Kraepelin's contribution was the establishment of dementia praecox and manic-depressive psychoses as separate entities. Under the broad framework of this twofold division, he identified multiple forms which he thought the diseases could take, and he theorized about the underlying causes. Although some of his concepts have been challenged, he laid many of the essential building stones for the future, and, by establishing the fact that every mental disease is a disease like any other and can be similarly distinguished and investigated, he bridged the gap between medicine and psychiatry. Once Kraepelin's work was accomplished, psychiatry could enter its classifying and prognosticating era with confidence. There was only one unfortunate consequence of Kraepelin's theorizing. He was certain that cases of dementia praecox, if not always, then at least with overwhelming probability, would terminate in irreparable deterioration. Attempts at therapy, therefore, seemed to be useless, and this nihilistic attitude was not reversed until more dynamic concepts of mental illness were introduced by psychoanalysis and by the psychobiology of Adolf Meyer.

Brief mention should probably be made at this point of Eugen Bleuler (1857–1939), a Swiss psychiatrist, though we

[20] *Psychiatrie: Ein Lehrbuch für Studierende und Aerzte* (Fünfte Aufl.; Leipzig: J. A. Barth, 1896).

shall encounter him in the next chapter and several times later on. Bleuler found it necessary to modify Kraepelin's concepts regarding dementia praecox and to broaden them and rename the disorder "schizophrenia," for many psychiatrists were unwilling to make a diagnosis of dementia praecox in individuals who were neither young nor demented. By schizophrenia, Bleuler meant a group of psychoses characterized by a specific type of alteration of thinking, feeling, and relation to the external world. The term "schizophrenia" was used because the splitting of the psychic functions was one of its most important characteristics. While it is true that changing the name of a disease does not cure it, in this case it made the symptoms more understandable and, in a way, made the outlook more hopeful.

Adolf Meyer

By the time Kraepelin brought order out of the confusion of nosology, psychiatry had swung almost entirely to the organic, impersonal orientation, and the deterioration in the care and treatment of psychiatric patients had become alarming. In America one glimmer of hope came with the introduction of nursing schools into mental hospitals. This began in the eighties and continued thereafter. Even more important was the appointment of neuropathologists to the staffs of the hospitals. The first of these physicians to devote himself full time to this work was Adolf Meyer, an exponent of the best traditions of European psychiatry. Well trained in neuroanatomy and pathology, psychiatry, and philosophy, Meyer was destined to exert an enormous influence on American psychiatry of the twentieth century.

In the view of Adulf Meyer, adequate studies of the living patient were fundamental in psychiatric research. His insistence on detailed case histories, exacting mental and physical examinations, and thorough laboratory studies helped change the emphasis in clinical psychiatry and psychiatric research. In addition, it led to a new concept of mental illness called "psychobiology," which might have made greater headway were it not for the unfortunately complicated terminology in which the concepts were couched. Meyer's early work in public mental hospitals, his collection of all available facts about a patient, his study of the psychoses in this way, made him suspect a relation between habit patterns and mental illnesses. He concluded that these were understandable as reactions of the total personality to life's stresses. Organic, sociological, general cultural, and psychological aspects of the life of the individual were all synthesized in his approach. His therapy was highly eclectic, including somatic procedures wherever they were indicated. Meyer, who became professor of psychiatry at Johns Hopkins Medical School, was the first to show how tendencies toward defective adaptation could be recognized long before the onset of overt illness, often very early in life.

Adolf Meyer and Sigmund Freud were contemporaries. Between them they made dynamic psychiatry an actuality, particularly in America. While Meyer never wholeheartedly accepted the theory or method of psychoanalysis, he perceived the importance of its basic concepts and some of his most gifted co-workers and students entered the field of psychoanalysis. Throughout the first half of the twentieth century Meyer was a recognized spokesman for American psychiatry. His views were fundamentally dynamic, intent on the mental conflicts which eventuate in mental disorders, and on the driving forces whose inhibition or antagonism lies behind the conflicts. This outlook is basically psychological, looking to such factors as drives and anxiety-generating situations, mental defense reactions and escapes, fantasies and illusions, and the other elements of psychic operation which form the core of much contemporary psychiatric theory. It is also an optimistic outlook, from the therapeutic point of view, for it implies that as the causes of mental disorder can be grasped, the effects can be reversed through the appropriate psychic treatment. Meyer's immense influence can be traced not only in psychiatric research and clinical psychiatry, but also in hospital organization, psychotherapy, psychiatric education, mental hygiene, child psychiatry, social psychiatry, and psychosomatic medicine. He, with the aid of a distinguished group, among whom were W. A. White, Ernest Southard, Smith Ely Jelliffe, Earl D. Bond, Edward A. Strecker, and others, brought psychology and psychiatry together and gave important impetus to the development of outpatient and community psychiatry and to psychiatric social work. These men were in the tradition of the great moral therapists of the past, yet were of the twentieth century. There were others, of course, but the listing of them would prolong this historical résumé unduly.

III

DR. FREUD, HIS THEORIES AND THEIR INFLUENCE ON AMERICAN PSYCHIATRY

To seize the truth here below by the intelligence, be it in an obscure and partial manner, while waiting to see it in its complete splendor—such is man's destiny according to Christianity. Indeed, far from scorning knowledge, it cherishes it. Intellectum valde ama.

Etienne Gilson[1]

The scientific world was teeming with new ideas when Sigmund Freud grew up in Vienna in the intellectual and cultural climate of the Victorian age. The span of his life, from 1856 to 1939, roughly coincides with far-flung advances in all the sciences. Pure and applied sciences, scientific method and research, all were on the move. Great names abounded; yet it is probable that of that group none shines with a greater luster today than the name of this lonely genius, who devoted himself to the study of the mind of man. That he has been a controversial figure is not to be denied; but he shares that position with many of the great figures of the historical past and the present. If his critics and detractors have been legion, he has also not lacked for followers and admirers. Nor does one have to be a psychoanalyst oneself, nor agree with all of Freud's doctrines, in order to stand in admiration of his genius and of the insights and directions which he gave to psychiatry. If we keep in mind the admonition in the first chapter of this book, that it is wise to know exactly what a man has said before venturing an opinion about his theories, we will be prepared to profit most from

[1] Gilson, E., "The Intelligence in the Service of Christ the King," *The Gilson Reader* (New York: Doubleday & Co., Image Books), p. 32.

what Freud has to teach. This has not always been the case with his critics, and the loss thereby has not seldom been theirs.

Freud was a dedicated, hard-working, good-living, honest man. Religious belief was not one of his attributes, however, and no amount of wishful thinking can attribute it to him. Yet, religion was much more a problem for Freud than even he knew. Karl Stern once stated that, had Freud possessed some of the spiritual insight of a St. John of the Cross or St. Teresa, he would have built his theories into a thing of grandeur and great beauty, but the fact remains that he had not and he did not. As we read his productions, therefore, and are impressed by his genius and his persistence, we need to recall St. Augustine's remarks which were quoted in the first chapter of this book.[2]

In explaining his choice of profession and his directions, Freud states that he felt "no particular predilection for the career of a physician," that he was "moved, rather, by a sort of curiosity, which was, however, directed more towards human concerns than towards natural objects."[3] For him science was truth and reason, and to him this represented the best hope for the future. In exploring the human mind Freud used the scientific method, objectively observing, recording, reducing data to common denominators, formulating working hypotheses and testing them meticulously over long periods. Influenced by prevailing scientific concepts, particularly those of physics, he conceived of man, and indeed of mind, as an energy system responsive to certain basic laws. In the human psyche Freud found primary forces operating at levels deep down and carefully concealed from the individual. Almost singlehandedly and against opposition and ridicule, he breached the ramparts behind which extremely important processes were taking place in man's psychic life.

An independent, resourceful thinker, Freud stood firm through the storms of controversy excited by his unorthodox views. For a decade he worked alone, living simply within the circle of his family, analyzing his patients and also himself, organizing and assessing his observations, writing prodigiously. "In Vienna," he points out, "I was shunned, abroad no notice was taken of me. My *Interpretation of Dreams* was scarcely reviewed. As soon as I realized the inevitable nature of what I had come up against, my sensitiveness greatly diminished."[4] It took courage to go on, however, for Freud had a scintillating reputation in neurology before his interest swung from organic to functional nervous disorders. In all, he published over twenty contributions in neurology and neuropathology, including, in 1891, a monograph on aphasia which became one of the classic studies of modern neurology.[5]

Freud was a research man by inclination, but the necessity of getting enough money to live on had forced him into clinical neurology. In the course of his clinical practice he found that neurotic patients far outnumbered neurologic patients and it did not take him long to see how much he (and psychiatry) had to learn about the neuroses and the reactions of man under emotional pressures. As soon as the opportunity presented itself, in 1886, Freud journeyed to Paris to study under Charcot, one of the leading neurologists of his time. Charcot had certain novel ideas which stimulated the inquisitive and restless mind of Freud. He had dignified hypnosis by using it in the treatment and investigation of certain puzzling nervous disorders. Most impressive to Freud was Charcot's work with hysterics, his demonstration of the genuineness of hysterical phenomena and also of the possibility of inducing hysterical-like paralyses and contractures by hypnotic suggestion. A year earlier Freud's older colleague, Joseph Breuer, had told him about a girl whose manifold hysterical symptoms had apparently been caused by certain highly emotional, forgotten experiences, which could be made conscious during hypnosis. Now, with his Paris experience behind him, Freud began to see mental behavior in another perspective. It appeared to be likely that such behavior might be determined by purely mental factors without any physi-

[4] Freud, *Autobiography*.
[5] Freud, S., *On Aphasia* (New York: International Universities Press, 1953).

cal ailment, even when the patient is completely unaware of these factors. As time went on, he specialized more and more in the treatment of neurotic patients. For these his therapeutic weapons consisted of electrotherapy, an accepted method of treatment in that day, and hypnosis. Freud soon became disenchanted with electrotherapy; he found it to be about as realistic as "the fantasies contained in any Egyptian dreambook."[6] His success with hypnosis, on the other hand, was considerable, though, unfortunately, some patients could not be hypnotized or could not be hypnotized deeply enough.

Like Breuer, Freud used hypnosis to explore the origin of the patient's symptoms (for patients could often recall under hypnosis events which were otherwise completely "forgotten") and for cathartic purposes. In the cathartic process, a patient under the influence of hypnosis could relive and talk out emotional experiences which were normally dammed up and locked away in his memory, and not infrequently this release of the emotions produced a real therapeutic effect. In a book published jointly in 1895 by Breuer and Freud, *Studien über Hysterie*,[7] the significance of the life of the emotions was tentatively, yet brilliantly, exposed. Foreshadowing things to come, the book made reference to mental acts which were conscious and to those which were unconscious, and suggested that neurotic symptoms arise through the damming up of emotions, and the consequent displacement of psychic energy from one purpose to another.

With the accumulation of experience, Freud was impressed by the frequency with which current or past sexual conflicts figured in the dynamics of neuroses. This was a finding which he had not anticipated. To him, however, the evidence became increasingly persuasive and he soon concluded that neuroses, without exception, were due to disturbances of the sexual function. When he ventured to say so before various medical societies, and when, in particular, he attributed sexuality to the infantile periods of life—though he did not mean exclusively genital sexuality—his colleagues ceased to

[6] Freud, *Autobiography*.

[7] Breuer, J., and Freud, S., "Studies on Hysteria," *Nervous and Mental Monographs* (New York, 1950).

listen to him. Even Breuer parted with him because of this issue, and the critics were forever to have something to allude to with scorn.

The years of ostracism began. Because of his increasing dissatisfaction with hypnosis, plus his strong impression that the personal emotional relationship between physician and patient was vitally important in the therapeutic process, Freud began to think in terms of another route to unconscious material. As his mind ranged among various possibilities, he remembered an experiment which he had seen Bernheim perform in Nancy. In it the subject, following arousal from hypnosis, carried out on schedule an order given by the hypnotist during the trance, and then upon persistent urging was able to remember that he had been given the order while under hypnosis. The events, therefore, experienced in the hypnotic trance were not entirely cut off from normal, waking consciousness after the trance was broken. Freud surmised on the basis of this fact that it might be possible to induce a patient to recall into consciousness the buried and pathogenic contents of his mind and to experience the catharsis, without the use of hypnosis at all. At first he would urge the patient to remember things which were associated with some theme which itself seemed to be associated with the pathogenic content. He found it was possible in this way to bring forgotten material to consciousness, but he also found the patient putting up an internal "resistance" to the process.

The materials which resisted resurrection in the patient's mind were always something painful to recollect, provoking affects of shame, self-reproach, anxiety, and the like. The resistance, however, was not deliberate; it was more like an unconscious and reflex flinching away from pain. Freud tried actively urging the patient to exert effort to overcome the resistance, and he tried tricks, like applying pressure on the patient's forehead to distract him from the need to resist, but these methods were only slightly effective.

The next step was the use of free association. If the patient could not directly break down whatever barrier was preventing his memories from emerging into consciousness, perhaps he could flank it. Perhaps by giving his thoughts free rein and uttering whatever comes into his mind, the train of the thoughts might lead from one to another until they touched on the buried materials and "pulled" them into view. According to Freud, free association is not random association. The succession of thoughts which come to mind in the analytic situation will almost always have some reference to that situation. The free associations will tend towards the crucial materials. This does not mean that resistances will not continue to appear. Freud found that sooner or later the associations would simply stop, or the patient would start making critical objections, or use allusions and approximations rather than a direct expression of the submerged materials. But this would give the analyst the opportunity to offer interpretations on the basis of what he believed to be the character of the unconscious material. Instead of trying to force the buried contents out directly, he would approach it through the interpretation of its various manifestations, including the fact of resistance itself. Thus psychoanalysis became an "act of interpretation" and thereby began to develop its corpus of unique and original knowledge about the unconscious mind of man.

The Principal Elements of Psychoanalytic Theory

The concept of resistance, the mental mechanism which acts to keep memories below the threshold of consciousness, is one of the key constituents of psychoanalytic theory. Allied to it is the concept of repression—the force which originally ejected from consciousness ideas or impulses which for some reason or other were unacceptable. Repression thrusts ideas out of consciousness and resistance keeps them out; if these two concepts are understood, the division between the conscious and the unconscious mind begins to come clear.

The assumption of an unconscious played a great role in philosophy, literature, and psychology before Freud. What is novel in Freud is the idea of the unconscious as a psychical system, that is, as a system of thoughts, images, fantasies, emotions, and drives actively and "purposively" operating outside the sphere of conscious awareness, harboring irrational or emotional elements derived from a person's remote past, alive with contents inadmissible to consciousness, possessed of boundless energy. The contents of the unconscious are presumed to be images or anticipations of modes of behavior that would bring gratification to instinctual strivings. To understand why these materials are kept in the unconscious, we must see the role of anxiety in the workings of the mind. In Freud's later speculative work, it is mental anxiety which triggers repression and maintains resistance, anxiety being understood as a signal of possible danger from within. Like fear of external dangers, anxiety is a reaction to a threat, but in this case, the threat is from within the mind itself. It is the propulsive force of the instinctual drives which causes anxiety—the hostilities, aggressions, and sexual impulses whose overt satisfaction would precipitate a personal crisis for the individual. The anxieties may actually be quite unjustified, given the real situation; indeed, they are often fantasied, misinterpreted, infantile, and irrational. The effect nevertheless is the same—repression of the contents which provoke them.[8]

The unconscious, then, is a storehouse of materials once conscious and now repressed, but it is more than this. It has its own dynamism in which tendencies, instincts, impulses, and dammed-up feelings remain operative. Repression gives it its fantasies and ideas, and also seems somehow to increase the force of the instinctual urges by blocking their discharge, but the urges themselves arise within the unconscious as the very driving forces of mental life. Hence the unconscious is active; images are associated there, ideas are worked out, "plans" are "formulated," symbols are evoked, emotions and feelings are aroused, tensions are raised. Basically this melee of psychological activity is polarized around two axes, aggression and sexuality.

The exact form in which the contents of the unconscious exist is problematical, but the same is true of the data of ordinary memory, which we know must be preserved in some way, since they are available to recall. The contents of the

[8] See p. 84 ff. "Anxiety According to Freud" for a fuller discussion of this very important point.

true unconscious are not so available. They emerge only when the mind's defenses are down, for instance, in dreams or in slips of the tongue and other lapses and symptomatic acts which Freud wrote about in his *Psychopathology of Everyday Life*.[9] If they never emerged they would, of course, be forever unknown. From what does emerge under specially favorable circumstances, some insight can be gained into the "midnight zone" of the mind.

The Instincts

The instincts, according to Freud, are inborn and unchangeable, and their demands persist throughout life. They are the psychological manifestations of basic biological needs. The law of the instincts is to find gratification in satisfying modes of behavior, and this gratification Freud termed pleasure. If an instinctual demand remains ungratified, it produces internal tension, and this is understood as pain. The "pleasure principle"—to obtain pleasure and avoid pain—inexorably rules the life of the instincts. The instincts do not enter into consciousness as such, but find representation there in the form of images of situations or conduct which afford them satisfaction. If there is no conflict with environmental forces (the rules of society), the individual can carry out the actions prompted by the instinctual drives and obtain direct satisfaction. If there is conflict, the individual must either seek gratification by a detour, by the pursuit of substitute goals (this is called "sublimation of instinctual drives"), or repress conscious representation of the satisfying behavior into the unconscious. The degree to which the individual is able to work, to fulfill his normal functions, to enjoy life, depends on the degree to which he can find suitable outlets for instinctual energies, and to the degree that he cannot, outlets may develop in the form of abnormal behavior of some kind.

At first, Freud envisioned two primary instincts—the sexual instinct, or libido, and the ego instinct, which serves the preservation of the individual. This classification was rather akin to the biological classification of instincts into those pre-

[9] 2nd ed. (London: Benn, 1948).

serving the race and those preserving the self. Later Freud modified his original views, giving a much wider meaning to libido, so that it included all life-seeking drive energy, and introducing an opposing destructive instinct to account for aggressive and "death-seeking" urges. The life instinct he called Eros, after the Greek god of love, and the destructive instinct, Thanatos, after the Greek personification of death. These, he said, were the two primal instincts, the two constant forces arising from the organism itself, striving through the psyche to secure specific forms of pleasurable discharge. The function of the life instinct is to bind, to unite, to maintain life. It expresses itself in three ways: through sexual or organ-satisfying impulses, through self-preservation impulses, and through sublimated impulses derived from impulses originally associated with organ satisfaction. This last mode of expression encompasses many and far-flung aims—artistic pursuits, all sorts of social relationships, sports and competitions, and, in fine, all positive, gratifying behavior. The death instinct also has three components: impulses towards regression, that is, towards more primitive, infantile forms of feeling and behavior; impulses which aim to injure or destroy the individual; and impulses which aim at the injury or destruction of other objects. Freud felt that these two primal instincts never operated in the pure form, but were actually complexly entangled with each other. The process of life, he speculated, was a conflict and compromise worked out between the two of them.

Freud's ideas concerning the life instinct have been unquestionably fruitful. He showed the many-sidedness of Eros in the life of the individual. The hypothetical death instinct, however, retains little popularity among psychoanalysts. Freud used it to clarify problems of aggression, sadism, and masochism, for these injury-inflicting behaviors seemed incapable of reduction to any other meaningful psychic element. They seemed to present themselves as prime data of evidence, to be accepted as such. Freud, however, was himself the first to recognize the tentative nature of these constructs, as is evident in the following declaration: "The theory of the instincts is, as it were, our mythology. The instincts are mythical beings, superb in their indefiniteness."[10]

The Oedipus Complex

The real force of Freud's speculations about the instincts cannot be grasped from a more or less abstract description of the different kinds of instincts. He was much more deeply concerned with the concrete forms the instincts assume in the life of the individual, and above all, in that instinctual phenomenon which he called the Oedipus complex. This, if anything, is the key to orthodox psychoanalysis; by Freud's own account, one may judge how much a psychoanalyst one is by the degree the Oedipus complex theory is accepted. This complex, Freud taught, emerges in the phase of late infancy. The child becomes emotionally fixed by an intense instinctual attachment to one of his parents, usually the boy to his mother and the girl to her father. The other parent is experienced as a rival, and powerful jealous and hostile feelings are aroused. In baldest terms, a boy child wants to possess his mother exclusively, and to destroy or somehow get rid of his father, and a girl child feels the same way, with the roles of the parents reversed. If this formulation sounds too harsh, the truth of the matter may be expressed as the Swiss psychoanalyst, Charles Baudouin, expressed it: In a child, love is extraordinarily wholehearted and jealous.[11] In any event, the situation, from the child's point of view, is intolerable. His hostile feelings towards one parent arouse his own anxieties, for a parent looms as a formidable figure on the limited horizon of a child. To escape anxiety, the child must repress his jealousy, and with it, the instinctual love which is its cause. This is the beginning of repression. How and how successfully the child manages to resolve his internal struggle determines the character of his later reactions when instinctual demands are involved. Ordinarily he succeeds fairly well in relinquish-

[10] Freud, S., "Anxiety and Instinctual Life," *New Introductory Lectures on Psycho-analysis* (New York: W. W. Norton & Co., 1933).
[11] Baudouin, C., *The Mind of the Child* (New York: Dodd, Mead & Co., 1933), p. 51.

ing his parental attachments and turns to other activities and interests; if he does not, the stage is set for psychological problems later in life.

Even if the theory of the Oedipus complex has not always been accepted in its most rigorous formulation, its influence on general psychological theory has been far from negligible. Freud's emphasis on the significance and often lasting effectiveness of experiences in early childhood has had great impact on our notions of education and of human life in general. The recognition of the crucial role of early childhood in the formation of character and general outlook on reality has been a landmark contribution. To be sure, generations of poets and philosophers have known that the child is father of the man, but Freud demonstrated this on the basis of careful study of real people, and within a context which made his statements particularly impressive. That his ideas have often been exaggerated and have led to educational excesses is not his fault.

The Id, the Ego, and the Superego

In his later years, Freud speculated about the anatomy of the psyche,[12] and formulated a theory which has proved extremely useful in the study of human behavior. He suggested that the psychic apparatus can be divided into three systems —the id, the ego, and the superego. The *id* is the reservoir of psychic energy or libido, and comprises the unconscious pretty much as it was described earlier in this chapter. In the id, the pleasure principle reigns supreme, and reality is ignored. The *ego* is the conscious system of personality; its sphere embraces external perceptions of reality, meaningful thought and organization of experience, deliberation and the control of behavior. It is attuned to reality, but in touch also with the internal strivings originating in the id. Its function is to bring harmony between reality and the demands of the instincts, controlling these latter until they can be satisfied in some way consonant with the limitations imposed by the

[12] In psychiatry, psyche is described as the mind, in distinction to the soma, or body.

real situation. The *superego* is an internalization of social norms and social pressures, largely unconscious. In some ways, it is like a conscience. It is formed for the most part when the Oedipus complex is resolved, when the primordial instinctual goals of the child are repressed and the external, environmental forces, particularly the demands of the parents, are accepted internally and become more or less automatic rules of conduct.

Behavior is a resultant of the interaction of these three psychic apparatuses. From the id comes a constant demand for instinctual satisfactions. The superego prohibits certain kinds of behavior as conflicting with what the individual has accepted as society's demands. The ego must find modes of behavior which gratify the instincts either directly or through substitute goals, taking into account both the prohibitions imposed by the superego and the opportunities and limitations afforded in the given real situation. It is not always an easy task. Sometimes the demands of the superego are harsh, rigid, and comprehensive, and if they are ignored, sharp anxieties will be aroused. Sometimes the urgings from the id become intense and compelling, and if they are not satisfied, tension builds up. Sometimes the ego can see no way realistically to satisfy the id's demands and the superego's prohibitions, and a state of chronic unrest ensues. Freud seemed sometimes to despair of the ego's ever satisfactorily resolving its difficult task: "Helpless in either direction, the ego defends itself vainly, alike against the instigations of the murderous id and against the reproaches of the punishing conscience."[13] It was a difficult role the ego played, but on its success devolved the issue of mental health or disease.

Dreams and Neuroses

The interpretation of dreams is the royal road to the unconscious. This now-famous dictum of Freud expressed both the satisfaction and the hope he experienced when he began to achieve some insight into the role dreams play in man's

[13] Freud, S., *The Ego and the Id* (London: The Hogarth Press, 1955), p. 78.

psychic life. In the state of sleep, the censoring action of the ego is somewhat relaxed and the contents of the id can make their appearance, not always directly and undisguised but still more abundantly and manifestly than is possible during waking hours. From what appears in dreams some notion can be gained not only of what goes on in the id but also how the ego goes about defending itself against it.

Freud distinguishes the manifest content of dreams, which is what the dreamer remembers, from the latent content, which contains the hidden meaning of the dream. The latent content usually embodies a wish, often a repressed wish. The manifest content is produced from the latent content via the dream work—condensation, displacement, secondary elaboration, and symbolization. Condensation takes several latent elements with some characteristic in common and weaves them into a composite. Displacement transfers the emotional value of one idea to another. Secondary elaboration welds the dream content transformed by condensation and displacement into a relatively coherent sequence of events, and symbolization uses some object to represent an unconscious or latent dream thought. Certain objects in dreams have a fairly constant symbolic value.

Freud's *The Interpretation of Dreams*,[14] published in 1900, is based upon far-reaching and meticulous research. The work was a fundamental building stone for psychoanalysis. From his work with patients and in studying his own dreams, he found that, if the dream is separated into its elemental parts, each element is capable of awakening lines of association. Abundant psychic material can be brought forth by association, much of it traceable to childhood life. In this way, an ingenious thought structure becomes recognizable in dreams. Acoustic and visual features predominate, and symbols, the language of the unconscious, are used in profusion. Freud discovered that what is outstanding in the manifest content of the dream has by no means the same importance in the dream thought. There have been adroit transformations designed to make the latent thought innocuous

14 London: The Hogarth Press, 1953.

enough to get past the prevailing censorship. As Poul Bjerre
explains it: "Even during the deepest sleep of the night the
sentries that guard consciousness from repressed experiences
do not slumber."[15] An interesting phenomenon also occurs in
the area of affects. In the dream something quite unimpor-
tant can be bound up with the strongest possible emotion.
The affect has been transferred from the real source to some
indifferent object.

Since Freud habitually analyzed his own dreams and recorded the results, we can find interesting samples of the
different kinds of dream phenomena throughout his writing.
The following case, which illustrates many of the basic ideas
about dreams, was a very simple dream in two parts:[16]

Freud records the dream thus:

I. My friend, R., is my uncle; I have great affection for
him.
II. I see before me his face, somewhat altered. It seems
to be elongated; a yellow beard, which surrounds it, is
seen with peculiar distinctness.

The presence of friend R in the dream was easily accounted
for. A professional colleague, he had visited Freud the evening before the dream and they had discussed their disappointment in not having been promoted to the much sought
after rank of professor. R told Freud that he had just found
out that the reason for their being passed over was their
religion. Freud felt he was more resigned to this than R was.

But what did it mean: "R is my uncle"? Freud's first
thought was that he had only one uncle, a man who had been
involved many years previously in a transgression against the
law for which he had paid a heavy penalty. (In fact, Freud
had several uncles; it is noteworthy that he thought of this
one, and as if it were his only uncle.) He remembered then
his father's remark at the time, that the uncle was not a
bad man, but just a simpleton. "R is my uncle," therefore,

[15] Bjerre, P., *The History and Practice of Psychoanalysis* (Boston: Badger, 1916).
[16] Freud, S., *The Interpretation of Dreams,* Chapter 4.

could mean "R is a simpleton." Freud realized, however, that he did not really think of R as a simpleton.

But then there was the elongated face with the distinct yellow beard. The uncle had had such a beard and, although R was black-haired and swarthy, his beard was turning yellowish with age. Another connection between R and the uncle.

But the uncle had been a criminal and R was not. At this point a second line of association suggested itself to Freud. He remembered another conversation he had had recently with another professional friend, who thought he would be passed over for a professorship because of an embarrassing criminal accusation which had once been made against him.

Now the role of the uncle in the dream becomes clearer. He does represent both R and the other friend, and neither of these were going to get professorships. But in the dream, one is represented as a criminal (as the uncle was) and the other as a simpleton (as the uncle was). Now the underlying meaning of the dream begins to emerge. Freud was not as resigned to being passed over (for religious reasons) as he had thought he was. And the dream was saying that his colleagues had been passed over for being respectively a simpleton or a criminal. Freud, therefore, could still hope for promotion, for he was not disqualified by either of these disabilities.

One last point about this dream: Freud realized that in fact he respected and liked both his colleagues, and he could not understand how, even in a dream, he could degrade them as he had. Thinking this over, he realized that he had had to do this to make his wish for promotion seem possible of fulfillment. But even in the dream his somewhat despicable acts could not be expressed so frankly and, therefore, in the dream, his defamation of R was covered up by the feeling of great affection: "I have a great affection for him." This affection, in the dream, compensated for the action for which he would have felt shame, and allowed him to make it. The reluctance he felt to analyze the dream stemmed from the same source, the desire not to admit that he had mentally defamed his friends.

When all this was clear, Freud felt that he had pretty well exhausted the meaning of this dream. The thoughts and images had acquired meaning through the associations they had elicited, the underlying sense of the dream emerged, and even the motivations behind the affect felt in the dream and the reluctance to interpret it later were accounted for. The dream had yielded up its meaning.

Freud regarded the interpretation of dreams as his greatest discovery and there is general agreement on this. Moreover, he was able to show striking analogies between dream psychology and the process of the construction of neuroses and psychoses. Although the neurotic retains a sense of reality, a part of the psyche operates according to the same rules which determine dream construction. There are similar condensations, associations, transfers of affect, censorship (resistance), and expressions, in symptoms, of unconscious wishes (impulses). Neurotic symptoms tend to be less directly related to real events than to fantasies embodying wishes. Even more apparent is the analogy of the dream to delusional and hallucinatory activity. Instances of this are found in the dream world, when unpleasant facts and feelings are disguised or censored out of existence, in order to favor the fulfillment of wishes, just as they are in delusions. The mother who cannot accept the death of a beloved child and chats with her neighbors about the child's doings, as if he were still alive, is censoring a fact out of consciousness for the sake of a wish. The voices heard in dreams, "warning" or "accusing" us of something, are like the voices heard by the hallucinated.

One of the best recognized contributions of psychoanalysis is the demonstration that, like dreams, delusions have a meaning and a symbolic content; that, like dreams, they are manifestations of or regressions to more primitive forms of behavior. In the dynamic processes of psychosis, the wish impulses which have been repressed succeed in imposing themselves on consciousness at the cost of reality. Not only do the delusions of the patient contain an element of historic truth; they reintroduce meaning into a world that has lost its meaning for him. The delusional activity obeys the patient's need to recreate the object relationships that evaporated as he fell prey to the psychosis.

Whereas neuroses are characterized above all by the repression of instinct, the psychoses show up as a loss of the sense of reality, and an internal liberation of immature instinctual impulses. There is a return to and a fixation on archaic, infantile modes of mental life, from which autoerotic and narcissistic satisfactions are derived. The patient regresses to primitive forms of thought, perception, and emotion. In neuroses, the regression is always partial; psychotic regression involves the whole ego. The synthesizing functions of intelligence and will are lost. Psychic energy is withdrawn, not only from the external world, when normal interests and desires for other people and things are abandoned, but also from the more evolved and matured portions of the ego, where judgment and purpose are exercised. The energies withdrawn are invested in dissociated portions of the mental apparatus, in rigid ideas and rationalizations, in circumscribed memories, and the like, and these proceed to live intense and volcanic existences, independent of the rest of the mind. These processes are not different from those of the dream. However, the patient cannot wake from this "dream"; for him reality and fantasy have become intermingled and there is no differentiation between them.

Some Other Freudian Concepts

This sketch of Freud's teachings is of necessity too brief to permit us to examine all of his ideas in depth. There are, however, a few other concepts which are so integral to the whole theory that we cannot afford to overlook them entirely. One of these is the notion of psychic determinism. Against the prevailing opinion that many mental events are merely fortuitous and random, and hence scientifically inexplicable, Freud insisted on a severely deterministic approach in psychology, unwilling to rest content until he could discover the causalities underlying even the most bizarre and apparently meaningless sorts of behavior. His insistence eventually paid off well, for he did make major discoveries concerning fundamental psychological structures and dynamics.[17] Having decided to search out the causes of all psychic phenomena, Freud postulated three points of view whose requirements must be satisfied before any psychological event can be considered adequately explained. The *dynamic* point of view took into account the moving forces underlying psychological activities. The *economic* point of view accounted for the distributions of psychic energies from their origins at the biological level, through their various channelings and blockages, to their eventual discharges. The *topographical,* or (later) structural, point of view considered the spheres, or areas, or structures of the mind to which various phenomena were functionally related, and the relationships between the structures. Originally Freud grouped the functions operating in the unconscious as belonging to one "area" of the mind, and the functions of the conscious and preconscious (things which are not being thought of at the moment but which are readily accessible to consciousness) as another. Later he preferred the id-ego-superego analysis.

Examining unconscious mental operations, Freud saw the need of introducing a distinction between what he called primary processes and secondary processes. Primary processes (called primary because they belong to the early stages of life when the id is predominant and the ego is immature) are characterized by the type of thinking we call infantile—magical, unrealistic, associative, exaggerated—and by emotional demands which cry for immediate gratification but are at the same time easily diverted from one object to another. Secondary processes are processes characteristic of mental maturity, logical and realistic, and emotional stability. In nor-

---

[17] There has been a tendency among psychoanalysts to interpret psychic determinism as opposed to human free will. Freud apparently did deny human freedom at times, and at other times he seemed to allow for it. In any event, the principle of psychic determinism, which is a methodological principle presupposed to analytic research, does not of itself preclude the possibility of human free choice. See Chapter X.

mal human development, the primary processes are gradually overlaid and controlled by the secondary processes, but a person may remain attached to an infantile object in an infantile way (fixation), or may, after reaching maturity, go back to infantile modes of behavior in times of stress (regression).

One of Freud's most significant contributions was his insight into the maturation of personality, the progress from primitive and childish ways of thinking and acting to those more appropriate to a realistic maturity. He theorized that instinctual life develops through phases, and that it can become fixated at one or another stage, and can regress from later stages to earlier ones. Many of the phenomena presented by psychiatric patients have become more meaningful in the light of this theory. Infantile life, for instance, is characterized by almost complete self-centeredness, in Freudian terms, by a centering of libido on the self. This infantile narcissism must be overcome as the child matures, and the energies centered on self must be turned towards other people and things. An inability to accomplish this outturning of libido is one of the specifying traits of emotional immaturity, some psychoses and neuroses, and many severe personality defects.

Anxiety According to Freud

Among Freud's later theoretical contributions, one which has become of great importance in contemporary psychiatry is his new theory of anxiety. In this theory the ego itself is the seat of anxiety. Only the ego can produce and feel anxiety. Indeed, the production of anxiety reactions is one of the most important functions of the ego. Anxiety—the mental experience of tense, painful excitation which cannot be mastered by discharge and cannot be avoided—emerges whenever the ego senses a threat to its integrity. In his *New Introductory Lectures*[18] Freud pointed out that it is the danger signal that anxiety represents, not the stuff it is made of, that is of importance in psychoanalysis. We must distinguish be-

[18] *Op. cit.*

tween objective and neurotic anxiety on this basis. In objective anxiety the danger is external, real, and perceptible, whereas in neurotic anxiety it is internal, mysterious, not recognized consciously. Neurotic anxiety can be traced to some intense instinctual demand, or to an instinctual demand which would bring the individual in conflict with the environment or with the superego. The nature of anxiety states may be illustrated by this example:

> A young man, a management trainee, began to experience intermittent palpitation, occasional headaches, and finger tremors when he came into close working relationships with people; at times his uneasiness and apprehension interfered with his ability to work efficiently and productively. His difficulties had become more marked when he thought that preferential treatment was given to another trainee. This young man was a courteous, almost subservient person, anxious to please others and agree with their opinions. These needs covered hostile-aggressive factors which he never consciously admitted, and which were a threat to him in his relations with others. The situation with the other trainee was of special significance for him because it reawakened conflicts from a childhood situation in his family. In therapy the young man gained insight into this segment of his difficulties and found that his tension was lessening and his headaches growing fewer. Gradually he became able to recognize and accept the existence of aggressive and hostile impulses within himself and to deal with them more constructively.[19]

In the struggle to handle anxiety the ego resorts to a variety of defense mechanisms, alone or in combination. Some of these defenses, which are all like mental reflexes operating natively and unconsciously, are primitive, going back to the earliest stages of ego development. If the mature ego resorts to them, it does so at the expense of its own strength and effectiveness. Repression is the primary and most powerful defense mechanism. There are evidences of repression in the

[19] Laughlin, H. P., *The Neuroses in Clinical Practice* (Philadelphia: W. B. Saunders Co., 1956), p. 47.

lives of all of us. Sometimes they appear under the guise of simple forgetting, as in the common phrases: "His name was in my mind a moment ago, but now I have lost it," or, "I worked with the man for ten years and now I forget his name." This may be but a temporary thing and usually is. Sometimes, however, it indicates that there is some type of association between the name of the individual and some objectionable idea, or feeling, or remembrance. A more complicated instance of repression is seen when someone reminds us of a whole series of incidents occurring at particular times in our lives which have been completely forgotten and only appear when they are recalled to us. More often than not careful examination would reveal that there was something painful or some traumatic experience which occurred at that time which resulted in a repression of the entire series of episodes.

Other mechanisms which appear early in life are introjection—taking into the mind the images and attitudes of loved or feared objects and making them one's own—and projection —attributing to others one's own thoughts and attitudes. Both introjection and projection are observable in certain psychotic states.

Doctor Henry P. Laughlin cites an example of psychotic introjection in which a patient believed that he had swallowed a mouse that was eating out his stomach.[20] The mouse represented a bad object introjected by the patient. O. S. English and S. M. Finch cite the depressed patient as an outstanding example of this mechanism.[21] Such a patient seems to have powerful undercurrents of hate in his relationships to loved persons. When one of these loved persons rejects him, he introjects that person—hate, love, and all—and so becomes the recipient of all the hate originally experienced toward the other individual.

A very common manifestation of projection is the tendency of one person to accuse another of inadequacies which the

[20] Laughlin, op. cit., p. 105.
[21] English, O. S., and Finch, S. M., Introduction to Psychiatry (2nd ed. New York: W. W. Norton & Co., 1957), p. 61.

first actually has. Thus, a woman who feels inadequate as wife and mother accuses her husband of possessing all her faults. She acts as if she were beyond reproach, but at an unconscious level she feels quite the opposite. The projection mechanism is also apparent in hallucinations. Thus, the paranoid psychotic patient projects onto the environment unconscious self-accusatory material. He literally hears voices which insult and threaten. Here the ego's reality-testing function is seriously disturbed.

When the ego is taken to be the seat of anxiety, and anxiety is taken as a danger signal, the role of the ego and the use of defense mechanisms appear in a new perspective. Now the ego becomes the principal agent, whose task it is to resolve the conflicting demands of instinct and environment, and anxiety is a warning bell, alerting the ego to the fact that a conflict has begun. The instinctual urges which are pressing for satisfaction may be wholly or partly unconscious, and the mind may be unconscious of the defenses it is using to control them, but anxiety serves notice that a struggle is under way. The issue will now depend on the relative strength or weakness of the individual's ego. The more intelligent he is, the more insight he has into his own emotional life, the more flexible he is in accepting new situations and adapting himself to new modes of behavior, the more he is able to govern his feelings by deliberate decisions, the more he can sustain frustration and disappointment, the better will be his chances of understanding and resolving his problem. If the ego functions—intelligence and will power—are strong and flexible, the individual will tend to be able to understand and resolve his own conflicts and enjoy mental health. If they are weak (i.e. if he lacks self-awareness and has inflexible behavior patterns), he may either succumb to neurosis, using the primitive and irrational mechanisms of defense to suppress and deflect his instinctual urges, or he may fall into psychosis, allowing the instinctual urges, buried fantasies, and primitive modes of thinking to overcome and dominate the reasonable and realistic parts of the mind.

An important implication of this later psychoanalytic formulation is that anxiety is not something that can be banished in some way from human experience, but an inevitable fact of life, one that will arise whenever the ego feels itself in danger. Of great importance, however, is the ego's capacity to endure a certain amount of anxiety without resorting to pathogenic defenses. This is a consideration of great importance to education, and stands, of course, in the forefront of therapeutic interest. Psychoanalysis today addresses itself above all to the fortification of the ego. It is not enough to liberate the instinctual forces and distribute them in one way or another; it is necessary to strengthen the ego so that it can tolerate more pain, renounce its outmoded defense methods, and adopt ones which are more appropriate.[22] Pathological defense mechanisms can be modified as the ego becomes stronger and more capable of mastering fear, which is to say, fear of the instincts.

The shift, then, in recent years has been from quantitative to qualitative aspects of normal and abnormal development. Attention is centered upon the particular methods of defense utilized by the psychic apparatus of the particular individual. There is more interest in that which does the repressing than in that which is repressed. As a result, the intimate relation between certain specific forms of defense and certain mental disturbances has been revealed more clearly. The importance of object relations in mental development and adaptation is also shown more distinctly. When object relationships break down, the sense of self is impaired, and vice versa. In psychotic states, the internal representations of objects may be seriously distorted.

[22] Freud was most clear on this point: "Analysis replaces the process of repression, which is an automatic and excessive one, by a temperate and purposeful control on the part of the highest mental faculties. In a word, analysis replaces repression by condemnation." ("Analysis of a Phobia in a Five-Year-Old Boy," *Collected Papers* [New York: Basic Books, 1959] Vol. 3, p. 285.) "But analysis enables the mature ego, which by this time has attained a greater strength, to review these old repressions, with the result that some are lifted, while others are accepted but reconstructed from more solid material." ("Analysis Terminable and Interminable," *ibid.,* Vol. 5, p. 329.)

Psychoanalytic Therapy

The aim of psychoanalytic therapy is a reconstruction of personality. Originally Freud attached considerable therapeutic value to the emotional catharsis which seemed to release internal tensions, but the effect of the catharsis was not always long-lasting. More importance was then attributed to the new insights the patient gained into his own personality and its conflicts, insights gained via the interpretations of the products of free associations. To the degree a patient could gain understanding of the origins and processes of his own conflicts, he could adjust himself to his strengths and limitations, abandon infantile modes of reactions and live on more mature levels. Eventually it turned out that the phenomenon of transference was one of the most valuable sources for insightful interpretation of the patient's troubles. Transference is an intense emotional relationship, either positive or negative, which arises between the patient and the analyst during therapy, and which cannot be accounted for by the actual situation. Basically, transference is a reliving and reflection of the emotional attachments the patient formed early in life towards important persons in his environment, and since these attachments generally lie at the root of his problems, the shape of the transference gives both analyst and patient a vivid picture of underlying instinctual structures. Moreover, the fact that the transference is formed affords the possibility of modifying these instinctual structures, which is the aim of the therapy. Freud maintained that analysis without transference is an impossibility and that, when the patient shows no inclination to a transference of emotion or when the transference has become entirely negative, there is no possibility of influencing the patient by psychological means.

Although psychoanalysis is the most powerful form of psychotherapy, its efficacy is by no means unlimited. Sometimes the analysts themselves seem quite pessimistic. At the World Congress on Psychiatry held in Montreal in June, 1961, Dr. Jules Masserman, himself a psychoanalyst, cast considerable doubt upon the therapeutic efficacy of psychoanalysis, stating that: "Patients treated by any of our current rituals may show temporary spurts of improvement but retain no discernible advantage after five years over those diagnostically matched, but left untreated." Freud himself was not a therapeutic enthusiast. He indicated clearly that psychoanalysis is *a* form of therapy, like any other method; that, like all other methods, it has failures as well as successes; that, like them, it does not invalidate or exclude other methods. Nor did Freud recommend psychoanalysis for all sorts of psychiatric disorders. He ruled out this form of therapy for the psychoses and what he called "the narcissistic neuroses," in which he apparently included pre-schizophrenic and borderline states, since he felt that in these there would always be a resistance, impossible to overcome, and that, also, the necessary transference does not materialize in patients who suffer from illnesses of these types.

From the other classifications, he regarded as suitable for psychoanalysis only the transference neuroses, by which he meant psychoneuroses affecting patients in whom there is a capacity to transfer feelings or affects to other persons. He mentioned the following disorders as examples of those most amenable to treatment: hysterias, obsessional neuroses, phobias, and abnormalities of character which have developed in place of these various disorders. The practical limitations of psychoanalysis implicit in Freud's own selection are magnified by other considerations, including the time-consuming nature of the therapy, and also the fact that only relatively young patients, with a considerable amount of intelligence and a real capacity for cooperation, are likely to benefit.

Freud derogated the tendency of some of his followers to extend psychoanalysis to all neurotic disturbances. He was antagonistic to the idea of "watering down" psychoanalysis by compressing treatment into a brief period, by intensifying the transference, and by combining other methods of influence with analysis. The time-consuming element of orthodox analysis could not be helped. It takes time to produce psychological changes in patients with neuroses. These disorders are by no means superficial; in fact, they are most complicated, as we shall see later when we discuss them. Matters of therapy have to be judged from the point of view of how long the illness would have lasted without deep and prolonged analysis.

The Impinging of Psychoanalysis on Philosophical Problems

Freud claimed for psychoanalysis the philosophy of science in general rather than a *Weltanschauung* of its own. Apart from science, Freud held that *Weltanschauungen* of any kind are more the products of emotion and illusion than of true knowledge. Thus, he believed, philosophy arrogates to itself the distinction of creating a complete and coherent picture of the universe, overestimating the power of reason and at the same time relying too often on intuition. Thus, he also stated, religion is a response to man's immature needs, wishes, and illusions, its rituals serving much the same function as those of the obsessional neurotic. It was this statement from Freud's limited view of religion and the publication of his *The Future of an Illusion* which crystallized the opposition of religious believers to his theories and to him personally.

Gregory Zilboorg has pointed out that Freud's challenge to religion is not the mere *parti pris* of one pledged to science and nothing else, but also the reaction to a lifelong inner conflict about religion.[23] In any event, it represents a personal point of view which should not be permitted to detract from the real contributions of psychoanalysis. Psychiatrists of all persuasions can attest that psychoanalysis is neither religious nor anti-religious, but an impartial instrument which there is no reason to reject when the clinical problem is such that analysis would undoubtedly afford the best therapeutic result.

Psychoanalysis is not concerned with the existence of God or the relationship of man and God. However, a good case can be made for its affirmation of moral principles. Psycho-

[23] Zilboorg, G., *Freud and Religion, a Restatement of an Old Controversy* (Westminster, Md.: Newman Press, 1958).

analysis confirms the importance of reason in man's life by showing the havoc worked by unreason and aggression in his daily existence. The ego, whose domain psychoanalysis endeavors to extend, represents reason and sanity. The troublesome id is the abode of the passions, whose demands the ego must screen and modulate in the light of reality. The ego ideal, composed of ideal models for identification and emulation, is an element of moral conscience. In his life and in his theory, Freud raised culture, art, and morality to an elevated position, and in the course of his investigations he widened the concept of libido to include and feature love itself. He actually put creative love at the center of his system; in the clinical situation he was more than dubious of the possibility of helping a patient who could love only himself.

Jacques Maritain, the well-known philosopher, believed that any discussion of this whole problem of psychoanalysis and its place in the scheme of things is doomed to failure unless the subject as a method of psychological investigation and treatment is sharply distinguished from Freudianism as a philosophy. In this there is general agreement by most observers.[24] Maritain went further than that and made a threefold division, distinguishing (1) the psychoanalytic methods, (2) Freudian psychology, (3) Freudian philosophy. In his opinion the psychoanalytic method shows Freud to be an investigator of genius. In Freudian psychology he finds him an "admirably penetrating psychologist, whose ideas, inspired by his astonishing instinct for discovery, are spoiled by a radical empiricism and an erroneous metaphysics that is unaware of itself." On the third plane, i.e. philosophy, Maritain feels that Freud "seems like a man obsessed." This is an excellent brief evaluation of the situation.[25]

In his many writings on psychoanalysis and religion Zilboorg has spoken eloquently on these propositions. He stated that one of the most flagrant mistakes religious thinkers make

[24] For an exceptionally penetrating and detailed study of this point, see: Dalbiez, Roland, *Psycho-analytic Method and the Doctrine of Freud* (New York: Longmans, Green & Co., 1941).

[25] *Cross Currents*, Vol. 6, No. 4 (Fall, 1956), p. 307.

is to assume that a good scientist, to be scientifically right, must be either a good theologian or at least an adherent of the theological tenets of an established institution. It would be well to heed the farsighted observations of Pius XII spoken in various contexts:

> Scientific knowledge has its own value in the domain of medical science no less than in other scientific domains, such as, for example, physics, chemistry, cosmology and psychology. It is a value which must certainly not be minimized, a value existing quite independently of the usefulness or use of the acquired knowledge. Moreover, knowledge as such and the full understanding of any truth raise no moral objection. By virtue of this principle, research and the acquisition of truth for arriving at new, wider and deeper knowledge and understanding of the same truth are in themselves in accord with the moral order. . . . Science itself, therefore, as well as its research and acquisitions, must be inserted in the order of values.[26]

> In your studies and scientific research, rest assured that no contradiction is possible between the certain truths of faith and the established scientific facts. Nature, no less than revelation, proceeds from God, and God cannot contradict himself.[27] Be assured that the Church follows your research and your medical practice with her warm interest and her best wishes. You labor on a terrain that is very difficult. But your activity is capable of achieving precious results for medicine, for the knowledge of the soul in general, for the religious dispositions of man and for their development.[28]

Acceptance and Influence

For more than ten years after his break with Joseph Breuer, Freud had few followers. Then his isolation gradu-

[26] "Moral Limits of Medical Research and Treatment," address of His Holiness, Pope Pius XII, September 14, 1952, *Catholic Mind*, Vol. LI (May 1953).

[27] *Ibid.*

[28] "Psychotherapy and Religion," address of His Holiness, Pope Pius XII, April 13, 1953, *Catholic Mind*, Vol. LI (July 1953).

ally ended as a small circle of students formed around him. After 1906 came the support of the Zurich group, headed by Eugen Bleuler (1857–1939) and featuring the outstanding young investigator Carl G. Jung (1875–1961). At first Jung grew close enough to Freud to be regarded as his heir apparent, but in a few years a serious quarrel separated them and each went his own way. In part, the quarrel arose from personal differences, in part from intellectual disagreements. Jung objected to Freud's conception of the libido as exclusively sexual, and by the time Freud had widened his concept, the division between the two was past repair. Jung went on to develop his own school of thought, "Analytical Psychology," and eventually contributed heavily to the development of many modern lines of thought, particularly in areas of cultural study.

The early influence of psychoanalysis was clearly visible in Bleuler's epoch-making monograph *Dementia Praecox, or, the Group of Schizophrenias* (1911).[29] Bleuler's concept of schizophrenia owed much to the psychoanalytic concept of emotions and also to the concept of psychological associations. He used the term "schizophrenia" to denote a *group* of psychotic reactions, not one disease, and we shall go more into detail regarding this later on. He was convinced of the psychic origin of certain schizophrenic alterations and recognized that many symptoms of these patients had a psychologically intelligible meaning. He made an important distinction between the primary and secondary signs of schizophrenia. The primary signs were a peculiar loosening of associations and a morbid ambivalence in the psychic life of the patient. The whole picture of dementia praecox detailed by Kraepelin, including the delusions and the hallucinations, would be secondary. Bleuler also showed that schizophrenia did not necessarily end in dementia.

Jung, too, made a basic contribution to the understanding of schizophrenia.[30] He demonstrated that the same symboliza-

[29] Bleuler, E., *Dementia Praecox, oder Gruppe der Schizophrenien* (Leipzig: F. Deuticke, 1911).
[30] Jung, C. G., "The Psychology of Dementia Praecox," *Nervous and Mental Disease Monographs* (New York, 1909).

tion which Freud utilized in his understanding of dreams might be used in the understanding of schizophrenia. Unlike Freud, Jung considered schizophrenic patients treatable by psychotherapy and reaffirmed this view in 1958 when he reviewed his experience of more than fifty years in the field.[31] His early uncertainty as to the primary cause of the illness he had by this time resolved in favor of a psychological cause, though he admitted that toxins produced in the body as a result of violent emotion might have a contributory effect.

Other well-known names appear in the list of Freud's early supporters. Alfred Adler (1870–1937) was, like Jung, one of the most promising of the early group which clustered around Freud, but he too soon seceded from the ranks of orthodoxy, again partly from personal differences and partly from differences in theoretical position. Adler struck out along lines of social and interpersonal forces at play in the development of personality—forces which he believed Freud was underemphasizing, and which Freud, in turn, dismissed as analytically superficial. The popularity of many of Adler's early conceptions was immediate and widespread, but as a school and a system his influence has diminished markedly. Otto Rank (1884–1939) was another early disciple and later dissident. He conceived the central psychological problem in terms of gaining personal independence against the forces and influences which work to keep an individual bound to his parents.

As time went on, Freud's works gradually received notice and interest was taken of him in various parts of the world. Certain important people were beginning to pass the word around that Freud "really had something there," especially in connection with the problem of hysteria. The very first volumes of the *Journal of Abnormal Psychology*, which began publication in this country in 1906, reveal the awakening interest.

In 1909 Freud was invited by Professor G. Stanley Hall to deliver a series of five lectures on psychoanalysis at Clark

[31] Jung, C. G., "Die Schizophrenie," *Schweiz. Arch. Neurol. Psychiat.*, 81:163–77 (1958).

University.[32] This, the first recognition of the importance of Freud's work by an official scientific community, was a harbinger of the unique success psychoanalysis was to enjoy in the United States. It was also a source of encouragement to Freud, who had been so long a prophet without honor in his own land and was soon to endure further distress when Jung and certain others upon whom he had counted most went off in different directions.

In America a number of respected neurologists and psychiatrists, such as James J. Putnam (1846–1918), Adolf Meyer (1866–1950), William A. White (1870–1937), and Smith Ely Jelliffe (1866–1945), disseminated psychoanalytic information in the scientific community. Moreover, all Freud's important works became available in English, owing to the translations of A. A. Brill (1874–1948), the first physician in this country to venture into the private practice of psychoanalysis. Thus, shortly after 1910, it was evident that psychoanalysis was taking a perceptible hold on American psychiatry. Jelliffe founded a special journal for the publication of psychoanalytic material, and he and White began publishing *Nervous and Mental Disease Monographs,* in which they included fundamental psychoanalytic contributions.

In his book *A History of Psychoanalysis in America*[33] Oberndorf shows the growth, the travail, the defeats, and the victories of the new science. Programs of education and training in psychoanalytic psychiatry made an early appearance. It is important to note that in America psychoanalysis was introduced as an integral part of psychiatry and an integral part of medical practice. American psychoanalysts insisted that psychoanalysis was the province of physicians. By 1919 psychoanalytic principles had made a greater impact in America than anywhere else. Freud ascribed this to the absence of embedded scientific tradition and the slight

[32] Freud, S., *The Origin and Development of Psychoanalysis* (New York: Gateway Editions, 1955). Reprinted from the *American Journal of Psychology,* Vol. 21 (April 1910).

[33] Oberndorf, C. P., *A History of Psychoanalysis in America* (New York: Grune & Stratton, 1953).

weight of official authority in America. He was somewhat apprehensive about Americans taking over his contributions, because of the dilution he could see in the offing, because he was not really much impressed by American culture, and also because he felt that there was plenty of room for gifted lay analysts in the psychoanalytic movement. In the international psychoanalytic conventions many a hot dispute centered about lay analysis, but the Americans stood firm, insisting on the highest standards for the practice of psychoanalysis.

America rapidly became the proving ground for the broad testing of psychoanalytic technique. Through the twenties the movement grew. In 1933 the American Psychiatric Association formed a special section on psychoanalysis in an effort to incorporate psychoanalytic concepts into psychiatry in a more satisfactory and accurate way. This marked the beginning of a new era in psychoanalysis and psychiatry in general. Now there was official recognition of the value of Freud's formulations in the understanding and treatment of the mentally ill and also of the worth of psychoanalysis as a method of investigation. Many able European analysts had already come to America. The darkening international situation in the thirties brought many more. The possession of this imposing supply of trained analysts made America the center of psychoanalytic teaching, training, and research.

Growth of Dynamic Psychiatry

Psychoanalysis, with a powerful assist from psychobiology, made American psychiatry increasingly dynamic. To understand the experiences, feelings, and thoughts of the mentally ill as basically similar to those of human beings in general, and similarly understandable, was to kindle hope for effective therapy in many cases previously despaired of. The crucial problem for the psychiatrist to solve was not what category the patient's symptoms belonged to, but rather the actual dynamic situation. He would view the patient as a person with a life history to be reconstructed, a person subjected to sensitizing and conditioning forces from far back, one whose psychological defenses and motivations had to be understood before progress could be made towards a better way of life.

The concept that other people are involved in both the origin and healing of mental illness is implicit in dynamic psychiatry. One of the people who helped make this concept understandable was Clifford Beers, author of *A Mind that Found Itself*.[34] This book was an impressive document of mental hospital experiences which tend to retard the recovery of a patient. Published at a most opportune time, when the teachings of Freud and Meyer were gathering momentum, the book and its author launched the mental hygiene movement. The National Committee for Mental Hygiene was founded in 1909. Although nominally dedicated to preventive psychiatry, this Committee and its member societies also sponsored surveys of the care of patients in mental hospitals and institutions. In 1950 the National Committee for Mental Hygiene changed its name to National Association for Mental Health, a change reflecting the comprehensive interests of today's dynamic psychiatry.

The American inclination to apply psychiatric knowledge to major social problems was important in the growth of dynamic psychiatry. Thus, as early as 1911, Elmer L. Southard (1876–1920) had decided to direct his energies to the buildup of social psychiatry. He was directly involved in the establishment of psychiatric social work as a profession. With this turn in psychiatric interest, there developed an increased interest in the human personality in a variety of social settings, including industry and education. One of the significant contributions of American psychiatry was the child guidance clinic pioneered by William Healy in the year 1909. Out of it came a rich store of knowledge about the emotional life of the child, his strivings for satisfaction and for grasp of the external world, his urge toward self-expression, his participation in the social group. The unmet needs of children became better understood, and problems of delinquency and adolescence came into clearer focus. Un-

[34] (New York: Longmans, Green & Co., 1908).

fortunately, the insights we have in these areas have not been consistently or extensively applied.

Thanks to psychoanalysis, child psychiatry has become a fruitful, ever advancing field, bringing increased understanding of the psychopathology of childhood along with steady advances in therapy. The contributions of Melanie Klein (1882–1960) and Anna Freud in England have been outstanding, but American psychiatry has been responsible for making this field almost a specialty in itself. Following Leo Kanner's description of "primary autism," much work has been done in connection with the problems of onset of psychotic conditions, as well as of neuroses and psychoneuroses, in children. René Spitz is among those who have made outstanding demonstrations of the importance of early emotional deprivation in the psychiatric problems of children. Special mention should also be made of the many contributions of American psychiatry to the handling of psychosomatic conditions and the psychological aspects of physical and handicapped conditions in young children.

Another significant movement to come out of psychoanalysis and psychobiology was the clinical application of psychopathology to medical problems. In 1833 Amariah Brigham had spoken of the influence of mind in causing and in curing dyspepsia, and a similar possibility in other diseases was mentioned by various writers after him, but it was not until 1915 that the great American physiologist, Walter B. Cannon (1871–1925), offered experimental proof that emotions can give rise to physiological changes. Cannon showed the relationship of the autonomic nervous system to epinephrine (i.e. the active principle of the medullary portion of the adrenal glands), a finding which was followed by studies showing the disrupting effect of fear-states and of epinephrine upon adaptive behavior. With this work and the work of Ivan Petrovich Pavlov on conditioned reflex, a scientific base for a modern psychosomatic approach to medicine was at hand, and we shall hear much more about it in a later chapter.

The preoccupations of American psychiatry today are many. A growing trend is apparent to integrate classic Freudian principles in a largely eclectic therapeutic approach. Research has shown the necessity of weighing interpersonal and social relations in psychiatric problems, to take into account the effect of emotions on body functions, to consider constitution and environment also. J. Sanbourne Bockoven describes the current situation as follows:

> The picture of mental illness which is emerging from research in the new strongly related fields of psychiatry, physiology and sociology is one in which a circular series of events occur, beginning with social factors which produce psychological changes. These psychological changes then, depending on the individual's constitutional inheritance, alter physiological function, which is accompanied by further psychological changes. Change in behavior elicits further reactions from society, which once again produce psychological changes in the individual and repeat the cycle.

> With progress of research, it is becoming increasingly clear that the treatment of mental illness involves the development of techniques for interrupting this cycle at one or the other or all of these levels. In some forms of mental illness, judicious change in the social environment alone will arrest the disease process; in others, individual psychotherapy or group psychotherapy may be needed in addition. More severe forms of illness may require electric shock, insulin coma, or even psychosurgery.[35]

The concept that mental illness is to a large degree a reaction to interpersonal relationships, past and present, figures largely in modern psychiatric thought. This is one of the most important legacies of Freud and his followers, notably Harry Stack Sullivan. New perspectives have opened in the direction of social psychiatry, which summon to our side thoughtful and brilliant investigators in the other social sciences and open important areas for cooperation between psychiatry and religion.

[35] Bockoven, J. S., "Moral Treatment in American Psychiatry," *J. Nerv. Ment. Dis.*, 124:167–321 (1956).

IV

SOME OF THE ILLNESSES IN QUESTION

No matter how much ability a person has, or how famous and how powerful he is, he shares the problem of all of us as part of the human predicament. He has to manage himself, and he becomes a tragic figure if he cannot do so.

Earl D. Bond

There is some question about the wisdom and advisability of going into clinical detail in a work of this kind, which does not pretend to be a textbook of psychiatry; yet some mention of the conditions about which psychiatry concerns itself should be made if we are to discuss our attitudes towards the subject. Necessarily, this mention will have to be brief, and only the salient facts of the more frequently encountered psychiatric conditions can be considered. When it is realized that, in addition to the various categories of illnesses which we shall mention here, emotional factors play a part in every illness to which mortal man is heir, then some hint of the size of the psychiatric problem will become apparent.

In contemplating many of the ills which we shall note here, one is moved to wonder what all the fuss is about and why there is so much hostility and misunderstanding of psychiatry. The conditions which it treats are real enough; no one is immune to them, and all of them, when they occur, are distressing to patients and families alike. Understandably, at times there will be differences of opinion among professionals regarding concepts of psychiatric treatment, and, just as understandably, there will be widespread differences of opinion regarding the philosophic overtones which accompany various psychiatric theories. None of these differences is cause for panic, antipathy, or sniping, however; rather, they are indications for careful consideration and scientific study of any issues about which there is dispute or divided opinion.

Mental or psychic disorders do not lend themselves to precise definition. They include a great variety of disturbances with many overlapping features. By the same token, mental or psychic well-being is even more difficult to define, for a wide range of behavior passes as normal. The modern psychiatrist is not unduly disturbed about these verbal difficulties, however, for he is no longer content with merely designating and categorizing mental disorders. What he is looking for are the dynamic processes of personality which are basically the same in all men and which may go askew in essentially similar ways, and the absence of sharp lines of demarcation among the shapes which disturbances might assume does not dismay him.

Neuroses are emotional maladaptations due to unresolved unconscious conflicts. Psychoses are severe emotional illnesses in which there is a departure from normal patterns of thinking, feeling, or acting. A certain degree of personality disorganization appears in the neuroses, and it is more extensive in the psychoses, but, in fact, the intrapsychic forces at work are the ones by which everyone is in some way affected. Every person is subject to anxiety, to changing moods difficult to explain, and at times to distorted and even primitive thinking. Each has available to him the same types of defense reactions and the same range of behavioral reactions, and it is now believed that anxiety lies at the core of most emotional disorders.

Most of the illnesses are a long time in the making, some observers stating that the trouble begins when we precipitate a soft baby into a hard world. Certainly the early emotional reactions of the child within the family and with others whom he encounters will determine the modes, attitudes, and fixations which will play a decisive role in his later emotional life and, should he become ill, will color his emotional disorder. This has been recognized for many years. Walter Pater, writing in 1878, observed in *The Child in the House:*

How insignificant at the moment seems the influence of sensible things which are tossed and fall and lie about us so and so in the environment of early childhood. How indelibly, as we afterwards discover, they affect us; with what capricious attractions and associations they secure themselves upon the white paper, the smooth wax of our ingenious souls, giving form and features and assigned house room in our memory.

Many distortions of later life are due to methods adopted by the personality to deal with the needs, conflicts, and problems that arouse intolerable anxiety. Constitutional factors, biological equipment, somatic functioning, or even organic disease may play a facilitating role, but even in conditions known to be organic in origin, the personality of the patient will influence the presenting type of emotional reaction. The shape this reaction takes and the symptoms it presents are, it seems, colored in large measure by the basic structure of the personality. Sometimes the organic impairment will simply allow the release of reactions hitherto repressed.

PSYCHIATRIC CLASSIFICATION

Down through the years numerous attempts have been made to construct a useful psychiatric nomenclature, but generally the results have been so involved that they served more to complicate matters than to simplify them. Ponderous groupings were constructed and new categories formed, sometimes by procrustean methods. Complicated names were given to symptom categories and bizarre causes alleged for their appearance, the latter ranging from "brain disease" to "abuse of tobacco" and "tight lacing."

Early in the nineteenth century some investigators promulgated the idea that mental diseases are diseases of the brain, of unknown origin, capable of showing themselves in various ways, and which are not to be thought of as separate diseases. This concept, which has much to recommend it, appears at times, then disappears, only to return again in a slightly different guise. Henri Ey, a contemporary French psychiatrist, believes that mental diseases should be looked upon less as disease entities and more as syndromes (groups of stably related symptoms) and pathological reactions resulting from a multiplicity of factors. Karl Menninger is more or less inclined in the same direction. He would have us think of patients as human beings whose relationships with their fellow man have gone awry in some fashion, rather than as persons to whom we must apply a diagnostic epithet and then set out to do it battle. He would have us regard these illnesses as a scale which runs from the mild "nervousness" of everyday life up through neuroses to the persistent, serious disorders typified by the psychoses. There is wisdom in this type of approach to the problem, for, as we shall note later, there is a tyranny in diagnostic terms which may at times be harmful to the patient and mislead the doctor.

In the present day, however, it is still necessary to classify illnesses in order to make statistical comparisons, indicate prognoses, and put psychiatric data in a broad frame of reference. Unfortunately, no regular order can be imposed on psychiatric phenomena. In a considerable majority of patients, classification is possible only on the basis of behavior; no specific disease entity can be identified and named. Circumstantial factors can contribute to the clinical picture, which, in any event, can show an exceedingly wide range of manifestation with many modulations. A clinical problem often presents a mixture of different symptom clusters and obstinately sits on the borderline between accepted classifications. It is always modified by personal experience both prior and subsequent to onset, and is greatly affected by the attitudes and reactions exhibited by others.

The symptoms which emotionally distressed patients present vary with the era and the culture in which they occur. Some pictures which were a commonplace a half-century ago, and even a quarter-century ago, are less in evidence today. Frequently the degree of the disturbed behavior in psychotic patients is much less than it used to be, and the differences we now observe are not explained solely by more active and successful forms of treatment. Pathological phenomena are no longer so clear, no longer so "classic," as they were in the custodial era of mental hospitals. Even schizophrenia seems to be taking on something of the *Zeitgeist* in which we live.

The most recent classification of mental and emotional disorders, adopted by the American Psychiatric Association (1952), was formulated in order to meet changing needs and changing psychiatric practice. Recognizing the descriptive nature of psychiatric diagnosis, it offered a more flexible and comprehensive system than its predecessors, which were more rigidly tailored to mental disorders observed largely in mental hospitals offering long-term care. Needless to say, this classification is far from perfect and, in the light of present-day advances in treatment, it is already in need of reconsideration.

Briefly, the emphasis of the classification is upon mental functioning and the disturbances fall into three overall groups: 1) Disorders Associated with Impairment of Brain Tissue Function; 2) Mental Deficiencies, Primarily of Familial Origin and Existing Since Birth; and 3) that great category subsumed under the term "Disorders of Psychogenic Origin Without Clearly Defined Physical Cause or Structural Change in the Brain."[1]

DISORDERS OF BRAIN TISSUE FUNCTION

In the first-mentioned disorders there is a brain syndrome, characterized by impairment of all intellectual functions, including comprehension, calculation, learning, etc., by impairment of memory, orientation, and judgment, and by shallowness and lability of feelings. The severity of this combination of symptoms parallels the severity of impairment of brain function; yet, upon this tissue impairment there may be an overlay of disturbances corresponding to psychotic or neurotic behavior reactions. These syndromes may be acute or chronic.

[1] Diagnostic Manual of the American Psychiatric Association.

Acute Brain Disorders

In acute cases the pathological brain changes may be reversible, i.e. reparable, or they may be acute to start with and eventually leave permanent damage. The behavior changes, whether they be psychotic or neurotic, are not necessarily related to the degree of brain damage, but they are rather more often due to factors inherent in the personality, to emotional conflicts, or to difficulties in interpersonal relationships.

Acute brain disorders are met with less frequently in psychiatric hospitals than in community hospitals and community medical practice, because of their rapid and dramatic onset and their obvious physical symptoms. A wide variety of afflictions can produce the acute brain syndrome; encephalitis, meningitis, brain abscess, or systemic infections like pneumonia, typhoid fever, or acute rheumatic fever. The cause also may be intoxications due to drugs of various types (bromides, barbiturates, opiates, etc.), or to poisons (lead, metals, gases, etc.), or, as is more frequently the case, to alcohol. Other provoking factors include trauma, such as head injury from any external forces, circulatory disturbances, cardiac disease, convulsive disorders, disorders of metabolism, intracranial tumors, etc.

In all of the above disorders the physician follows the same principles of management as he does in any delirious reaction. Treatment is always directed toward the basic disorder, providing, of course, it is known and treatable. These patients sometimes have episodes of hallucinatory and illusory experience, to which they may react in a way dangerous to themselves and others, and it is at this time that psychiatric help is sought. Hallucinations may occur in all spheres of sensation, but most often they are auditory. Visual and tactile hallucinations occur particularly with drug intoxications. Delusions of a fear-producing nature are common, and the doctor in such instances is sparing with sedation, lest perhaps, under its influence, the patient should lapse into stupor. Most individuals recover from the original acute symptoms mentioned, but at times there is fear that some organic damage may persist. The mental symptoms usually disappear but occasionally leave in their wake an irritability or, in some instances, mild persecutory ideas.

Chronic Brain Disorders

The chronic organic brain syndrome is much more prevalent in psychiatric hospitals than is the acute reaction. It varies in degree, depending usually upon the amount of brain tissue destruction. Though such destruction is irreversible, the chronic brain syndrome itself may become milder or it may show fluctuations. It may also progress. Previous personality traits become exaggerated. Thus, some aggressive people become more so; seclusive and suspicious personalities become paranoid; the quiet pessimists become frankly depressed. There is decreased tolerance to toxic substances, so that delirium follows intake of small doses of alcohol or drugs. This phenomenon the layman frequently sees and has difficulty understanding. The history is one of gradual change in personality, with reduction of mental capacity and development of defects of judgment. Behavior changes are basically those of habit deterioration. Secondary to the organic brain syndrome, there may be psychotic or neurotic symptoms. Emotional instability, with irritability and rapid shifts of mood, is prominent. The emotional reactions are extreme and out of line with the provocative stimulus. The individual, heretofore often above reproach, becomes quarrelsome, shows poor direction of energy, and may indulge in injudicious actions or even shameless behavior.

Some of the most formidable conditions with which psychiatry must deal belong in this chronic group. There are disturbances in brain function arising from congenital cranial defects—Mongolism, birth trauma, etc. Classed here, also, are the various types of *central nervous system syphilis;* fortunately, these are much rarer than they used to be, and highly treatable. The use now of large doses of penicillin usually quickly controls the original infection, so that the progressive mental deteriorations, once common in this disease, and inevitably leading to dementia and death, have been strikingly reduced in number. Brain tumors and various brain traumata are also causal factors in producing chronic brain syndromes, as are various diseases of the heart and circulatory system, glandular disturbances, and diseases, such as pellagra, which result from vitamin deficiencies. Prominent among the chronic brain disorders are those associated with senile brain disease; the syndrome ranges from mild to severe, and psychotic or neurotic reactions are often superimposed upon the basic organic change. Finally, the chronic syndrome may appear in the absence of any recognizable cause.

The overall picture, then, shows a brain syndrome which is basically the same in all cases, although the initiating causes are quite heterogeneous. Some of the cases have a favorable prognosis; in others there is little, if any, prospect of recovery. With the advances of medical science, there has been a revolutionary change in outlook for patients in some of the subgroups. Perhaps the most dramatic example is the therapeutic success now being obtained in cases which originate in acute infections of the central nervous system; not only has there been a remarkable decline in mortality, but also fewer patients have been gravitating into the chronic group. General systemic infections, intoxications, vitamin deficiencies, and the like are also under better control now, so that the associated brain syndrome is more susceptible to successful treatment. Brain surgery and antibiotics have salvaged numerous individuals with serious organic lesions of the brain, people who earlier would either have been lost or destined for a life of invalidism.

Psychoses of Old Age

An aspect of mental illness which must always be taken into account is the so-called historical coefficient. The effects of the patient's actual experiences and of the period of life in which he is situated have important bearing on the illness from which he suffers. A prime example of this can be found in the organic psychoses of old age. The control of infections has increased the life expectancy of the population. A generation ago people surviving to an advanced age presumably represented a better physical selection than do many of those surviving today. One result of this is that circulatory and degenerative diseases are creating an ever increasing problem for psychiatry. By 1959 about one third of all patients in state mental hospitals, and 27 per cent of all first admissions to mental hospitals, were over 65 years old. Approximately 80 per cent of this latter group were suffering from mental disorder primarily associated with old age.[2] Few of these people are ever released and most of them die within a relatively short time.

From psychic senescence to senile dementia there are all gradations of mental deviation. Rigidity of thought and loss of flexibility are characteristic of old age. With a drift into pathologic senescence, an impairment of perception and memory is a common occurrence, and there may follow mental impoverishment and personality regression. Reduction in voluntary activity is an early symptom of the psychosis. Mental processes operate with difficulty; there is a lack of alertness, a narrowing of interest, and defective orientation. Fantastic images become divorced from criticism and the patient confuses imaginary facts, dreams, and reality. Days of dream state may be followed by periods of comparative lucidity. Depressed and manic states occur, as do delusions and paranoid behavior. The old-age psychoses connected with hardening of the arteries to the brain are more prevalent in males; senile psychoses, on the other hand, seem to be more common among women.

The age of onset of the mental disease of senescence is usually between 55 and 70 or older, rarely between the ages of 45 and 55. More cases are common before the age of 60, however, than is generally believed.

Psychiatric problems of senility constitute one of the most urgent of contemporary problems. Not only are more elderly people entering mental hospitals; they are entering at an increasing rate. Many of these patients could be profitably treated elsewhere, medically, psychologically, and socially. Various measures to improve blood circulation to the brain have improved the outlook for cerebral arteriosclerosis, and

[2] Figures from *Fact Sheet,* Joint Information Service, American Psychiatric Association and National Association for Mental Health, No. 14 (January 1961).

general medicine can aid in the prevention of other organic deteriorations. In the definitely psychotic groups, too, since the pathological mental mechanisms are frequently of a very simple kind, measures can be taken to deal with the secondary psychiatric symptoms, which are the individual's reaction to his situation and his impaired capacities of adjustment, even when the brain damage cannot be repaired. Especially in presenile deterioration, psychotherapy can be remarkably effective, even though it is superficial and merely instructive. Many individuals who seemingly present a picture of senile psychosis are actually only depressed, their depression due in the main to the manner in which older people are treated in the present culture. Some of these patients will respond to active treatment and the administration of anti-depressant drugs.

Psychoses Due to Alcoholism

A lot has been said and written about alcoholism which does not require repetition here. It is only necessary for us to consider the psychiatric aspects of the problem and to leave its sociological, philosophical, and theological implications in more capable hands. We have already noted the number of chronic alcoholics in the nation and estimated the number who are trying to earn that cognomen. This group is sad to contemplate. They rarely consult psychiatrists, and ofttimes the people to whom they turn do not know how to advise them properly. Threats, cajoling, pathos, promises, discipline, reasoning, desertion by family, loss of job, none of these are of proven efficacy. It is the psychiatrists' contention that these folk are sick and in need of treatment and that many of them are unable to help themselves. Whether this treatment is to be of the group variety, which is promulgated by that excellent and effective organization, Alcoholics Anonymous, or by individual psychotherapy at the hands of an experienced clinician depends upon many factors which can only be determined by careful examination and consideration of each individual problem.

Despite the real problem of alcoholism and its increasing incidence, alcoholic psychoses have been decreasing in frequency since 1910, when they constituted 10 per cent of mental hospital admissions. However, there have been shifts or fluctuations in rates at various times, from a low in 1921 to a high in 1941, and another drop during the war years. At the present time the rate is 7 per cent of admissions to mental hospitals. Cultural determinants are of importance in alcoholism, certain classes and national groups tending more to addiction than others.

The relation between alcohol and alcoholic psychoses is complex. Often alcohol just releases a reaction that is primarily psychogenic. In other cases there is a combination of psychogenic and metabolic factors. In others, the psychosis seems to be primarily an organic event.

One form of organic brain syndrome is that known as acute pathological intoxication. The mental state is one of impaired consciousness, confusion, disorientation, illusions, visual hallucinations, and transitory delusions with destructive behavior. This acute state lasts from minutes to a day or more, and the patient has no memory of the episode once he has slept. Relatively large doses of two new drugs, chlorpromazine, or chlorpromazine and meprobamate combined, are now being used extensively to produce prompt control of motor excitement and of nausea and vomiting, to relieve tension and anxiety, and to permit restful sleep.

The acute reaction of delirium tremens, which occurs in chronic alcoholism, is sometimes a withdrawal syndrome after sudden deprivation of alcohol and sometimes a sequel of metabolic disturbance or nutritional deficiency associated with its use. Early evidences of the reaction are aversion to food, restlessness, irritability, and disturbed sleep. In the delirious state of this illness there are illusions and hallucinations of a terrifying nature. The patient experiences clouding of consciousness, confusion, disorientation, incoherence, motor restlessness, and temperature elevation. The reaction runs a course of three to ten days. Death may ensue from heart failure or pneumonia (this happens in 5 to 15 per cent of the cases). The treatment of delirium tremens is symptomatic and supportive. Chlorpromazine is used advantageously today to relieve anxiety, though it does not modify the delusional or hallucinatory state. The drug is contraindicated, however, in association with or immediately after other drugs and in the presence of serious infection or cardiac disease. One hesitates to even mention drugs in the treatment of these conditions, for the indications for their use change. At present a drug of choice in these situations is Librum.

Other pictures associated with alcoholism are acute hallucinosis, alcoholic paranoia, and alcoholic deterioration, none of them pleasant to contemplate. In *acute hallucinosis,* there are vivid auditory hallucinations which provoke marked fear reactions. Recovery occurs in five days to a month, but the condition will recur with repeated overindulgence. When the illness takes on a chronic march, it eventuates in a condition resembling a paranoid-schizophrenic picture. Treatment of these afflictions consists in the withdrawal of alcohol, continuous baths, chlorpromazine or other tranquilizing drugs to relieve fear and anxiety, and the administration of vitamin B complex. In *alcoholic paranoia* frequently there are delusions of jealousy and infidelity. The pre-psychotic personality is a predisposing factor in the appearance of this illness. Prognosis is poor. After a long period of alcoholism, *alcoholic deterioration* is a frequent manifestation. The possible impairment covers a wide range, from emotional instability to dementia, with much of the damage due to vitamin deficiency. These individuals unfortunately show an increased tendency towards impulsive action, in accord with primitive instinctive forces and with sudden, overwhelming emotional pressures. Hopeless people that they are, they provoke rejection from others, and consequently this adds to their experiences of frustration, resentment, hostility, and guilt. Further, they become untruthful, unreliable, egocentric, careless in habits and appearance, and increasingly unable to face the facts of reality. As if this were not enough, after a time memory is impaired and the picture may march on toward dementia. If the use of alcohol is discontinued as soon as early character changes are recognized, complete restoration to mental health may be possible. However, the chances for continuing healthy are not the best, since the alcoholic is a person with longstanding problems of adjustment, and because alcohol is an easy, readily procurable escape from difficulties, he is loath to give it up. What he needs is psychiatric treatment that includes active physical therapy, constructive occupational therapy, agreeable social relaxation and, most particularly, psychotherapy. Group psychotherapy may be beneficial, and membership in Alcoholics Anonymous has much to recommend it. For symptomatic control, new agents, such as antabuse (disulfiram) and the newer citrated calcium carbimide, are now available, but their disadvantage lies in the fact that the patient may willfully discontinue their use.

Investigations have revealed that there is no specific personality disorder that leads to alcoholism. However, despite personality differences and patterns of mental defense, there seems to be one common denominator—a personality in which there are excessive demands for indulgence of whims and desires, frustration because these demands are not met, subsequent rage, hostile acts and wishes and, as a consequence of these, guilt and self-punishment. The alcoholism serves to pacify disappointment and rage, and to enable the individual to carry out hostile impulses which ordinarily would be suppressed.

Mental Retardation

Mental retardation is a public health problem of great magnitude, in terms of both the number of people affected and the wide range of causative and contributing agents. In the official definition, mental retardation means subaverage intellectual functioning which originates during the developmental period and is associated with impairment in adaptive behavior.

Mentally retarded individuals form a heterogeneous group. They are found at all ages from infancy to the senium and present a wide range of symptoms and various degrees of impairment. A large number of diseases of varying etiology can produce the syndrome. The estimated prevalence of such impairment in the population is 1 to 3 per cent, but a large segment of this total is never identified as mentally retarded.

In general, cases of mental retardation can be grouped into two major categories—mental retardation secondary to brain changes, and primary mental retardation in which no such changes can be found.

Mental Retardation Secondary to Brain Changes. This group, which makes up about 10 per cent of the total, is characterized by moderate to severe retardation. A single causative agent—though the agents are many—can usually be implicated. It is often possible to diagnose the condition at birth or during early childhood. Superimposed physical handicaps are common, and morbidity and mortality rates are higher than in parallel age groups in the general population. The brain changes in this group can be caused by numerous forces. In most cases heredity plays a much less important role than was once assigned to it. On the other hand, metabolic, infectious, toxic, and traumatic factors operating during pregnancy, labor, or childhood years are of prime importance.

During the *prenatal period,* development of the brain may be impeded or disturbed by factors at work in the pregnant mother. Thus, virus infections in the first three months of pregnancy, particularly German measles, may affect the developing organism and lead to brain damage. The spirochete of syphilis can be transmitted to the fetus, with adverse effects on the central nervous system; this particular problem has lessened considerably in recent years because of the adoption of routine serological tests of pregnant women and the institution of immediate treatment. Another causal factor is toxoplasmosis, which is an infection detrimental to immature nerve tissue and producing severe damage to the fetal brain. Exposure to radiation may also be injurious to the developing nervous system. In rare instances toxic substances taken by the mother during pregnancy may injure the brain of the fetus. Tissues which have achieved a certain maturity or are still in a dormant condition are affected little if at all.

Perinatal disorders, i.e. those which occur at the time of birth, are responsible for perhaps 8 per cent of all cases of brain alteration. Incompatibility of blood groups, including the Rh factor, operates in some cases; it is after birth that the symptoms occur, with jaundice, paralysis, and convulsions, and subsequent mental retardation. Replacement transfusion immediately after birth is effective in preventing this train of events. In addition, the brain may be injured during birth by mechanical interference or by asphyxiation and anoxemia of brain tissue. Cerebral hemorrhage, a frequent perinatal complication, is caused most often by prematurity or difficult labor. The brain may also be damaged by precipitate birth. Fortunately many children showing clinical evidence of brain injury do not become mentally retarded, and the removal of subdural hematoma, i.e. removal of a blood clot under one of the brain coverings, by surgical means, in an effort to prevent major brain damage, has yielded encouraging results. The effects of damage from various causes at time of birth range from mild palsies with little involvement of mental functions to severe retardation. In cerebral palsy intellectual functions may or may not be affected. The picture presented by a child subjected to severe asphyxiation at time of birth resembles that of the autistic child in the weakness of contacts with the outside world, defective language development, and unawareness of the environment.

Postnatal factors account for 25 to 50 per cent of the cases of mental retardation secondary to brain changes. Among these factors are viral and bacterial encephalitis. The high mortality rate formerly associated with some of these infections no longer obtains, but organic changes conducive to mental retardation may be the end result. Similarly, toxemia and vitamin deficiency, if long continued, may produce irreversible changes in the cortex of young children.

Gene-connected mental retardation is less common than the varieties previously mentioned. Syndromes with a single dominant gene transmitted from parent to child include those associated with lesions of the skin, with angiomata (i.e. a tumor made up of blood or lymph vessels), or with lesions of the bone. Mental retardation due to a single recessive gene is very occasionally found. The recessive types of mental retardation are usually associated with abnormality of carbohydrate, protein, and fat metabolism resulting from faulty enzymatic systems. Phenylketonuria, a congenital faulty metabolic condition which occurs in about one out of every 25,000 or 30,000 births, is an example of mental retardation connected with a recessive gene. Physical development is often normal but mental retardation is usually present, often accompanied by abnormal behavior problems. The use of low phenylalanine diets in infants in whom phenylpyruvic acid has been demonstrated in the urine will prevent the development of mental retardation. A simple recessive genetic pattern of inheritance is also seen in the condition known as galactosemia. This is a rare familial disturbance of carbohydrate metabolism characterized by an inability to utilize galactose. Symptoms are precipitated by the ingestion of milk and develop shortly after birth. As a result of the accumulation of galactose (a milk sugar) or the products of its intermediate metabolism, the child presents jaundice, enlarged liver, malnutrition, cataracts, neurological abnormalities, and mental retardation. Diagnosis can be established with the help of laboratory tests. The disorder can be treated by eliminating milk or lactose from the diet and substituting non-lactose feedings. Symptoms then disappear. The mental retardation has persisted in a few cases despite early diagnosis and treatment. The intolerance to galactose remains in all cases. However, a galactose-free diet may not be required after the first few years; later, small amounts of lactose-containing foods may be tolerated without symptoms.

Chromosomal abnormalities may produce severe mental retardation. Chromosomes (microscopic rod-shaped bodies) are conveyers of genetic material and control development from the time of conception. Numerical and structural abnormalities of chromosomes have been found in a number of syndromes associated with characteristic physical and often mental aberrations. Technical advances in the last few years have made it possible to study the chromosomes in a cell, to count them accurately, and to distinguish one from another with some degree of assurance. In 1956 the correct number of chromosomes in a human somatic cell was established at 46. A normal set of 46 includes a pair of each of the 22 non-sex chromosomes, called autosomes, and 2 sex chromosomes. In 1960 a special study group meeting in Denver set up a chromosomal classification in which the autosomes are numbered according to their length and general appearance.

The gametes, or germ cells, male and female, have at maturation half the number of chromosomes present in the primary cell—one of each autosome and one sex chromosome. When they unite they produce a zygote (i.e. the cell resulting from the fusion of two gametes; the fertilized ovum) a cell with 46 chromosomes. From the zygote the individual is developed. Various mishaps can occur during the formation of the gametes. Part of a chromosome may be lost, one chromosome or part of one chromosome may become fused with another, there may be unequal transference of material from one chromosome to another, or two instead of one of a given chromosome may become incorporated in a single cell. The incorporation of two instead of one of a given chromosome in a single germ cell is due to non-separation of a pair of chromosomes in the course of miotic cell division (i.e. the reduction of the chromosome number by half). Both members are swept into the same daughter nucleus and the resulting cell is chromosomally imbalanced. When a gamete of this kind unites with a normal germ cell, the zygote is said to be "trisomic," i.e. it has a triplication instead of a duplication of the genetic material supplied by the chromosome and has a total count of 47.

Mongolism is a trisomic syndrome. It is found in 5 to 10 per cent of the patients who are severely retarded and occurs at least once in 1,000 births. The somatic cells of a large majority of mongolians contain 47 chromosomes. The extra chromosome is No. 21—one of the two smallest autosomes—and its triplication in the mongolian is believed to be due to failure of separation of the non-sex chromosome during the development of the ovum, so that the fertilized ovum had 24 chromosomes. The chances for non-separation of this type evidently increase with maternal age. In a small percentage of mongolians, clinically indistinguishable from the others, the chromosome count is 46. However, the chromosome set is structurally abnormal. In these cases maternal age is irrelevant and there is a strong familial trend. One of the parents, usually the mother, has only 45 chromosomes, but all of the genetic material of the missing chromosome is carried in one. Though without symptoms herself, the chance that she will produce a mongoloid child is about one in three. In one familial case of mongolism, the fused chromosome was demonstrated in three generations of normal females, including mother, grandmother, and the normal sister of the patient.

Trisomies of at least two other non-sex chromosomes, associated with gross defects present at birth, have been reported. In the so-called Kleinfelter's syndrome, named after the man who described it—a condition affecting males and characterized by eunuch-like body build, small testes, and sterility—there are 47 chromosomes, the extra one being a sex chromosome. Kleinfelter's syndrome occurs in the general male population about once in 1,000, but the frequency is ten times as high among the retarded. In the female abnormality known as Turner's syndrome, marked by ovarian agenesis (failure to develop), short stature, webbing of the neck, and other defects, the somatic cell has 45 chromosomes. One sex chromosome is missing. Slight mental retardation is found in some patients, but the condition does not appear to be concentrated among the severely retarded.

Psychiatric Considerations

Most of the mental disorders that affect normally intelligent people may also affect the mentally retarded. Thus, the mentally retarded sometimes have acute transitory psychotic attacks, with episodes of excitement, depression, paranoid trends, or hallucinatory experiences. Such events are often precipitated by situational factors and are therefore potentially preventable and treatable.

In cases of mild retardation secondary to brain changes, it is possible to increase the individual's social capacity. Affording the child affection, security, social recognition, achievement, and new experience is of great importance. The emotional problem of parents with a retarded child is often exceedingly difficult, and every effort should be made to assist them in handling it, lest their difficulties in doing so have a further effect upon the child. Many retarded persons are more incapacitated by their emotional difficulties than by their intellectual impairments. The social training of the retarded child is of immense importance and is as significant as is educational training of whatever abilities and aptitudes he may happen to have. It should be obligatory upon the state to discover, classify, and provide suitable education for retarded children who can benefit from it, and to do so as early as possible. According to present estimates, 50 per cent of those admitted to state schools can be returned to the community socially improved and often equipped to take on gainful employment. The problem of the treatment of the severely retarded, on the other hand, consists largely of physical care and custody, with simple training in self-help, if possible, and self-protection. Tranquilizing drugs are now being used advantageously in the management of noisy, overactive, aggressive, and destructive patients.

The prevention of mental retardation is a problem of enormous importance. With advances in our knowledge of contributing prenatal, perinatal, and postnatal factors, greater inroads can be expected to be made upon many types of secondary mental retardation.

Primary Mental Retardation. Classed in this group are cases in which the central feature is mental retardation from no discernible prenatal cause and with no brain disease demonstrable during life or post mortem. The group as a whole stands at a crossroads between normally endowed individuals, whose range of intelligence is very wide, and the group handicapped because of organic brain damage. The group with primary mental retardation is a large one, and for the most part the degree of retardation is moderate or relatively small.

Various studies support the widely held hypothesis that intelligence is genetic in nature or that certain factors of general intelligence are gene-connected. In any given population the group of people with superior intelligence is counterbalanced by a group less fortunately endowed. However, a lack of early environmental stimulation is often important in producing mild mental retardation. In fact, the literature on mental retardation suggests that early environment is of equal, if not greater, importance than genetic forces.

In general, the intellectual deficit is not enough in itself to prevent some adaptation to society. Adverse emotional and social factors are of great importance. Sometimes institutional training is needed to counteract antisocial influences at home. A mentally retarded person may get into a great deal of trouble because of faulty reasoning, planning, and judgment, and limited ability to modify behavior through experience. Yet many retarded individuals are fairly well adjusted. Retardation does not make emotional immaturity inevitable, nor does superior intelligence guarantee superior adjustment and emotional health.

It is estimated that between 1 and 2 per cent of the total population are mildly retarded. In the school population the figure is about 3 per cent, with another 5 per cent at the borderline. Intelligence can be affected positively or negatively by cultural and other environmental stimuli. In areas with high rates of illiteracy and cultural isolation it is difficult to evaluate mental retardation, for what happens to natural endowment depends a good deal on environment. Heredity and environment operate reciprocally; both supplement and reinforce each other from the beginning of life.

Mental illness is an important contributing factor to the admission of these individuals to institutions. The cases of mild retardation in institutions are but a small sample of those with a comparable degree of handicap in the general population. Being at odds with their social environments, often because of a mentally disordered state, they require care and control. Various forms of psychoneurosis, such as obsessional and anxiety states, probably occur as frequently among the mentally retarded as in the population at large. Hysteria may be more common. Psychoneurosis adds to the difficulties of institutional supervision.

Retarded children often commit neurotic misdemeanors and they are more likely to be caught than those of greater mental ability. They are also suggestible and easily led by more intelligent malefactors. Neurotic states are therefore of no small importance in the gravitation of the mildly retarded to institutions. Sex perversions, closely allied to personality disorders, occur rather frequently, but probably no more frequently than in any other sector of the general population. It is because the retarded person is less competent to conceal unacceptable behavior than one more normally endowed that he tends to stand out more and to be credited with a greater degree of danger to the community. The sexual promiscuity and illegitimate pregnancies which occur among the retarded can be attributed to lack of judgment, impulsiveness, suggestibility, and inability to resist victimization. It is not a question of increased sexual drive. Training, supervision, and guidance through special classes, sheltered workshops, vocational guidance, community programs, and mental hygiene clinics can be used to advantage in correcting most such deviations of the mildly retarded. Adjustment may then become quite satisfactory, with the achievement of a fair degree of self-sufficiency and self-direction.

This is the area of mental health to which psychiatry has directed too little attention. Most community facilities do not accept children who have retarded ratings. Doctor Malcolm Farrell, of the Walter E. Fernald State School, states the problem as follows: "It has to be recognized that the marginal group lives in a psychiatric and social no man's land. They need more attention. This is the group especially responsive to educational and psychiatric proceedings and, if neglected, contributes largely to the minor forms of delinquency, misdemeanors, and social disturbances."

DISORDERS OF PSYCHOGENIC ORIGIN

This group presents the greatest challenge of all to the psychiatrist. Included in it are major forms of psychopathology, the causes of which are still obscure. No physical basis for the disorders in this area has yet been found, though the search continues for biological abnormalities that might help explain the baffling behavior that many patients show. The best explanation for them at the present time is that they are predominantly of psychological origin. Characteristic of disorders in this group is some degree of personality disturbance or disintegration, some degree of failure in testing and evaluating external reality, and some degree of impairment in interpersonal, occupational, and other social relationships.

Disorders of psychogenic origin fall into five large groups:

1. Major Functional Psychotic Disorders.
2. Psychophysiological or Psychosomatic Disorders.
3. Psychoneurotic Disorders.
4. Personality Disorders.
5. Transient Situational Personality Disorders.

Appearing in the first group are the major functional disorders, which have been traditionally the focus of interest in psychiatry: 1) the so-called involutional psychoses, characterized most commonly by depression; 2) the affective psychoses, marked by a primary severe disorder of mood, made up largely of manic-depressive reactions and reactive depressions of psychotic magnitude; 3) the schizophrenic reactions; and 4) the paranoid reactions in which there are systematized delusions but ordinarily no hallucinations and no significant intellectual deterioration. Giving each of these illnesses as much attention as is possible in a work of this scope, we will describe the involutional psychoses in the latter part of this chapter, and devote the next chapter to the affective psychoses, schizophrenias, and paranoid reactions, as their importance warrants.

The second and third large groups, the psychosomatic and psychoneurotic disorders, will also have a chapter to themselves. One category, the fourth, will have to be slighted somewhat, namely, the personality disorders, for an adequate appraisal would take us far afield, into discussions of personality development and especially of adolescent traits, which deserve a book in themselves. We will take up some of the more general aspects of this category in this chapter. The fifth category, the transient and situational personality disorders, will be handled in various sections towards the end of the book.

The group which we denote as personality disorders is made up of personality types which are difficult to influence in any radical way by any form of therapy, though it may be possible to improve their functioning by prolonged psychotherapy. The defects in the personality are developmental and of long standing, and the individuals concerned have a minimum of anxiety and little, if any, sense of distress. The disturbance is manifested at the level of behavior rather than of thought or emotion. From the descriptive point of view, personality disorders fall into three groups: 1) personality pattern disturbances which are considered to be deep-seated; 2) personality trait disturbances, making the individual unable to maintain emotional equilibrium and independence under any degree of stress; 3) sociopathic personality disturbances, placing the individual at odds with society and the prevailing cultural milieu.

These disorders, in varying intensity, are now being found in young individuals who are "acting out" the ideas and the fantasies which ordinarily are held in check in normal life. Some psychopathic behavior results in brushes with the law. This type of behavior is not new to our culture, but now, in the milieu of better economic circumstances, the culture recognizes some of it as a form of illness resulting from unresolved personality difficulties in individuals who have lost their beliefs and their moorings. These individuals, many of whom are bright and personable, believe in nothing but the satisfaction of their own desires. The heartbreak that they cause in parents and loved ones is vast and incalculable.

The Psychoses

The psychoses, which are psychogenic rather than organic in onset, are mental disorders in which all forms of adaptation —social, intellectual, professional, etc.—are disrupted and personality disorganization is extensive. Psychoses are rare until adolescence, when their incidence climbs abruptly, and the trend thereafter is upward. There is a growing body of opinion among psychiatrists that most functional psychotic behavior has a common dynamic basis and that the amount of similar behavior among the types distinguished from one another in the classification is great. Some authorities maintain that there are no dividing lines at all. In broad psychiatric experience, patients with mixed symptoms are more common than those who run true to type. Perhaps the four major functional psychoses—involutional, manic-depressive, schizophrenic, and paranoid—should be put in one group, and called schizo-affective diseases, as some advocate. "Schizo-" would refer to the more common symptom, namely, disorder of thought control; "affective" would refer to the mood disturbances. Involutional psychoses present an excellent example of a mixture of mood and thought disturbances.

Involutional Psychoses

The patients who succumb to involutional psychoses have no previous history of a psychotic break. The condition arises for the first time in the involutional period and is presumably associated with it etiologically, i.e. causally. The involutional period is notoriously difficult to define, but roughly it corresponds to the ages 42 to 46 in women and about a decade later in men. These are the illnesses popularly thought to accompany the "change of life" in the female.[3] This, too, is rather a fuzzy designation; actually the term is a misnomer, for all of life consists in "change." Most frequently the picture takes the form of melancholia, though an involutional paranoid reaction with depression is not uncommon. The term "melancholy" dates from the time when depression was considered to be due to disorders of the bile. In cases where black bile (*melana chole*) predominated, it supposedly gave rise to a mournful nature.

Involutional melancholia is characterized by intense agitation and depression and is two to three times as frequent in women as in men. Among first admissions to hospitals for mental illness, it ranks fourth in frequency behind schizophrenia, senile dementia, and psychosis with cerebral arteriosclerosis. It is believed that the physiological changes that occur in the involutional period are of less importance in the genesis of the pathological reaction than are the psychological implications of these changes. For certain individuals the loss of prized

[3] Involutional depressions are differentiated from manic-depressive depressed states by the symptoms mentioned above: 1) no previous break; 2) an agitated depression in the individual age group. It differs from psychoneurotic depressions in that the latter appear in the presence of other neurotic symptoms, are due to unresolved unconscious conflicts, and are less severe reactions with a minimal loss of contact with reality.

biological functions and the fear of aging are highly disturbing. They have too much insecurity in their personalities to accept their declining powers, and, consequently, upon encountering more than ordinary stress, they become anxious and depressed.

One of the most important factors in this type of disorder is the personality makeup of the individuals who become ill. There is conclusive evidence now that the persons who become depressed in this age group were basically insecure and prone to increased anxiety. Typically, these individuals have been inhibited, compulsive, and self-depreciative with exacting, inflexible standards and a proneness to blame and punish themselves for trifles or non-existing faults. The rigidity which they exhibit is a neurotic defense against anxiety. In addition, they are prone to overcompensate for their feelings and intellectualize their difficulties. This leads to a certain amount of psychological isolation from their friends and peers.

The punitive conscience of these individuals, plus their own unconscious immaturities and mixed feelings about people and themselves, combine to produce serious conflicts which remain unsolved. At the involutional period, which constitutes a period of stress, the personality structure breaks down, precipitating a depression. The symptoms preceding the depression are usually vague; the patients complain of fatigue, feelings of inadequacy, irritability, and sleeplessness. Physical complaints are also varied and consist of vague pains, pressures in the head, difficulty of thinking, flushing, vertigo, etc. An unfortunate aspect of this illness is that it occurs in individuals who are usually capable, hard-working, dedicated, and efficient.

Prior to the advent of electroshock treatment, about 40 to 50 per cent of these patients with involutional melancholia recovered, and not infrequently the illness lasted for two or three years. A large percentage went on to chronic illness, and a number of others destroyed themselves. Suicide is an ever present danger in this illness, and sometimes it takes place despite all efforts to prevent it. With the use of electrotherapy nearly 85 per cent of these patients recover. In some the improvement is dramatic after eight to twelve treatments;

in fact, it is in this illness that electrotherapy is most efficacious.

Lately one of the major phenothiazine drugs has been used successfully in the treatment of this disorder, and now, with the synthesis of the new anti-depressant drugs which we shall discuss later, the picture takes on a brighter hue. Hormones may help the physical symptoms which accompany the menopause, but they are of little value in the psychiatric aspects of the problems which occur at this time.

Once the depression has lifted, psychotherapy ought to be undertaken in an effort to help the patient understand some of the origins of the pathological reaction. The greater the deterioration of personal habits, the more grotesque the delusions or hypochondriacal ideas which tend to occur in this illness, the greater the hallucinatory activity, and the more marked the poverty of thought and tendency to depersonalization, the worse the prognosis.

The involutional paranoid reaction is rarer than the melancholic. The pre-psychotic personality pattern in these cases is also one marked by lifelong insecurity. This insecurity has been handled through a different pattern of defense: hypercritical attitudes, hypersensitivity, jealousy, obstinacy, and a tendency to blame others for one's own failures. These defensive character traits lose their effectiveness in the involutional period when added physiological and psychological burdens must be coped with. Then the patient resorts to the more extreme defenses provided by the paranoid psychosis, with its misinterpretations and well-organized delusions. These lack the fantastic quality of schizophrenia. In the involutional paranoid reaction, prognosis is less favorable than in involutional melancholia. Here electroshock treatment is of limited value, but the phenothiazines may be helpful, especially for symptoms of aggression and excitement.

Sexual Deviation

Sexual deviation is one sociopathic personality disturbance which it would be wise to mention briefly. True sexual deviation, in which there is a profound personality disturbance and a pattern of repetition, should be distinguished from perverse acts which the individual is capable of resisting. True perversion stems from unconscious forces. Obviously, therefore, the sexual deviant is a psychiatric problem. Only skilled dynamic psychotherapy can help with these problems, and even then the outlook is often poor.

Sexual deviation is basically a psychosexual immaturity. "Oversexuality" or "undersexuality" has little if anything to do with it; neither do abnormalities of constitution and anatomy. The underlying feature in all of these cases seems to be an inability to bring the emotional and instinctive aspects of sex into harmony with the whole personality. Unable to obtain satisfaction in the mature love of another person of the opposite sex, outlets are sought in voyeurism, exhibitionism, homosexuality, rape, pedophilia, masochism and sadism, and their derivatives.

Whether or not an individual achieves psychosexual maturity depends on critical experiences in the course of his personality development. Parental influence may be unfavorable, or unfortunate sexual experiences in childhood may serve to block further development. In some instances, the infantile drive towards aggression and destructiveness is not successfully tamed, and it becomes bound up with the sex instinct. Later sexual behavior may then be not just deplorable, but often extremely dangerous to society.

A repetitive compulsive character is evident in all sexual deviations. Deviant activity seems necessary to relieve intolerable tension; but the relief is always temporary and must be sought anew, for what the individual seeks, though he is unaware of it, is the satisfaction of aggressive and other infantile drives. Some deviants have no desire to be cured. Others seek treatment and, if they have not committed a serious social offense, the outlook under intensive psychotherapy is hopeful.

V

THE AFFECTIVE REACTIONS
AND THE SCHIZOPHRENIAS

We read that heaviness of the heart of man maketh it stop but a good word maketh it glad. A cheerful heart doth good like medicine but a broken spirit drieth up the bones. . . . A great many of our diseases either arise from a weight of care lying on the minds of men or are thereby increased.

Cotton Mather

DEPRESSIVE REACTIONS

All people feel sad, depressed, blue, or melancholy at one time or another. Sometimes the cause seems obvious and rational; at other times the emotion seems to come from nowhere and sweeps over the individual in the mood of "blackest midnight born." Occasionally the mood passes as it came, and yet again it seizes upon the individual and cuts him off from activity, from pleasure, and even from his fellow men. There is no intention of implying here that those individuals who suffer from mild or transient attacks of the blues are to be considered as pathologic along with those who suffer from the more serious affective reactions. They are mentioned here merely to clarify and differentiate them.

Aristotle once asked the question: "Why is it that all outstanding men, no matter how they have distinguished themselves, are obvious melancholics?" This question is important, for it indicates that the term "melancholy" has always had several meanings. On the one hand it describes an illness which disables a man and renders him ineffectual, and on the other it describes a quality which seemingly is part of a creative and energetic nature. It is obvious that these last-mentioned persons are neither sick nor ineffectual. Somberness is their way of life and they have come to terms with it.

Ordinarily, feelings of depression are only welcome to the morbid. Even though one hears a lady say occasionally that she enjoyed a good cry, this is but a figure of speech; it was the relief which she received from the free expression of her low spirits that she was grateful for, not the depression itself. It is only the truly ill who find "naught so sweet as melancholy." The normal person, with a garden variety case of the blues, is more likely to say ruefully with Robert Burns:

> It's hardly in a body's pow'r
> To keep, at times, frae being sour.

Seemingly occasional depression is an ordinary accompaniment of intelligence and experience. Throughout history we find that it is the clown and the jester who were expected to produce consistent merriment, certainly not the serious men of the realm. "I'd rather have a fool to make me merry, than experience to make me sad," Shakespeare wrote. But in his case, if experience did not make him sad, it gave him deep insight into melancholy moods, and throughout his works he described them in all of their forms and gradations. Most of his melancholy characters are well known—the brooding Hamlet; Don John, sour, ill tempered, surly, and discontented; Jaques in *As You Like It*, morose and in love with his own melancholy. It is interesting to note that Goethe had a touch of depression and late in life wrote contemptuously of what he called "lazarette poesy." (A lazarette is a contagious disease hospital.) He said: "Poets write as if they are ill and the whole world a hospital." This observation is suggestive of the poesy of the modern angry young men and the beatniks, and one can only conclude, again, that "there is nothing new under the sun."

There are, at times, passing and usually easily handled fits of depression in young people, but resiliency and adaptability ordinarily limit these attacks. Then, too, the reasons for their lowness of spirit are often apparent, and even though the events cannot be changed, attitudes toward them can be. As an individual grows up, occasional bouts of sadness cannot be avoided. It is understandable that the middle years, about which we spoke earlier, should be a time when one might become vulnerable to periods of depression. In this period there is a lessened ability to tolerate loss, frustration, and disappointment. This is accentuated when the possibilities of attaining the goals one had erected for oneself begin to fade and declining personal resources and physical powers emphasize the failure, while competition from younger claimants grows more intense.

It should be remembered that the man of achievement also has depressive moments, like the rest of us. The trophy he chased too hard and which claimed too much of his time to win is now and again found to be empty. That life, which from a distance appeared to be so exciting, is found to be a merry-go-round of obligation with no time left for spiritual contemplation, pleasure, or relaxation. Occasionally a man in middle life goes through a "success depression," a feeling of being pushed beyond his powers, an aloneness on the heights which he has attained, a frightened look down from a pinnacle from which there is always a danger of falling.

We noted earlier that the depressive feelings of women in middle life are not due to hormones nor anything mysterious, but, rather, are simply exaggerations of moods and elaborations of disposition which are perhaps developed early in life. Her family unit is slowly changing; the children are off on their own; the husband is busy about his own affairs; and she falls prey to "that hint of the sadness of all things completed." It is a time of change for her, an end to her more arduous duties; and yet, with it comes the need of letting go of the past and taking hold of the future. There is the difficulty of deciding what to do with the new leisure and the methods of undertaking a new stage of life. Then arises that distressing feeling—the "need to be needed." If a woman can come to terms with this, she has some chance of being at peace with her surroundings; if she does not, then, understandably, a depressive reaction might result.

Grief

Grief may herald the beginning of a depression at any time of life, but should not be confused with it. In grief the loss is objective, external, and readily understandable. The response it calls forth is realistic and proportionate to what has been lost. In depression the loss is emotional, of internal origin, and much more complex. At the core of it there is an intricate set of reactions which lead to a sense of loss of self, to feelings of self-doubt, self-contempt, and even self-loathing. Grief is self-limiting and gradually subsides; it merges into a depression only when the sorrow and bereavement are somehow turned inward instead of being openly expressed. Of late we have relearned the fact that there is something salutary in the controlled expression of grief. Leigh Hunt in 1797 spoke of this: "It is only for sophists to contend that we, whose eyes contain the fountains of tears, need never give way to them. It would be unwise not to do so on some occasions. Sorrow unlocks them in her balmy moods. The first bursts may be bitter and overwhelming, but the soil on which they pour would be worse without them."

Depressive Feelings in Older Age Groups

The depressive reactions in these ages have various causes. Frequently the male is pushed into retirement before he wants or needs to be. This is an enforced leisure; the person is declared old by the fiat of a board of directors and a calendar. In our present culture too often retirement means loss of privilege, loss of status, and financial stress. Depression is the almost inevitable reaction to this change, but the symptoms differ widely. Some men become peevish and irritable; others tend toward a useless overactivity, as if they were attempting to show themselves and others that they are capable of superhuman achievement. Others show the more typical symptoms—wakefulness at three or four in the morning and the loss of interest in family and friends. Early morning awakening is a common symptom and no harm comes from it; it is simply inconvenient.

The feeling of uselessness in a man heretofore holding a responsible job; the pained courtesy of listeners; the feeling of being shunted about in the homes of children, from one to the other; the feeling of loneliness and time on one's hands; all of these things contribute to the deeper depressions with more serious outlook.

AFFECTIVE REACTIONS

The Psychoses

Beyond the fits of melancholy and moods of depression, whether passing or chronic, and divided from them by a line that would be impossible exactly to descry, lie the affective psychoses, which are characterized primarily by severe mood disorders, sometimes with various accessory symptoms, such as illusions, delusions, and hallucinations. The best known are the manic-depressive reactions. The manic type is evidenced by elation or irritability, with overtalkativeness, flight of ideas, and increased physical activity. Transitory, often momentary, episodes of depression may also occur. The depressive type is evidenced by mood depression, with mental and motor retardation and inhibition, and, in some cases, uneasiness and apprehension. Perplexity, stupor, or agitation may be prominent. Mixed forms of manic and depressive symptoms occur and, rarely, circular forms in which the manic and depressive attacks alternate. The depressive and the manic attack look altogether different; yet they are basically similar, for it is the same mental functions which are altered in opposite ways and push the mood to one extreme or the other. The dynamics of these conditions are best understood in terms of the unconscious.

Psychodynamics (i.e. the Underlying Mental Processes)

Basically these patients are narcissistic and egocentric, with many early infantile drives still present within them. The depressed personality is at the mercy of an extremely severe superego (internalized parental authority), is usually over-conscientious, overly serious, compliant, subservient, obsessive, or maybe even overly agreeable. He is invariably an individual who finds recognition of his own hostility entirely too threatening to his own security, and he cannot allow a vestige of it to appear. He reacts by clamping down hard and quickly on any impulse which might in the slightest way betray aggressiveness, and so he moves along under an unrelaxing constraint from which he eventually begins to suffer feelings of depression. A typical case is as follows:

An elderly woman who, all her life, had been a quiet and submissive type, although in a quiet way, had also been intensely critical of anything sloppy and disorderly. She had complained for many years of feeling "sad" and dissatisfied, and as she entered her sixties, these periods of depression had become more pronounced. Sometimes she would go for days hardly eating anything, sitting in a darkened room, apparently doing nothing at all. She was disinclined to speak and, although she would not exert herself to get rid of visitors, her lack of response soon discouraged them. These periods of depression were broken occasionally—every five or six months—by sudden flurries of excitement and activity. She would go on shopping sprees, buying exotic hats and shawls, and wear these around the house, often walking from room to room humming or singing to herself. During these periods she used the phone constantly, calling all her acquaintances and chatting at length with them, although not always perfectly coherently. After such a period of excitement, a period of deeper depression set in. Finally the depressions became so deep that she entered what for all practical purposes was coma, and she could only be brought out of these by shock therapy in a hospital.

Some observers see three personality groups most commonly associated with depression. A member of the first group reacts to his hostile, aggressive impulses by an overserious, somber, overly studious, overly conscientious pattern of behavior. This pattern aids the repression of the impulses but also depresses the spirits. Those in the second group have developed traits which deny hostility and are formed by the process of reaction formation, i.e. the unconscious

adoption of attitudes and behavior that reflect impulses opposite to those which the individual is attempting to disown.
These are the overly compliant, overly polite, subservient,
and obsequious types. The third group employs obsessive-
compulsive habits, which are repetitive thoughts or acts provoked by unconscious urges, such as meticulousness, concern
with detail, rigidity of behavior, parsimony, in order to master
these impulses. Attempts to desist from this behavior result
in anxiety of unknown origin.

As long as the defensive traits of the depressive person
serve their purpose, the status quo of adjustment is maintained. But if internal or external stresses increase, the defenses may become inadequate, and then depression may
develop as part of the urgent need to conceal from everyone,
oneself included, the feared aggressive and hostile drives.

Because of the efforts required in the concealment of hostility, plus the gloomy outlook and obvious rigidity, other
people feel uncomfortable around these individuals. As they
are severely critical of themselves, they frequently spill over
and are critical of others. Building themselves up by the device of tearing others down, they are not comfortable companions.

Depression, it can be seen, is closely related to the conflicts
arising from the frustrations of denial, loss, and failure. In the
resulting deep disappointment, the individual is literally unable to handle his hostility. Depressed people suffer deeply,
much more so than in any other medical condition, and the
acme of this suffering is seen in severe cases of agitated depression in middle life.

It is conjected that the *manic* phase of this illness occurs
when the ego, ordinarily submissive, achieves an overthrow
of the repressive superego, i.e. when the individual over-
throws or ceases to be held in check by the inhibitions he has
acquired in his earlier life. Then the ego runs wild with exaggerated self-esteem and reveals the underlying narcissistic
and megalomanic qualities present. There are normal inter-
vals too, but the balance is precarious and easily upset by
intrapsychic as well as environmental stimuli.

About 5 per cent of first admissions to mental hospitals belong to the manic-depressive category, if cases are excluded which are complicated by an admixture of other symptoms. The question now in the forefront is: Is there a real decline in the pure manic-depressive disorders in our culture? A profusion of data suggests an affirmative answer. In a period of twenty years the incidence in New York has decreased by one third, and the trends are similar elsewhere. It may be that new therapeutic methods at the beginning of an attack are bringing the illness under better control, so that fewer cases develop to the acute stage that makes hospitalization mandatory. It may also be that diagnostic trends are changing in such a way as to assign more cases to the mixed group. In any event, the pure affective reactions are curiously rare, and cases with mixed affective and thought disturbances are on the upsurge. The impression obtains that manic-depressive and schizophrenic groups form a continuum. Some authorities suspect that there is a causative factor in common, the difference in symptoms arising from such factors as variations of constitution or of age at onset. Patients with a lifelong psychosis have been known to show each pattern. Moreover, both manic-depressive psychosis and schizophrenia can be found in the same families—the former disorder appearing first, and then, after a few generations, an increase in schizophrenic reactions. This does not mean that either psychosis is due entirely, or even largely, to heredity. Psychological and environmental precipitants are almost surely of major importance.

Psychosociological explanations are often invoked to explain the marked differences in frequency and pattern of manic-depressive reactions found in different cultures. True manic-depressive psychosis is rare in technologically backward areas. In Kenya, for example, manic states of the acute and chronic form are fairly common, but there is no slowing up of physical activity nor ideas of sin or unworthiness, such as Western cultures show. A relatively larger incidence of manic-depressive psychosis than of schizophrenia apparently obtains in the lands of the Mediterranean basin. In Italy manic-depressive patients are found more commonly than in the United States, but even there Italian psychiatrists note a decline in this psychosis, especially the manic type. Thus, the decline is not universal, but it seems to affect many countries and at different speeds.

There may be a relation between what David Riesman calls "inner-directed personality and culture" and the affective psychoses. An inner-directed culture, with its emphasis on duty and self-responsibility, may, as a by-product, promote the severe, strong superego and the strong introjective (as against projective) tendencies of the personality. This type of superego, these introjective tendencies, are prominent in the personalities of patients who succumb to manic-depressive psychoses.

The first attack of manic-depressive illness occurs most frequently between the ages of twenty and thirty-five. The individual attack generally subsides and, even though the patient has repeated attacks, there is little intellectual impairment. During the depressive attack the greatest danger is that of suicide. In many cases suicide occurs, not when the state of depression is at its depth, but when the worst is over. In the depths of his depression the patient is too retarded to take action. It seems sometimes that the patient bent on suicide can redeem himself entirely only by destroying himself. For other patients the suffering inflicted by the depression is adequate and, after the acute attack, remarkable relief is experienced. They are free of guilt for a while. But neither the depression nor the manic state solves the deeply rooted conflicts. In an increasing number of cases a typical schizophrenic picture develops in the wake of one or more attacks. In these, projective tendencies have presumably been present and, once the manic-depressive mechanism has failed, the projective one takes over.

On the whole, the treatment of manic-depressive reactions has become increasingly successful. Hospitalization is ordinarily advisable if the attack is severe. It has become possible in some cases to avoid hospitalization because of the effectiveness of convulsive treatment. Electroshock therapy until very recently was unchallenged as the best treatment for affective disorders, regardless of the phase. The number of treatments required varies. The ordinary depressed patient will begin to show improvement after the third or fourth treatment. Two or three more are given to consolidate the result, and in some cases as many as twenty may be needed. Lately, drugs have appeared which also have been effective and bid fair in some ways to supplant electrotherapy. Certainly since their advent the use of shock in depressions has markedly decreased. The phenothiazine drugs are useful for tranquilizing manic patients, and the new stimulating drugs are now often used successfully in the treatment of depression.[1] It is true that electroshock and drugs do not cure the basic illness, but, once symptomatic control is obtained, psychotherapy may help the patient understand what has been happening and he may be able to avoid future attacks. He needs to understand and modify his rigid superego, as well as to bring closer to maturity his unconscious infantile needs.

Psychotic depressive reactions are not all of the manic-depressive type. As indicated above, in the manic-depressive situation there is usually a history of previous mood swings without obvious cause. Some psychotic depressions lack these distinctive features. They arise when the patient has been confronted with a personal situation of great stress. The environment and certain personal experiences have been so frustrating, arousing such intense feelings of guilt or remorse or feelings so damaging to personal pride, that the patient reacts with a psychotic depression. Associated with this may be gross misinterpretation of reality, delusions, and frequently suicidal ruminations or attempts, intense feelings of guilt, and retardation of thought and activity. The prognosis in such cases is favorable. The program of treatment is the same as in manic-depressive psychoses, physical forms of treatment

[1] Again one hesitates to mention the names of drugs used in the treatment of depression, for they may be supplanted by the time the book is in print. At present, however, Tofranil, Parnate and Stelazine and Nardil are some of the drugs enjoying favor. Tofranil, though it is somewhat slow to take hold, does seem to be quite efficacious.

bringing symptoms under control, with follow-up psychotherapy to maintain the patient's equilibrium in future situations of stress.

SCHIZOPHRENIC REACTIONS

Oh, this poor brain ten thousand shapes of fury are whirling there and reason is no more.

Fielding

We noted earlier how, in 1896, Kraepelin separated from other mental patients a group which seemed to be following a deteriorating course and called their illness "dementia praecox." We noted, too, how Bleuler found it necessary to rename this disorder "schizophrenia" because many psychiatrists were unwilling to make the diagnosis "dementia praecox" in patients who were neither young nor demented. By "schizophrenia" Bleuler meant a group of psychoses whose course is at times chronic, at times marked by intermittent attacks, and which can stop or retrogress at any stage but does not permit a full *restitutio ad integrum.* It was characterized by a specific type of alteration of thinking, feeling, and relation to the external world. The term "schizophrenia" was used because the splitting of different psychic functions was one of its most important characteristics. For the sake of convenience, the term was used in the singular, although Bleuler was sure that the group included several entities.

Schizophrenic reactions are the commonest of the major mental disorders extant and the most difficult to understand. They have always posed the greatest challenge to psychiatry and are at present the focal point of concentrated research throughout the world. The genesis of the illnesses remains uncertain, but it is obvious now that more than one causal factor is involved. A wide variety of therapeutic approaches, used in combination, is at last making definite inroads in this formidable territory.

Numerous theories as to the origin of these conditions have been advanced. They have been all-inclusive, from the hereditary and the strictly anatomical and biochemical to the psychological and environmental. At present the most useful concept holds that the schizophrenias are reactions of faulty adjustment to difficult life situations. The anxiety thereby worked in the victim is overwhelming, and the only way he can handle it is by resorting to drastic narcissistic defenses. Freud had, in fact, designated these illnesses and those which Kraepelin terms "manic-depressive psychoses" as "the narcissistic neuroses."

Thus far it would seem that the varied assumptions widely held in years past that the illnesses are produced by heredity, endocrine changes, toxic factors, etc., lack sufficient supporting evidence, despite constant investigations by able scientists. This is not to say, however, that these various factors play no part in the illness. They might well be contributing elements, but the primary role at the present time has to be assigned to the psychodynamics of personality development and early traumatic relationships with other persons.

Schizophrenic reactions are characterized by marked disturbances in interpersonal relationships. They usually involve a strong tendency to withdraw from reality, although intellectual and perceptual capacities, orientation, and memory are not really impaired. What occurs is a split or breakup of basic personality organization. The sufferer becomes incapable of blending feeling, thought, and action in a meaningful and constructive fashion. Because of insoluble conflicts within himself and with his environment, his ego becomes increasingly handicapped in its effort to maintain a balanced, comfortable, and purposeful attitude. When sufficiently weakened, it is no longer able to prevent dangerous unconscious ideas and fantasies from emerging into consciousness. The line between fact and fiction grows blurred and we have the phenomenon of the once rational person living a large part of his waking life —perhaps all of it—in a "dream myth" fashion. The price exacted for this fantasy is high. Reality, human contact, and the whole shared world are yielded in payment for it, and all that the patient gets in return is a permit to operate at a lower level of integration and often at an extremely primitive level of behavior. As autistic thinking, i.e. thinking which attempts to gratify desires without regard to reality, finally reigns unchallenged, the individual loses his emotional rapport and empathy with his fellow men. His emotional energy is directed to the world he has created for himself alone, the only one in which he now finds satisfaction of his basic needs. External objects of satisfaction are no longer necessary.

Schizophrenia, we have noted, is an ubiquitous disorder, occurring at all times in all cultures. The statistics of incidence vary, however, with social and historical factors. Thus, the illness occurs more frequently in urban than in rural areas, in industrial rather than in non-industrial groups, among the foreign-born and immigrants, and among ethnic minorities. It is most frequent in the center of cities, where other indices of social disorganization abound. In less advanced cultures it is reported less frequently than in so-called sophisticated communities. Actually, of course, the closer the ordinary logic of a culture is to primitive thinking, the less tendency there is to regard as abnormal certain aberrant thinking which we consider to be of schizophrenic magnitude. However, in patients of primitive cultures, who are ostensibly schizophrenic, the symptoms are often quieter than they are in the Western world. The richness of the variety of symptoms manifested may depend on the intellectual and cultural resources of the patient. In any event, social, historical, and geographic factors have a definite influence upon the incidence and form of schizophrenic reactions.

Even in Western countries statistics are by no means representative of the scope of the problem of schizophrenia. Such statistics deal only with the more overt forms. They have to do for the most part with patients disturbed enough to get into mental hospitals. On the basis of a half century of observation, C. G. Jung estimates that the incidence of mild or latent cases, as compared with more severe cases, is ten to one. Yet, cases of schizophrenia already account for more than one quarter of all admissions to mental hospitals. In this country this number is somewhere in the area of 30,000 new cases yearly. Because a schizophrenic reaction tends to become chronic unless vigorously combatted, preferably at an early stage, one finds an enormous representation of these patients in any large mental hospital at any given time—as high as 60 per cent, according to some observers.

The illness may manifest itself at any age, from childhood (somewhat rare) to age sixty or so. The age of greatest frequency is the late teens and the decade of the twenties. Occasionally the onset of a schizophrenic reaction is sudden and acute. When this is the case, the abandonment of relationships with other people is often precipitated by the patient's fear of losing control over dangerous impulses. More typically, the onset is insidious. There have been gradual changes in behavior over a period of months or years. One can trace either a shy, retiring pattern of behavior, with a limited social existence, or a sustained display of coldness, moodiness, and perhaps irritability. It is as if the individual were trying to build up a wall of indifference around himself. His interest is beginning to attach itself to unconscious material, as are his feelings. Because of this displacement, the patient feels vague, detached, depersonalized to some extent, and the environment in which he moves thus becomes unnatural and unreal. As the psychosis takes on more definite outlines, emotional impoverishment increases. Finer feelings fade away. The patient becomes careless in appearance, sloppy in work habits, and impervious to responsibility. As the illness grows in strength, he may show an incredible indifference to his own fundamental physical comforts and needs. As the subjective creations of his fantasy exert their increasing fascination, thought becomes more and more disorderly. Associations and symbols are formed in the unconscious, whence they arise into consciousness and lend dreamlike features to the patient's thought—the symbolism, displacement, and condensation so mystifying to the untrained observer. Irrational thought proceeds unhampered by the premises of reality, logic, and science. Schizophrenic thinking resembles the prelogical thinking of children and primitives, which makes little distinction between the external and the internal world.

Often the dominant thoughts of schizophrenic patients are grotesquely delusional. Incomprehensible as they may seem, they have a meaning for the patient and are shaped to his psychological needs. The delusions tend to be loosely organized. They are frequently centered around themes of persecution or grandiosity and of sex. The function of delusions is to deal with thwarted drives and hopes, with inadequacies and insecurities, with disowned qualities and other contents of the unconscious. Hallucinations occur more frequently in schizophrenia than in any other form of mental disorder. They tend to be highly disguised and are of more serious significance than the hallucinations that occur in delirium. Highly significant material in the patient's inner life assumes hallucinatory vividness and the "voice" of conscience can be heard. So vivid are the hallucinations that the patient is completely incapable of recognizing the origin of the "voices" and ascribes them to others, often to "enemies" bent upon his destruction. Hallucinations are not an early symptom of the illness. The patient's personality must be extremely disorganized before they can appear.

There is often a sense of tragedy accompanying the onset of schizophrenia, for the sufferers are frequently bright and talented persons. The following is a typical case:

A young man, intelligent and well liked, was away from home for an extended period, undertaking graduate studies in a foreign country. At first he got along very well and gave signs of high professional promise. Then he began to withdraw and limit his associates to two or three close friends; he complained that people were watching him and criticizing him and going out of their way to make things difficult for him. His friends did not take this seriously until he withdrew entirely, remained in his room and refused efforts to dislodge him. Wherever he went he thought that people were watching him through cracks in the walls, behind drawn curtains. On one occasion he broke down completely, was noisy, destructive, overactive, and out of control. There was no doubt now about the seriousness of his condition and it was necessary to hospitalize him temporarily, for he felt that eyes were watching him from the ceiling and voices were accusing him from behind the walls.

Psychiatrists now classify schizophrenia in greater diagnostic detail than ever was possible before. A number of subtypes have been added to what were considered the standard forms. However, each diagnosis is descriptive and it is often difficult to assign cases to a single subgroup. The first four subgroups dominated psychiatric thinking in the past and they embrace the classical pictures which, except for the paranoid reaction, are becoming rarer in psychiatric practice. A brief description of these categories is probably in order.

Schizophrenic Reaction, Simple Type

The main characteristics of this type of schizophrenia are the reductions in external attachments and interests and an impoverishment of human relationships. The individual, perhaps one who had given promise of superior accomplishment, gradually slackens and begins to function on a lower psychological plane. This letdown is characterized by marked apathy and indifference. It is a gradual and insidious reaction and is often seen as a willful indolence rather than an illness, until the time when blunted affect and preoccupation with fantasy indicate that something serious is wrong. Lack of interest in important and vital concerns, in family, and in doing anything constructive soon pinpoint the difficulty.

Conspicuous hallucinations and delusions are rare. The illness is marked by a gradual deterioration in character and a loss of the finer sensibilities. These patients are generally found on the fringes of society—drifters, hoboes, prostitutes, and vagrants—and their eventual habitat is "skid row" rather than the mental hospital.

Schizophrenic Reaction, Hebephrenic Type

When the illness takes this form, there is no doubt but that the patient is seriously affected. He regresses markedly and his behavior is characterized by silly actions, mannerisms, shallow affect, inappropriate giggling, etc. This behavior and appearance is close to the caricatures of the "madman" of old. The patient's delusions are fragmentary and often concern bizarre bodily distortions. The hallucinations are extremely grotesque. There is a dissociation of thought and feeling, which is readily discernible, and there is no doubt that the underlying process in this illness is more malignant than in any of the other subtypes described.

The onset of this reaction is also insidious and it begins usually in early adolescence. The apparent intellectual changes are attributable in large part to the patient's lack of attention and the looseness of his associational processes. As the illness progresses, there is an impressive incoherence of speech, and neologisms, i.e. new words coined by the patient, not readily understood by others, are common. The patient leads a fantasy life, completely wrapped up in his own thoughts, and the eventual disintegration of his personality and habits is perhaps the greatest of any occurring in schizophrenic illness.

Schizophrenic Reaction, Catatonic Type

This form of schizophrenic reaction is seemingly not as common now as it was a decade or two ago, and it is probable that some of the bizarre aspects of the illness were embroidered into the picture by the failure of the meager treatment procedures and the incarceration and neglect of patients in large hospital groups.

The picture here is indeed striking, even dramatic, because the motor activity of the patient may be either inhibited or stimulated. If inhibited, the patient may progress to the point of stupor, and display that condition called "waxy flexibility" (an ability to remain in uncomfortable, imposed postures for hours on end), which used to be commonly noted in mental hospitals. Conversely, these patients may show excessive motor activity and excitement to the point of furor. These varied phases may alternate, sparked by vivid delusions and hallucinations. If allowed to go untreated, the catatonic becomes the backward, apparently vegetating, yet periodically destructive patient, who in the past did much to inspire fear and horror of the mental hospital in the minds of the layman.

The most frequent age of onset is between adolescence and the mid-twenties, and the prognosis for recovery, with reintegration of personality, is more favorable after a catatonic episode than after other symptom patterns. Unfortunately, however, this reaction does have a tendency to recur, and after several attacks a personality defect may become apparent. Sometimes the illness may take a hebephrenic or a paranoid course, with consequent further damage to the personality.

The Paranoid Type

This is one of the commonest forms of schizophrenia; certainly it is the one seen most frequently today. Its peculiarity, which sets it off from pure paranoia and the other paranoid reactions,[2] lies in the *mixture* it presents of typical schizophrenic and paranoid reactions. As in schizophrenia, there is a disorganization of personality, although to a lesser degree than is found in the other subtypes. As in paranoia, there is marked delusional thinking—delusions of grandeur, or of persecution, or of both. Ideas of reference, i.e. incorrect interpretation of casual incidents as having direct reference to one's self, may be present, and sometimes hallucinations occur. The behavior of these individuals may be unpredictable, and their prevailing attitudes, those of hostility and aggression.

This disorder may come on at any time, but as a rule its onset is about ten years later than the other forms of the illness. Its onset, too, is gradual, but it may be precipitated by toxic or traumatic episodes. Because personality organization is better preserved, some of the sufferers can go through life undetected, thought of only as grouchy or peculiar people; yet they may be quietly but grossly delusional. As long as they interfere with no one and remain inside the bounds of propriety in their conduct, many of them can go about their duties and can be carried as outpatients for years.

When the patient's personality disorganization becomes marked in degree, his delusional beliefs become less logical and he is ruled by vague magical forces, while his affective responses become more and more blunted. Some of these patients, under certain circumstances, may become dangerously assaultive.

[2] See the last section of this chapter for a fuller account of paranoia.

Schizophrenic Subtypes

A number of subtypes of schizophrenia are listed in the most recent nomenclature, and a brief reference to them might be in order here. There are the *undifferentiated types* which present mixtures of symptoms, usually hebephrenic and paranoid or catatonic and paranoid. When these types are acute, the attacks are transient with the likelihood of recurrence; when they are chronic, the disorder is often mild. The *schizo-affective type* shows an admixture of schizophrenic thinking with marked elation or depression of mood. The *child schizophrenic reaction,* which some authorities prefer to call autism, appears extraordinarily early in life, presenting itself as a failure to develop normal interest in external reality. *Pseudoneurotic schizophrenia* involves an underlying psychotic condition overcast with the typical symptoms of neurosis—anxiety, phobias, obsessions, hypochondria, etc. Although a third of these patients go on to frank psychosis, many remain only mildly ill and can be treated in the community.

Overall View of a Complex Illness

A quantitative change has been slowly taking place in the percentage of the various types of schizophrenia encountered in both community and hospital psychiatry. Until about twenty years ago the incidence of hebephrenic, catatonic, and paranoid subtypes of the illness was much the same. Today the paranoid form is by far the most common. It is suspected that one of the reasons for the greater rarity of the hebephrenic reactions is the greater effectiveness of psychiatric treatment and also earlier diagnosis, which in combination avert a rapid slide into the more regressive forms of the illness. Similar considerations may hold, to some extent, for the decline in catatonic reactions. It is thought that perhaps a parallel can be drawn also between the decline of catatonic schizophrenic reactions and the decline of manic-depressive reactions. One determining factor would be a change in the present-day cultural environment, by virtue of which fewer guilt feelings are incorporated into the personality. On the other hand, comprehensive programs of treatment must also play a very important part in the prevention of the patient's total withdrawal and in controlling the most disabling symptoms of these illnesses.

The prognosis of schizophrenic reactions in general has improved considerably in the last quarter-century. In some cases the course is still continuously progressive; nevertheless, in a large proportion of cases a chronic, inexorably deteriorating picture is no longer to be expected. This does not invalidate the axiom, however, that expectancy of recovery falls with each year of continued illness.

Therapeutic progress has been many-sided. On the one hand, effective physical methods of treatment are available, including insulin coma, electroshock, and, more recently, powerful new drugs. On the other hand, individual and group psychotherapeutic programs have been improved and extended to more and more patients, and there has been a more constructive use of the older occupational, physical, and recreational programs, designed to reduce the withdrawal of patients. The philosophy of the mental hospital as a therapeutic community rather than a custodial institution, has also wrought noteworthy changes. As a result of the summation of these many influences, we find much less apathy and regressive behavior among schizophrenic patients, more of them making good hospital adjustments, and more of them improving enough to return to the community. The therapeutic optimism of staff and personnel is a decided change, also.

Treatment should aim to help the patient achieve a more adequate level of personality organization and adjustment, as well as to improve his relationships with people. Despite the aloof, withdrawing, apathetic, or even hostile attitude of the patient, it is crucially important that he be immersed in an atmosphere of kindness and respect, for we believe that the patient's intolerable lack of self-respect, his feelings of rejection and abandonment, have done much to propel him into the gross disorganization of psychic life we call a schizophrenic reaction. Effective treatment includes exposing him to a variety of experiences which help curb autistic thought and alienation from the world of his fellows.

Of the various shock treatments, insulin coma remains the most effective for schizophrenia, in the opinion of most workers. However, electroshock, alone or in combination with insulin coma, also yields benefits in many cases. Within the last several years, however, the so-called tranquilizing drugs, particularly those of the phenothiazine series, have become a major therapeutic instrument. Chlorpromazine has done as much as anything else to change therapeutic attitudes to schizophrenia, and the treatment of early cases is now undertaken with considerable optimism. In both acute and chronic overactive and disturbed cases this drug has been remarkably beneficial. Its greatest usefulness is with patients who show tension, psychomotor overactivity, agitation, impulsiveness, aggressive outbursts, destructiveness, and antagonistic, paranoid reactions. In the acutely ill patient the drug frequently suppresses the hallucinations and delusional ideas in a period of several weeks. The longer the illness has been in existence, the less likelihood is there that chlorpromazine will bring about a lasting remission, i.e. enable the patient to return to the community. The best results have been recorded in patients who have been ill less than two years. Even in these patients, however, success depends upon the type and the severity of clinical manifestations. So-called productive symptoms, that is, overactivity, excitement, and other symptoms indicating that the patient is still struggling against the psychotic material, respond best to the drug. Patients who are underactive and apathetic, who have come to terms with their illness, as it were, who are comfortable with it and find it the natural state of affairs are less likely to respond. Patients who have been hospitalized for more than five years have a poor prognosis as a rule. Their chances of discharge from the hospital, despite real improvement in their behavior as the result of drug therapy and the other therapeutic programs to which they are exposed, are rather remote. Between 5 and 10 per cent manage to make the grade, but there remains the danger of recurrence, particularly if the patient stops taking the drug or fails to make an adjustment in the community. Nevertheless, the use of tranquilizing drugs has changed the climate of mental hospitals, and this is a development well worthwhile.

In recent years psychotherapy has been used increasingly in the treatment of schizophrenia, not only in combination with physical and other methods of therapy, but also as the only treatment. In the hands of some workers modified psychoanalytic techniques have produced social remissions in schizophrenic patients. This, however, is a very difficult field of endeavor, one which requires an enormous investment of time and devotion by the psychiatrist; therefore, it cannot be applied on a wide scale. Moreover, complete resolution of the schizophrenic process is rarely obtained. It is of interest, perhaps, that a "spontaneous" remission occurs in some schizophrenic patients. Often the improvement really seems to be due to the fact that the patient was able gradually to establish a relationship with another person over a long period of time. The other person may have been a nurse or some other member of the helping team, or it may have been another patient; but the relationship established was undoubtedly crucial in helping the patient find the way back to reality.

Paranoia and Paranoid Reactions

The difficulty of setting up categories of mental illness is well exemplified by so-called paranoia and paranoid reactions. There is a paranoid type of schizophrenia, as we have already indicated, but periodically all paranoid reactions are assigned to the schizophrenic class, only to be taken out again soon afterwards. They are characterized by severe delusional thinking, usually grandiose or persecutory. Ordinarily there are no hallucinations, and intelligence and personality organization are well preserved.

A distinction is made between *paranoia*,[3] a rare clinical picture, and *paranoid states*, which are frequent. Paranoia

[3] Actually there is some question in our minds as to whether this particular condition exists as a separate entity. Formerly called *paranoia vera* (*true paranoia*), it seemed that if one waited long enough these patients would develop schizophrenic symptoms.

is an insidiously developing, chronic disorder, characterized by persistent, unalterable, and logically reasoned delusions, often elaborated at the outset after a false interpretation of an event. Frequently the patient is convinced that he has superior or unique endowments, and there is often some truth in his self-estimation. The delusional system is isolated from much of the normal stream of consciousness. A paranoid state lacks this logical systematization of the delusions, and tends also to be of relatively short duration, though in some cases it is persistent and chronic. Patients in this classification often suffer mild or moderate attacks without requiring hospitalization and sometimes without being recognized as ill in any way.

It is believed that the causes of both paranoia and paranoid states are psychological. High on the list of psychological influences are frustrated ambition, defenses against undesirable tendencies and repudiated impulses, feelings of insecurity, guilt, and other anxiety-arousing factors, and a need to enhance self-esteem or prestige. There may also be specific traumatic life experiences in the background—being brought up in a severely authoritarian environment, early effective frustrations with subsequent withdrawal, feelings of rejection and resentment. In this way a paranoid element may be integrated into the developing personality. In some cases repressed homosexual impulses seem to be of genetic importance.

Suspicion and mistrust are widespread in non-psychotic people. There is no clearly defined point at which their expression becomes psychotic. Diagnosis depends on the degree of distortion of reality and of impaired adjustment. Paranoid tendencies rarely become of psychotic magnitude before the age of thirty. The disorder is more common in men. In both paranoia and paranoid states the content of the morbid ideas varies widely, depending on the particular psychological needs they are created to fulfill, and also on the type of rationalization to which the individual is partial. The patient's own inclinations are attributed to others. He projects his hostile impulses and his hate, and then experiences them as being directed against himself.

In all forms of paranoia there is a central, all-pervasive delusional theme. All events, however irrelevant, are interpreted in terms of the delusion, and incidents of the past are reinterpreted to fit into the same framework. As a result, the system constantly extends. The patient is always confident that he is right, no matter what or how much contrary evidence may be put in front of him. A rather frequent form of paranoia is the *litigious* type, which often materializes following a legal experience unacceptable to the individual. Thereafter he keeps instituting legal actions to prove his case. With each adverse decision he feels more violent sentiments of injustice. In the *exalted* type of paranoia, ideas of grandeur appear either from the onset or after a long preceding stage of persecution. Ideas of invention are a frequent symptom in these cases. Other patients think that they are chosen of God and have supernatural powers. In *obsessional* paranoia there is an erotic delusion expressed in the belief that someone of title or wealth, usually a complete stranger, is in love with the patient.

As indicated above, the so-called true paranoiac is often a person of superior intellectual endowment, but his achievements are not in line with his abilities. His personality handicaps have been too disabling. For such a person rationalization and projection are more natural defenses than regression and other inferior mechanisms. The paranoiac shows an intense drive in the service of his delusional system, and his affect in this connection is appropriate and sustained. The prognosis of this illness is very poor. It is doubtful that the so-called "true paranoiac" ever recovers. Yet, because general personality organization is well maintained and the behavior of the patient is so often within the bounds of tolerable behavior, a large number of these cases do not gravitate to the mental hospital. Oddly enough, the reverse is true of paranoid condition. Patients who suffer from these are less industrious, less social, and less restrained by social custom and law, hence more liable to display their disorder openly. It is preferable that a paranoid patient with good self-control remain in the community, if possible. Commitment and restraint have an unfavorable effect and tend to lead to an extension of the delusional system. When danger signs appear, of course, hospitalization cannot be avoided. Danger signs include a centering of the delusional system on a few individuals, or on one, and the presence of overt hostility. For both paranoia and paranoid states psychotherapy is of insignificant value, and the same is true of the shock therapies. A congenial environment, however, may be advantageous, and congenial employment is highly desirable.

VI

PSYCHOSOMATIC DISORDERS AND THE PSYCHONEUROSES

. . . the thought whereof
Doth like a poisonous mineral
Gnaw my inwards.

Othello

If there is one invaluable and lasting contribution which psychiatry has made to general medicine, it is the conclusive demonstration of the futility of attempting to treat bodily ills while neglecting the mind, or, conversely, of treating the mind as if it were detached from the body. This contribution constitutes the cornerstone of what is now called "psychosomatic medicine." This medical concept has had hard sledding for many years. Up until the end of the eighteenth century, the mind was the province, for the most part, of the philosophers. Physicians were relegated to the care of the body—the body alone—and mental symptoms they encountered were considered as unfortunate complications or, perhaps, as completely irrelevant to the disease at hand. Unfortunately, there are still some evidences of this dichotomy visible in the practice of medicine today.

Between the realm of actual physical ailments and the field of "pure" neuroses (which are psychological in origin and symptoms), there exists a group of conditions designated as "functional." They are thought to be due to the inappropriate use of the function of an organ or an organ system to discharge unconscious emotions. This implies that anxieties, hostilities, aggressions, guilts, bottled-up resentments, and other disturbing emotions and attitudes can and do produce or aggravate bodily disease. The diseases in question are grouped under the general category of "psychosomatic" ills.

Though ordinarily fleeting, they can be prolonged, and, when they are, they are capable of causing actual tissue change in the organ or organ system involved.[1]

It is unfortunate that the terms "functional" and "organic," applied to illnesses, have acquired such widespread usage. Because of ignorance, prejudice, and oversimplification, the word "organic" has come to imply real, important, legitimate, or demonstrable illness, while to the word "functional" has been related the unreal, the neurotic, the illegitimate, or the imaginary. By means of the tyranny of these terms the sheep are separated from the goats: the organically ill are studied carefully and treated tenderly, while the functionally ill are not infrequently dismissed with the admonition to "buck up," "snap out of it," "there is nothing really wrong with you; you are just a little nervous." Though a reaction has set in against the use of these functional-organic categorizations, they seem to be too well ensconced to be eliminated.

Psychosomatic medicine, then, is the discipline which is concerned with the study and treatment of the illnesses in question here, and it is only within the last few decades that it has come sharply into focus. It was not until 1935 that one of the earliest workers in this field was able to make the statement:

> Scientific study of the bodily changes that accompany diverse emotional experiences marks a new era in medicine. We know now that many physiological processes which are of profound significance for health, not only of the individual but also of the group, can be controlled by way of the emotions.[2]

Though the scientific study of emotions in physical health and illness is of recent date, the recognition of the interplay of emotions and physiological forces is so ancient that we cannot trace its beginnings. Apparently writers and observers from the earliest times have instinctively used expressions

[1] Dunbar, H. F., *Emotions and Bodily Changes* (New York: Columbia University Press, 1935).
[2] *Ibid.*

such as "my heart leaped," "his heart stood still," "she was paralyzed with fear," etc.

The close relationship and reciprocal influence of body and mind was known to the ancient Greeks and commented upon by Aristotle and Plato. Plato in one of his dialogues (*Charmides*) quotes the Thracian king Zamolxis:

> . . . this is the reason why the cure of many diseases is unknown to the physicians of Hellas, because they are ignorant of the whole, which ought to be studied also; for the part can never be made well unless the whole is well. . . . this is the great error of our day in the treatment of the human body, that the physicians separate the soul from the body.[3]

This recognition of the intimacy between mental and physical phenomena has continued down through the centuries. In one of his letters, St. Augustine stated: "I am of the opinion that every act of our mind produces some effect in the body and that, however heavy and slow our senses may be, they feel this effect in proportion to the intensity of the mental act, as when we are angry or sad or joyful."[4] Historians, philosophers, and dramatists apparently paid much more attention to this phenomenon than did the physicians, though the latter were certainly aware of it.[5]

Shakespearean drama is replete with instances, not only of the "mind which makes the body rich," but also of the mind which makes the body ill. Unfortunately, however, medicine de-emphasized this knowledge as it began to put itself on a more scientific footing. Experiencing so much success in treating so many distressing illnesses on the basis of physical and bacterial agents—Koch's bacillus[6] in

[3] "Charmides," *The Dialogues of Plato*, translated into English by B. Jowett (New York: Random House, 1937), Vol. I, pp. 6–7.

[4] St. Augustine, Letters (Letter 9), translated by Sister Wilfred Parsons, SND, New York.

[5] Hippocrates knew that the illness from which the king's son suffered was due to unrequited love rather than to a rare physical phenomenon.

[6] Koch's bacillus—named after Robert Koch, German bacteriologist (1843–1910), discoverer of the tubercle bacillus.

tuberculosis, the spirochete pallida in syphilis, the typhoid bacillus in typhoid fever, etc.—the physicians began naturally to look forward to explaining all diseases in similar terms. Little attention was being paid to the insights that philosophers or literary men might be offering.

Consideration of the "Whole" Man

What was not recognized sufficiently in those times, however, was that all diseases have multiple causes. There is no single isolated cause even for illnesses as specific as the ones mentioned above. Only a small proportion of people who harbor Koch's bacillus develop clinical tuberculosis, and the same may be said for other bacterial diseases. Man does not become sick in a vacuum; he becomes sick in his own particular surroundings and under various personal and environmental influences, and emotional pressure is one of these conditions.

In recent decades a number of developments led to a return to consideration of the whole man in his various illnesses. On one hand, physiological research demonstrated that emotions, acting through the vegetative nervous system, could produce profound effects upon bodily organs. As mentioned earlier, the Russian scientist Pavlov had shown experimentally that physiological processes could be correlated with behavior, and American scientists confirmed this and went on to show that even experimental animals are affected organically by their feeling relationships with their human observers.[7] All of this work has furnished background for the development of modern psychosomatic concepts.

Recently other scientists have emphasized the role of the pituitary and adrenal glands in reaction to physical and emotional stress.[8] At the time these investigators were at work, psychoanalysts were developing concepts of considerable importance for the understanding of physical disorders; for ex-

[7] Cannon, W. B., *Bodily Changes in Pain, Hunger, Fear and Rage*. An Account of Recent Researches in the Function of Emotional Excitement (New York: Appleton, 1929).

[8] Selye, H., "General Adaptation Syndrome and Diseases of Adaptation," *Journal of Clinical Endocrinology*, 6–117 (1946).

ample, they suggested that anxiety touches off repressive and regressive disorders which lead to the revival of old infantile patterns, many of which involve increased activity of internal organs. Sociologists and anthropologists, approaching the phenomena of man from different angles, produced material supporting and amplifying the concepts of the physiologists and psychoanalysts.

By the mid-thirties of this century the conception that the storm and stress, the wear and tear, of life's difficulties involve physiological derangement, which may under certain circumstances lead to visible damage in organ tissues, had been so well accepted, and so many papers on the subject had appeared, that H. Flanders Dunbar in her *Emotions and Bodily Changes* could cite hundreds of scientific references in the literature. She quotes, for instance, as one of the commonplaces of medical lore: "That people develop gastric disturbances after financial losses and suffer from them until their financial conditions turn to the better, is an everyday experience."[9] She gives the more colorful example of a patient who for months had an attack of asthma every evening at 7:00 during dinner. He blamed the odors of cooking, and one might also have suspected an allergy to some food. It turned out, however, that before the first attack had occurred, the subject of venereal disease had been discussed at the dinner table. The patient's family did not know that he had once suffered from venereal disease. But it was the fear of detection that had brought on the attack at this time, and further attacks occurred when he was reminded of the situation; finally they began to come automatically at this hour.[10]

Her volume was followed in 1939 by the founding of a journal, *Psychosomatic Medicine*. The editors of this journal stated in their opening number that the object of psychosomatic medicine is "to study in their interrelation the psychological and physiological aspects of all normal and abnormal body functions and thus to integrate somatic therapy and psychotherapy." Designating a method of approach rather

[9] Dunbar, *op. cit.*, p. 269.
[10] *Ibid.*, p. 254.

than a delimitation of the area, the psychosomatic approach becomes both a special field and an integral part of every medical specialty. It is a part of the "art of medicine," having to do with the understanding and therapeutic use of the psychic component of disease, and the relationship between the doctor and the patient.

Psychosomatic medicine is especially concerned with "functional" medical conditions as they are related to, or are manifestations of, problems of adjustment of the personality in stressful life situations. Though these conditions have considerable importance today, since so many of them tend to become chronic, it should be understood that neither practitioners nor patients are particularly happy about the diagnostic term "psychosomatic," especially the patients, for the thought of having any kind of an illness which has the prefix "psycho-" attached to it has connotations which are not considered quite legitimate.

These are the patients, however, who haunt the physicians' offices. They feel wretchedly and know that something is the matter; they do not understand their illness; they know only that they are sick and that they need help. Though underlying the illness there may be anger, fear, rage, hopelessness, disappointment, depression, guilt, or hatred, these feelings may manifest themselves and be presented in the doctor's office as aches, pains, breathlessness, insomnia, nausea, headache, diarrhea, palpitation, angina, etc. What happens then and in the future depends upon the skill and psychological insight of the doctor. These psychosomatic symptoms must be understood as defensive instruments which the patient has unconsciously adopted to handle some difficult situation. Thus, although he consciously desires relief, he will unconsciously resist relinquishing these devices until some solution of the underlying problem is in sight. Psychological tensions are particularly common in today's middle-class urban culture, with its heavy burden of striving, conforming, and repression, and the presence of a physical symptom can often be appreciated when a survey of the patient's emotional problems is undertaken.

Early Studies

Early studies in psychosomatic medicine focused on such disorders as peptic ulcer, essential hypertension, rheumatoid arthritis, ulcerative colitis, bronchial asthma, and hyperthyroidism. Since then the list of illnesses in which emotions play a part has grown enormously. In addition, it has been realized that personality factors can influence the course and onset of almost any illness. In organic disease at times there may be disability entirely out of proportion to the causative factors, for emotional disturbances can influence the course of the illness either by undermining resistance or by leading to the neglect of treatment. Even the amount of tooth decay has been associated by some investigators with emotional disturbance.

One scientist and his associates studied all illnesses over a period of years in 2,924 subjects and found that sickness episodes appeared in clusters, and that these clusters were usually associated with periods when the subjects were attempting to adapt to what they conceived of as difficult life situations.[11] They concluded that man's relation to his social environment, as he subjectively experiences it, has a profound influence on his general health, and influences the development and progression of all forms of illness, regardless of their nature and regardless of the influence of other causative factors.

Theories

The mechanisms by which actual physical symptoms and organ dysfunctions are produced by life experiences and their resulting anxieties, hostilities, insecurities, fears, and emotional tensions are not fully understood. They are the subject of many theories, often conflicting. A possible explanation might start with the common observations that emotions cause physical results—grief causes a flow of tears, embarrassment produces blushing, fear is hair-raising. Cannon and

---

[11] Hinkle, L. J. *et al.*, "Studies in Human Ecology's Factors Relevant to Occurrence of Bodily Illness, etc.," *American Journal of Psychiatry*, 114:212 (1957).

others showed that the emotions also cause internal changes —secretions, muscle tensions, changes in circulation, and the like.

Two resourceful scientists observed a patient with an artificial opening in his stomach, through which the stomach lining could be seen, and found that pleasurable emotions of appetite led to some increase in secretion and of blood flow to the mucosa with increased movement of the stomach wall.[12] Sadness, discouragement, and self-reproach led to prolonged pallor of the stomach lining and decreased secretion. Anxiety increased blood flow, secretion, and activity. Resentment and hostility led to a great increase in secretion and blood supply and to some increase in motility. The same investigators also studied patients in whom portions of the colon were exposed. They found that when these patients felt conflict, resentment, and hostility there was increased action of the colon with increased secretions. In some patients overactivity was sustained during resentment and anger, and led to minute hemorrhages. Dejection and fear were associated with underactivity of most of the large intestine.

The bodily reactions which accompany emotion serve a useful purpose when the emotion is brief and appropriate. For instance, the person who finds his home threatened by an intruder or by fire feels anger and fear, and at the same time his adrenal system is stimulated, his blood pressure is elevated, and blood is moved out from the abdominal area into the muscles, the lungs, and the brain. The person is then prepared to take action, either by fighting or by running away. However, when the emotions are unrelieved, either because they are unconscious and part of a basic personality conflict, or because the person is involved in a repetitive or trap situation (such as being compelled to work for a father-in-law whom he hates), the physiological effects continue and can even eventually lead to "organic" change in the area.

One brief, and perhaps oversimplified, way of understanding this type of psychosomatic phenomenon would be to view the emotionally burdened patient as having retreated to a

[12] Wolf, S. G., and Wolff, H. G., "Human Gastric Function," *Journal of the American Medical Association* 120:670 (1942).

level of adjustment more appropriate to the earlier years of life. In infants, the borderline between world, body, and mind is dim. It is this infantile vagueness that recurs in the psychosomatic disorders. Emotions are discharged into organs or organ systems instead of being expressed outwardly toward objects and situations that provoke them.

We shall only briefly touch upon some of the various theories underlying psychosomatic concepts. Some of them seem fanciful and some of them sound plausible; none is complete. The early psychoanalysts—Sandor Ferenczi, Smith Ely Jelliffe, Felix Deutsch, and their confreres—saw psychosomatic disorders as resulting from repressed instinctual drives which had been unconsciously displaced into organ systems, very much as are conversion symptoms, but not all later observers agreed with this.[13] One psychiatrist suggests that patients with psychosomatic disorders have difficulty in communicating by verbal symbols, so they use what he calls a "regressive body language."[14] As an example, two men, finding themselves talking at cross purposes, gradually become more animated, use signs and gesticulations, and then become heated and flustered and experience unpleasant visceral sensation. So whenever communications break down, emotional energies stir up the physical reactions used in intense communications, and bodily processes are affected.

The same physician also noted a retention of residues of infantile reactions in the personality organization of such patients. Many other investigators have been impressed by the serious ego weakness of these individuals. They express primitive emotions and have an intense physiological response to them. Some psychiatrists feel that this regression in itself reawakens intense emotions, while others have suggested that the physical signs are simply accompaniments which follow upon the psychological reactions.

[13] Lidz, T., "General Concepts of Psychosomatic Medicine," *American Handbook of Psychiatry*, ed. Silvano Arieti (New York: Basic Books, 1959), Vol. I. Reusch, J., and Bateson, G., *Communication, the Social Matrix of Psychiatry* (New York: W. F. Norton & Co., 1951).
[14] *Ibid.*

Silvano Arieti, a psychoanalyst, sees in these psychosomatic reactions a form of self-deception which serves to ward off recognition of situations which provoke anxiety and other disturbing emotions.[15] Their development would lead to an organized neurosis. Basically, the person who is subject to psychosomatic disorders has suffered serious insecurities early in life but has erected no adequate defenses against the emotions aroused. Consciously or unconsciously he avoids recurrence of the feeling of insecurity by making sure he will never be exposed again. But if his defensive pattern of living collapses, due to one of many circumstances, he is subject to the unpleasant emotions that were experienced early in life with an intense physiological accompaniment. Thus, the patient with peptic ulcer has need of being dependent but defends himself against recognition of that fact by developing an intense self-sufficiency. But he may overreact in this, and thus become prey to any form of ordinary setback in his daily life.[16]

Writing from the biosocial point of view, J. Groen offers a classification of personalities according to how they find outlets for their inner drives. According to him, a "normal" person finds adequate outlets for his drives or substitute gratification for them within the framework of acceptable behavior. A neurotic behaves acceptably but does not find gratification, and expresses his emotional disturbance in symptoms such as phobias, obsessions, etc. Psychotic individuals develop unreal forms of behavior, while psychopaths achieve gratification by indulging in unacceptable behavior. The person with a psychosomatic disorder cannot find gratification in accepted ways, yet he avoids neurotic and psychopathic behavior patterns. It is Groen's belief that such patients inhibit and control all reactions expressing emotional distress except those beyond their control, and these become intensified. These individuals have learned to control weeping and complaining and all other voluntary outlets of

[15] Lidz, *loc. cit.*

[16] Groen, J., "Psychosomatic Disturbances as a Form of Substituted Behavior," *Journal of Psychosomatic Research*, 2:85–96 (1957).

emotional upset, but the ones they cannot control—those depending on hormonal and visceral changes—become facilitated from carrying the whole burden, and as they chronically overact, they produce somatic disorders.

J. O. Wisdom has suggested that conflicts evoke psychosomatic reactions when they are experienced in the medium of tactile and kinesthetic sensations, and psychological reactions when the conflicts are experienced in visual imagery.[17] (Psychotherapy would then be effective if it succeeded in making it possible for the patient to see his conflict in visual or symbolic forms.) Most investigators feel that the conflicts and emotions leading to psychosomatic disorders are and must be unconscious. However, others feel that any long-continued unpleasant emotion can have deleterious physiological effects, whether it is unconscious or not.[18]

No stable relationship has been found between neurosis, psychosis, and psychosomatic disorder. It has been assumed by some that these disorders should be more or less mutually exclusive, but there is little experimental evidence to prove this.[19] Psychosomatic disorders may coexist with neurosis or psychosis, and some patients may alternate between neurosis and a psychosomatic disorder, or psychosis and a psychosomatic disorder. It is interesting, and not at all encouraging, in this connection to follow the progress of patients who have had their psychosomatic disorders cured by medical or surgical means. One group of investigators studied thirty patients whose peptic ulcer symptoms were relieved by either medical management or by surgery (partial gastrectomy). One year after their symptoms were relieved, sixteen patients had new psychoneurotic and/or psychosomatic symptoms. Twenty-one patients showed changes of attitude, behavior, or habits. Some patients developed

[17] Wisdom, J. O., "One Differentiating Mechanism of Psychosomatic Disorder," *International Journal of Psychoanalysis*, 40:34–146 (March–April 1959).

[18] Kaplan, H. I., and Kaplan, H. S., "A Psychosomatic Concept," *American Journal of Psychotherapy*, 11:16–38 (January 1957).

[19] Badal, D. W., Driscol, T. E., and Maultby, M., "The Role of the Symptom in Psychosomatic Disease," *American Journal of Psychiatry*, 113:1081–88 (June 1957).

unfocused anxiety, some showed hysterical reactions, and others became neurotic invalids. Specific changes seemed to depend on the patient's basic conflicts and the way he worked them into his pattern of defense.

Response to Stress

Another problem which has been mulled over considerably is why one particular organ or system becomes the seat of a psychosomatic disorder—this is known as the problem of specificity. Here again there is much difference of opinion. Flanders Dunbar has said that persons suffering from the same psychosomatic ailments have certain personality traits in common and has drawn up personality profiles for the various disorders; but now most psychiatrists agree that the conception of a personality constellation specific to each psychosomatic disorder has no foundation. Other investigators have related specific repressed emotions to symptoms and illnesses. Thus, weeping has been related to skin eruptions, the suppressed cry for help to asthmatic attacks, hungering for love to peptic ulcer, etc. Such observations are usually placed in a broader theoretical context, though there is no general agreement upon them.

Some psychiatrists feel that the organ system affected in any given psychosomatic illness is determined, not by psychological factors, but by an inherited or acquired weakness. Thus, a patient with a "weak" stomach might develop peptic ulcers in any conflict-laden situation.

There have been reports of physiological responses to various stresses, which indicated that the response to stress tends to differ from individual to individual, but to be constant in each individual, regardless of the nature of the stress. This finding is consistent with the idea that in any individual the choice of a psychosomatic symptom will depend, not on the nature of his emotions, his personality, or his specific conflict, but on his own peculiar way of responding to stress itself. It suggests, too, that the psychological treatment for psychosomatic disorders should not be specific; rather, the therapist should endeavor to discover and reduce whatever conflict may be present.

Sociological Aspects

Sociologists and anthropologists have contributed to our understanding of psychosomatic disorders by studying persons suffering from these disorders in the larger context of their families and society. For example, the late Thomas A. C. Rennie and Leo Srole have studied the distribution of psychosomatic disorders in a group of 1,660 persons, a true cross section of a population of 172,000 in New York City.[20] They found that arthritis, hypertension, neuralgia-sciatica, and possibly diabetes increased progressively in incidence as the groups studied approached the bottom of the social scale. Colitis, hives, rashes, and hay fever increased in incidence with higher social status. Asthma and bladder trouble were found most frequently in persons of very high or very low social status. Stomach ulcer was found in all social groups, in persons whose fathers were strivers, as shown by the fact that they had less education than their occupational peers. Multiple ailments were most common at the top and the bottom of the social ladder. There was a correlation between a high level of tension-anxiety and multiple ailment rates, and between a high level of tension-anxiety and each of the ailments studied except asthma and hypertension.

In both Great Britain and the United States sociologists have been directing their attention toward the family as the unit of treatment. Examples of this have been the Peckham experiment[21] in London and the study made by the Cornell University College of Medicine and the Community Service Society, described by Henry B. Richardson in *Patients Have Families* (New York, Commonwealth Fund, 1945). Both studies had their roots in the concept of homeostasis, the concept that the physiological system of the body seeks to

[20] Rennie, T. A. C., and Srole, L., "Social Class Prevalence and Distribution of Psychosomatic Conditions in Urban Population," *Psychosomatic Medicine,* 18:449–56 (November–December 1956).

[21] Experiment conducted at the Pioneer Health Center in the Peckham district of London. See *The Peckham Experiment* by Innis H. Pearse, M.D., and Lucy H. Crocker (New Haven: Yale University Press, 1945).

maintain a dynamic equilibrium between internal and external environment. According to this concept, disease is a disturbance in equilibrium, while the symptoms of disease are evidences of the body's attempt to regain an optimum state. This concept is extended to include the family, which must also maintain a dynamic balance in its internal relations and its relations to the community. Family life, through a disturbance in these relationships, may become a compelling influence in the origin and perpetuation of chronic or recurring illness.

An anthropologist, William Caudill, points out to us that there may even be connections between culture and deep psychodynamics.[22] Psychoanalysts have already noted that such cultural factors as the nature of infant care (weaning habits, toilet training, sleeping arrangements, etc.) may affect the nature of the defenses. Caudill, however, makes the point that culturally determined aspects of the ego and superego may be repressed, which brings culture itself into the realm of the unconscious. To illustrate his point, he discusses Alexander's statement that our culture puts great emphasis on independence and personal accomplishment, and that this cultural emphasis accounts for the frequency of the hyperactive, go-getter type of personality among peptic ulcer patients. This surface picture, according to Alexander, is but a defense against deep-seated dependent longings and has no direct correlation with ulcer formation. But the anthropologist might feel, Caudill says, that the dependent longings of the ulcer patient are culturally determined as well. The urban middle-class American family is pruned in its structure to the bare minimum of a father, a mother, and one or a few children. The father is frequently away during the child's waking hours and, since the family moves often, the child encounters no one stable set of playmates. Under these circumstances, the child develops an intense and culturally determined attachment to the mother. Since our culture also emphasizes independence, the child must overcome this deep

[22] Caudill, W., "Applied Anthropology in Medicine," *Anthropology Today*, ed. A. L. Kroeber (Chicago: University of Chicago Press, 1953).

dependence, and this is a difficult task; more than likely it may even activate deep-seated dependent longings.

It should be clear from all that has been said thus far that a patient's illness can be understood only in terms of the individual as a whole man or woman, with a home and a job, a past, a present, and a future, visualized as he is situated in his own particular culture. The attention of the physician must be focused upon the whole person, even in purely physical cases such as a fracture, for emotional overtones may affect the patient's condition and delay recovery, no matter what the illness may be.

Many times relatives, friends, and physicians of patients with psychosomatic disorders become impatient with symptoms which seem so refractory to treatment. Sometimes, at their wits ends, they are driven to attempt to "pep up," or to "humor" the patients, hoping to make them forget their troubles. This, of course, only further complicates matters, for the patients, sensing criticism, expressed or implied, are given to cling more tenaciously to their symptoms.

The necessity for psychological insight in anyone who is consulted by sufferers should be apparent. Physicians, counselors, clergymen, all are constrained to make an effort to understand the individual, no matter how bizarre his symptoms or how personally difficult he may be. Unfailing kindness, gentleness, and sincere interest, all are requisite qualities of a healer, whether of mind or body. It is assumed, of course, that each therapist will recognize his limitations and will not go beyond them. Premature or indelicate confrontation of the patient with psychological interpretations does not help matters; in fact, it may exacerbate the illness. None of this is work for a tyro. It requires patience, skill, understanding, dedication, and that real love of sick people which identifies the true physician.

PSYCHONEUROTIC REACTIONS

Of late the terms "neurosis" and "psychoneurosis" have been used interchangeably to designate emotional maladaptations due to unresolved, unconscious conflicts. Unfortunately, neither term is a particularly happy one; in fact, in some instances both seem to have attained the dimensions of an epithet. Frequently, even today, the designations are used in derogatory fashion, by some who forget that all of us, including the critics themselves, at some time in our lives exhibit psychoneurotic symptoms. It would seem, therefore, that it ill becomes anyone to criticize another whose symptoms are only more apparent and manifest than his own.

The psychoneuroses are relatively benign reactions, as compared to the psychoses, and are much more frequently encountered. True enough, the psychoneurotic reactions can be disabling, but they do not place the individual at so great a distance from his fellow man as does the psychotic adaptation.

Neurotic patterns are believed to arise from conflicts and feeling attitudes developed in childhood, and anxiety is of fundamental importance in all of them. Normally, impulses, feelings, and desires that tend to arouse anxiety are dealt with by repression and by cultivating behavior patterns which lend more security to the personality in meeting its internal and external requirements. In psychoneurotic individuals repression is only partially successful. The hostility or rage or other destructive feelings, or the drives of sexuality or dependency, or other needs which are felt as dangerous to the peace and order of the conscious personality will not stay submerged. When they show themselves, the ego is alerted by anxiety.

Anxiety is an extremely unpleasant experience. There is a feeling of impending disaster, along with a mobilization of physical resources for purposes of fight or flight. But the individual does not know what he fears and, since the threat is internal, there is no possibility of fight or flight from it. One kind of anxiety stems from the ego's dread of being overwhelmed by instinct, and this is the earliest type of anxiety. But, with the development of the superego, or the internalized parental authority, an anxiety is also experienced when a "morally" unacceptable impulse threatens to assert itself. Many of the strictures of the superego are unconscious and unrealistically exaggerated. If the individual were aware of the nature of the threat producing the anxiety, he would be

better off. As an adult, he might no longer desire the fulfillment of the impulse, highly dangerous in the past, and it
would no longer be a threat.

The neurotic individual tries to control emerging, unconscious, dangerous material, if not by repression, then by distortion or displacement, or by some other defensive reaction.
Only in this way can he escape the discomfort of anxiety.
The defenses mobilized for the purpose vary. The differentiation of psychoneurotic types is based on the nature of the
principal defense mechanism used. It is not a question of
specific morbid entities, specific causes, or unvarying manifestations. No sharp line can be drawn between any of the
psychoneurotic reactions, and many of them show mixed
features.

Anxiety Reaction

Anxiety is the primary symptom in the anxiety reaction, no
specific defense mechanism being used to control it. The
anxiety is diffuse, free-floating, and uncontrolled. The reaction is ushered in by an exaggerated physiological response
to the underlying anxiety, with physical sensations related to
the heart and other autonomic systems. It tends to become
chronic and the patient is in a constant state of anxious ex-
pectation. The free-floating anxiety will settle on anything at
any time, whether or not anything in the environment has
disturbing implications. The patient's sleep pattern is often
upset; he has difficulty in getting to sleep; his sleep is restless;
or he has nightmares in which the unmastered dangers of
childhood recur, often in the wake of daytime events reminiscent in some way of the original situation. There are acute
attacks of anxiety which descend suddenly on the patient,
with physical alarm symptoms, a sense of faintness, or a feeling of impending loss of control. When the attack is severe,
the patient is overwhelmed by feelings of helplessness, panic,
and an urge to escape. Having once experienced this panic
state, the patient is ever fearful of a recurrence, and this fear
of fear makes him all the more susceptible. In the chronic
anxiety state the patient feels fatigued all the time and may
fear for his reason. As time goes on he becomes increasingly

concerned over bodily functions and health in general. This concern may serve to rationalize or bind the anxiety.

Some traumatic neuroses, i.e. those following upon severe psychological or physical injury, take the form of anxiety reactions. There may be, in addition, an impairment of intellectual functions, ranging from confusion and misinterpretation of environmental data to attacks of fainting and unconsciousness. These symptoms prevent the intrusion into consciousness of repressed material associated with the traumatic events. The picture may also be characterized by fear, irritability or rage, by sleeplessness or distorted sleep, threatening dreams, and other derivatives of anxiety.

For the basic neurosis the treatment of choice is psychotherapy. The patient must first be convinced that his symptoms are psychological, then helped in the doctor-patient relationship to understand the connection between immature needs and current attitudes and situations that cause frustration and tension. The use of sedative drugs can be no more than a temporary expedient, pending discovery of the underlying sources of anxiety. Telling the patient to relax or to get hold of himself is worse than useless, for the patient is not consciously producing the symptoms. Although many patients can be helped by simple reassurance and by the recognition that a particular environmental stress has something to do with the anxiety reaction, many others do not respond, for the problem is too deep-seated. Such patients require the services of a skilled psychotherapist.

Dissociative Reaction

The reaction classified on the basis of personality dissociation is relatively infrequent, but extremely dramatic. It is a psychological condition in which the emotional impact of an idea, object, or situation is suppressed automatically and hence detached or separated from the object that arouses it. In some instances the personality disorganization is marked enough to resemble that of a serious mental illness. Again, anxiety is the major force but now it is managed by walling off certain areas of the psyche from consciousness. Formerly viewed as a form of hysteria, these reactions are now believed to be more closely related to the severe anxiety reactions. The individual who presents dissociative reactions has serious problems in dealing with other people and ordinary situations. In common with all neurotics, he has unconscious conflicts, and these are exacerbated by the anxiety-producing conditions in the environment. The personality makeup is so immature that very ordinary responsibilities and tasks present insurmountable difficulties. When an environmental situation reaches a certain level of intolerance for him, he dissociates, excluding a portion of his conscious memory and feeling, or developing a dreamlike state in which he reacts with little, if any, reference to ordinary reality situations. The mechanism used in dissociation is that of repression of whole segments of experience to the unconscious.

The best known dissociative syndrome is *amnesia*. The amnesia is more than forgetting. It is an active process, removing unpleasant data completely out of awareness. The amnesia is sudden in onset. It may be circumscribed, involving a particular period of time only, so that memory for earlier or later events remains intact. Most dissociative amnesias are of brief duration, but long-lasting cases are sometimes encountered. It appears that the amnesia can last for years in the absence of proper treatment or of the occurrence of some highly charged emotional situation which restores remembrance spontaneously.

Somnambulism, or sleepwalking, is another familiar phenomenon of dissociation. Though most frequently encountered in children, it is by no means limited to the tender years of life. In the somnambulistic state the individual is not living in the immediate environment, despite the fact that his eyes are open and that he may be moving about with considerable agility and responds to questions. Often the patient returns to bed voluntarily. On the other hand, he may become involved in a precarious situation, in which case attempts to awaken him may prove disastrous. It is preferable, in any event, not to awaken the somnambulist, but rather to attempt to lead him back to bed.

Multiple personality is a rare and exceedingly dramatic form of dissociation. There is a curious alternation of the patterns of two or more partially or completely separate personalities, each taking over in turn the current stream of consciousness and controlling behavior.

Fugue state, though more frequent than multiple personality, is still rather uncommon. In this condition the state of consciousness is suddenly changed and the personality of the individual is completely apart and different from the usual personality. The patient may be impelled by unconscious forces to perform complicated activities, such as embarking on a long journey. To all appearances the individual acts normally. Sometimes he loses his indentity completely and assumes another name. After recovery from the attack he may experience complete amnesia concerning it. The fugue state is usually of brief duration but may last for years until, one day, the individual suddenly remembers who he is and where he came from.

Dissociative *stupor* is a reaction in which a patient becomes unaware of and unresponsive to his environment. It resembles psychotic or toxic stupor in many respects, but differs from these conditions in that the history of the patient frequently reveals a psychological traumatic event immediately prior to onset. Stupor represents a temporary solution to the problem.

The treatment of psychoneurotic dissociations may be directed to the swift suppression of the symptoms or, whenever possible, to a gradual improvement of the patient's basic personality structure and to a more mature adjustment with the help of psychotherapy. Simply restoring the memory of the amnesic patient, for example, does not solve the basic problem, and amnesia is likely to recur when a similar stressful situation presents itself. The application of hypnosis or of drug therapy is advantageous, as far as restoring the patient's contact with his environment is concerned, or returning him to his memories. However, a permanent gain from this expedient is doubtful, and it is preferable to make more thorough psychotherapeutic procedures available to him. The immature, dramatic characteristics of the patient become increasingly evident after removal of the dissociation, but the repression that exists is still very extensive. When, through psychotherapy, this repression is loosened and the unconscious immaturities become conscious, a more realistic adjustment is possible. The prognosis of an uncomplicated dissociative reaction is relatively good.

Dissociative reactions must be distinguished from malingering, which is a conscious simulation of illness, used to avoid a personally unpleasant situation.

Conversion Reaction

This reaction, referred to in previous classifications as "hysteria," was the first of the neuroses to receive serious attention. In conversion reactions, anxiety-producing impulses or repressed conflicts, highly charged with emotional components, are "converted" into physical symptoms which are symbolic in some way of the psychological state. These reactions are excellent examples of what is called "the primary gain of neurotic symptoms," i.e. that some psychological advantage is achieved by means of these symptoms. For example, if repressed hostile impulses are converted in limb paralysis, the person cannot execute his aggression, and this relieves him from anxiety. The "secondary gain" from these manifestations is that the patient escapes from an intolerable situation, is able to evade an unpleasant responsibility, and yet have an obvious, sometimes dramatic, excuse for failure.

Behind the phenomenon of psychological conversion is a psychic trauma, painful ideas being associated with a conflict unacceptable to the conscious personality. The ideas are repressed but remain as a potential source of disturbance. When a stressful situation occurs, or tensions have built up long enough, the ego is unable to keep the conflict buried. Somatic conversion symptoms then serve to relieve the pressure.

The conversion reaction takes many forms. Classic symptoms involve systems under voluntary control. One finds anesthesias, paralyses, and loss of vision and hearing. Typically, the symptoms involve body segments, not according to anatomo-physiological division, but according to the patient's own idea of function. Thus motor symptoms characteristically involve an entire extremity. Muscular contractures are not uncommon, and the same is true of tics, tremors, and gross muscular movements. When conversion takes place via the autonomic nervous system, symptoms are much less dramatic and colorful and more subtle and insidious in development. They include visceral disturbances, disturbances of circulation, respiration, gastric, and rectal function, and the activity of the bladder and of other vegetative functions. Chronic coughs, some asthmatic conditions, and certain susceptibilities to colds can be conversion symptoms. Painful complaints, particularly, are often a conversion symptom and, according to some observers, are the commonest expression of this illness today. Despite their complaints, these patients demonstrate an indifference which Jean Martin Charcot, in the latter part of the last century, named *la belle indifférence*. Placebos, i.e. inert substances given for psychological effect, may relieve the symptoms of such individuals, and one may find an intermittent history of the same symptoms occurring in relation to incidents arousing emotional conflict. The existence of organic symptoms does not necessarily exclude the presence of conversion symptoms also. Sometimes organic symptoms imperceptibly take on a psychic purpose.

It is possible to handle superficial, simple forms of conversion by supportive psychotherapy and reassurance and, occasionally, by narcoanalysis and narcosynthesis, the first-mentioned being psychotherapy conducted under the influence of drugs, the second a psychotherapeutic measure originally used to treat combat cases. Some of these patients respond to direct suggestion. The preferred treatment, however, is again intensive psychotherapy, particularly if the reaction is a complicated one and the patient has a high intellectual capacity. Patients with conversion reactions often have fixations to earlier levels of development which complicate and prolong treatment. Their chief ego defense is repression, and therapy must bring about the release of repressed material so that it can be assimilated on the conscious level and in a mature manner. Psychotherapy helps bring about an understanding and abandonment of the pathological mechanism of defense, with a working through of the unconscious conflicts. In many cases, however, a brief form of treatment, based on psycho-analytic principles, proves satisfactory.

With adequate treatment, prognosis in the average un-complicated case is fairly good. Many patients, however, are difficult to treat because of their dependent attitudes, their habitual evasive tendencies from early life, and other person-ality deficiencies. Prognosis is also affected by the amount of secondary gain. The childish, egocentric patient who becomes dependent on his symptoms has a poor prognosis. If the ad-vantages of the disability are considerable, the patient is less apt to respond satisfactorily to treatment. Conversion symp-toms develop in a large variety of personality disturbances and there are factors in each case to be evaluated carefully —history of childhood development, childhood experience, en-vironmental stress and its modifiability, which type of treat-ment and how much the patient and his family will accept.

Some forms of conversion neurosis, especially those which seem to follow upon a trivial incident, have been called com-pensation neuroses. This means that there is something for the patient to gain by hanging on to his symptoms; either he is relieved of responsibility or given financial reward. Work-men's compensation acts and indirect accident insurance have increased the incidence of compensation neuroses.

Phobic Reactions

In phobic reactions, the anxiety of the patient which has become detached from its real cause—idea, object, or situa-tion—is displaced onto some idea, object, or situation which symbolizes the original, and this latter thereafter serves as the specific neurotic fear. Some of the dynamics leading to the development of phobias are illustrated by the following case:

A successful young journalist had had a strong phobia of theaters since his graduate school days. At that time the highly coveted editorship of the School Review was awarded to another student, in spite of the fact that the patient was the logical candidate. He went to the chair-man of the editorial board, who gave him little satisfac-tion. To relieve his feelings of helplessness, murderous hostility, and self-destructiveness, he attended a theater and happened to see the chairman there. His feelings reached a peak, and he fled from the theater. Thereafter he avoided theaters. He had displaced his dangerous feelings onto theaters, and could therefore run away from and avoid facing them. The loss of the editorship revived earlier conflicts. The patient had had a cold and distant mother who aroused a hidden and threatening rage in him by setting such impossibly high standards that he could not meet them and win her love. With the new failure, the old rage and helplessness reappeared; the phobic defense kept these unpleasant emotions repressed.[23]

By avoiding his sources of fear, the individual keeps his anxiety under control. Many people get along quite well in this way. Self-imposed limitations on various activities, in an effort to avoid sources of fear, become an integral part of their lives. Phobias in childhood are widespread; they arise from the immaturity of the evolving personality, but the phenomenon is usually transient, except when there is a woeful lack of security.

The history of a phobic patient usually contains evidence of emotional neglect during earliest childhood and a failure of parents to realize the child's need for love, security, and stability. The outcome of such an environment is a self-centered adult, unable to love adequately himself, though needing love greatly. Because love continues to elude him, he is bitter and resentful, obstinate and ambivalent, i.e. he may have opposing feelings of love and hate toward the same person. Unable to express his needs openly and forced to cope with the anxiety which these evoke, he projects his fears on an outward object, situation, or place and then avoids it. Thus the basic mechanism in all phobias is similar—inner insecurity and conflict, the anxiety entailed by these being then tied to a phobic situation. The patient's underlying hostility is also served by the symptoms, which handicap and immobilize the people with whom he lives.

The range of phobias is extremely wide. Common forms

[23] Laughlin, H. P., *The Neuroses in Clinical Practice* (Philadelphia: W. B. Saunders Co., 1956), pp. 182–83.

include fear of syphilis, dirt, closed places, open places, high places, animals, travel by a certain type of vehicle, etc. Freud divided phobias into two groups, depending on the nature of the object feared: 1) Common phobias—an exaggerated fear of all those things feared or detested by everyone to some extent, e.g. night, solitude, death, illness, dangers in general, snakes, etc.; 2) Specific phobias—the fear of special circumstances that inspire no fear in the normal man, e.g. fear of open spaces (agoraphobia) and other phobias of locomotion.

There are fashions in phobias; they change with the times. In earlier times patients attached their fears to sorcery, witchcraft, etc. Forty years ago syphilis was a preferential possibility for people to hang their fears upon, but syphilophobia is much less common today. Currently cancer phobia, fear of airplanes, fear of poliomyelitis, and, to a lesser extent, atomic phobias have been on the upswing. The popularity of such phobic objects as water, height, closed spaces, open spaces, insanity, dirt, and certain animals appears to remain much the same.

A phobia represents the patient's effort to keep himself comfortable, that is, in a sense to treat himself. The self-treatment, however, is inefficient. Skilled psychotherapy is required. Personality, inner difficulties, and the life situation of the patient must all be evaluated, along with the problem of secondary gain or satisfaction from the symptom. Psychotherapy must help the patient to gain an understanding of what is basically wrong, teach him how to cope with his insecurity, and point out and correct poor management of his childish impulses. Unskilled interference with the phobic symptom must be avoided. It may be dangerous, for example, to remove the symptom rapidly, since the symptom may be keeping a more serious disturbance at bay.

The outlook for recovery in these situations depends upon the severity of the reaction, the reality elements in it, the degree of incapacitation and secondary gain which the patient receives from it. Phobias connected with objects and situations disliked by most ordinary people are easier to deal with than those connected with more unlikely objects and situations. If the phobia has become an integral part of existence, prognosis is guarded, and the same is true if marked secondary gain is involved. The most difficult phobias are those based on deep, severe, and long-standing conflicts.

Obsessive-Compulsive Reaction

Obsessive-compulsive reactions are psychoneuroses in which anxiety is automatically controlled by persistently repetitive thoughts and ritualistic acts. There may be persistent recurrence of an unwelcome and often distressing idea or an urge to perform a repetitive, stereotyped act, or both together. Often the ideas are at complete variance with the patient's conscious moral or esthetic feelings. Sometimes the thought is pointless and absurd but the patient is unable to control the obsessive rumination. Or it may be in the pattern of *folie du doute,* when the patient, beset by doubts, vacillation, and indecision, usually with compulsive rumination, engages in repetitive, stereotyped acts to dispel the doubts. Moral scruples are of this nature. If the compulsive acts cannot be carried out, the patient suffers great anxiety. Most patients have mixtures of obsessions and compulsions, and sometimes phobias are added for good measure. The frequency of mild obsessive or compulsive rituals in the population is high, and especially in childhood between the ages of seven to eleven years. The mild forms are relatively innocuous, but the severe forms can be incapacitating.

Obsessive-compulsive reactions date back to difficulties encountered in early childhood, making for unstable relationships. The individual who presents them is generally of a rigid and meticulous makeup, though he often has superior intellectual capacity. His makeup, despite his capacities, is marked by insecurity and he manifests a proneness to superstition, doubt, and indecision. These symptoms serve to protect the ego, substituting for an unconscious urge unacceptable to the conscious personality. They are a symbolic method of carrying out the unacceptable urge and, at the same time, of expiating the guilt connected with it. The obsessive-compulsive individual is superficially passive, but underneath this façade there is certain to be a great hostility which is expressed in indirect and subtle ways. Everything is intellectualized and subject to cold, logical scrutiny. The superego is rigid, punitive, and tyrannical. The original unacceptable urges are masked by superficial attitudes just the opposite of what they formerly elicited. The mechanism of *undoing* is very important. Undoing is a belief in the omnipotence of ritualistic acts, in an effort to negate or neutralize real urges.

In general, the unacceptable impulses are of two types: 1) aggressive, sadistic, and destructive; and 2) sexual. Usually there is a mixture of the two. In milder reactions the patient is ambitious, hardworking, and perfectionistic, and when he must delegate responsibility, he becomes anxious and unable to do so lastingly.

The onset of these symptoms is usually before the age of twenty-five, and if the reaction continues to increase and extend, it may become disabling before the age of forty. It is obvious, therefore, that early treatment is indicated. The patient must be given an understanding of his problems in order to reach a more mature level of adjustment. It is necessary for the therapist to align himself with the patient in his reality situations in order to strengthen him against the onslaught of unconscious pressures and against the tyrannical demands of his superego. The most effective psychotherapy is thought to be either formal psychoanalysis or psychotherapy based on analytic principles. It is true that some patients respond well to superficial, explanatory psychotherapy of the supportive type, but most of them require prolonged, intensive, dynamic psychotherapy. Such treatment is especially worthwhile because of the superior capacities of many obsessive-compulsive patients and because of the great handicap imposed by the disturbing symptoms of these illnesses.

In adults the prognosis is less favorable than it is with other psychoneuroses. However, many individuals have only sporadic attacks and with help can get along in reasonable comfort. If the individual is to be rid of his symptoms, he will generally have to be treated over a long period of time. The outlook in these illnesses is understandably more serious if the onset of the continuing morbid condition was in the early years.

Psychoneurotic Depressive Reactions

The final large subgroup of the neuroses is made up of the psychoneurotic depressive reactions. These illnesses occur in individuals who are prone to dejection or despondency and self-depreciation. The outright depressive reaction typically follows upon an event which would ordinarily produce temporary unhappiness in almost anyone: death, loss of savings, failure in school or business, or some other unfortunate crisis.

The dynamics of all varieties of depression show some similarity; however, in the type in question, personality function is less severely disturbed, and the physiological concomitants are not as noticeable as in the psychotic type of the illness. In all depressions, it is agreed, there are hostile feelings which were once directed towards some important loved person, and which have subsequently been directed against the self, for fear of losing the love of the other. There was ambivalence of feelings, dating back as far as childhood, and it was solved, in a sense, by hating oneself for hating the beloved person. The internal conflict is often sharpened if the person who is prone to depression suffers the loss of someone important to him or of something which symbolizes such loss.

The symptoms of this form of illness vary in severity from a minor diminution in spirit to a severe depression. In a typical reaction there is insomnia, a wide-ranging loss of interest, and a multitude of complaints. Though ordinarily inclined to show a form of compulsiveness, meticulousness, and perfectionism, the patient is now no longer interested in either previous goals nor accomplishments. At times he displays some preoccupation with physical symptoms, but not to the degree shown in psychotic depressions. Throughout, it becomes apparent to the practiced eye that the sufferer is a self-centered individual, chronically wrapped up in his own problems.

The treatment of choice is intensive psychotherapy. However, if the depression is severe, especially if it borders upon a psychotic reaction, electroshock therapy may be indicated, to be followed by psychotherapy. In most instances of psychoneurotic depression, shock therapy is less effective than it is in psychotic depression. In certain selected mild depressions drugs may be useful temporarily, but, again, psychotherapy is essential. The physical therapies may suppress symptoms, but the patient has no insight into his problems and, under stressful circumstances, may develop another depressive reaction.

If there has been at least a superficially good adjustment heretofore and the patient has had some basically good relationships, the outlook with psychotherapy is reasonably good. However, excessive rigidity, perfectionism, and other compulsive tendencies, with few, if any, warm relationships, make the outlook less favorable. Treatment goals include a readjustment of the patient's level of aspirations, in keeping with reality, a mellowing of the harsh, internal, unreasonable, and unreal conscience, the recognition and study of ambivalence, and the discovery and cultivation of new objects of interest. In a reasonable number of patients such psychotherapy is successful.

VII

PSYCHOTHERAPY IN ITS VARIOUS ASPECTS

Console yourself, dear man and brother, whatever you may be sure of, be sure at least of this: that you are dreadfully like other people. Human nature has a much greater genius for sameness than originality.

James Russell Lowell

Psychotherapy is the name given to that type of treatment which is based primarily upon verbal, or non-verbal, communication with the patient, as distinguished from the use of drugs, surgery, or physical measures such as electro- or insulin shock, hydrotherapy, and others. It is a potent method of treatment and most physicians regard its use in an intensive manner as a medical responsibility. At present, however, there are various claims and counterclaims regarding its efficacy and as to who may and may not practice it, and methods employed are as numerous as are its definitions. Revisions and innovations continue to appear as psychiatry gains new recruits, new investigators, and new insights.

The efficacy of this type of therapy has been known for centuries. Even in ancient times, psychological forces were brought to bear upon man's mental and emotional disorders and, in fact, upon his physical complaints too. Instead of its present designation, however, this therapy was known as "mental healing," a time-honored concept as old as man's need for relief from mental and physical anguish and turmoil. We learned in Chapter II that its practitioners were sorcerers and medicine men, expert in the manipulations of magic forces, who provided a crude sort of help to all manner of sufferers.

Later, mental healing came to be a function of philosophy and religion—theistic and non-theistic—and medicine inherited its role from these varied forebears. On his pilgrimage to

Delphi, Socrates sought help in his endeavors to unmask hypocrisy, false piety, and self-deceit in himself and in others, and it was on this journey, we recall, that he received the familiar injunction: "Know thyself." Socrates, and later Plato, held that each individual, through intuition, dreams, or fantasies, remembers truths learned in a previous existence. Today dynamic psychiatry holds that a person knows much more than he is consciously aware of, that the personality has unconscious depths in which there lurk not only impulses and desires, but observations, previous learning, and past experience blocked from conscious awareness. The old wisdom thus retains much of its cogency.

Psychotherapy rests squarely on a constructive patient-therapist relationship. Its first prerequisite is the respect which the therapist must have for a mental patient. Within this interpersonal situation, an important exchange of ideas takes place; needs must be recognized and met, including deep symbolic needs, and the emotional experience called transference must occur. In this experience, a strong emotional rapport, reflecting the emotional attachments the patient formed for important persons early in life, springs up between patient and therapist; this fortifies the patient in the difficult task of recognizing and acknowledging his inner weaknesses, and, hopefully, gives him better insight into his problems. The crux of psychotherapy is this therapist-patient relationship. The general aim of psychotherapy is not only the relief of presenting symptoms, but also an improvement in the patient's capacity to deal with his problems and to make more advantageous use of his own emotional and intellectual resources. If possible, the therapeutic effort is directed towards positive personality growth and development.

It has been pointed out that the methods used in psychotherapy usually reflect the values of a culture. Thus, in some cultures psychotherapy is largely authoritarian. In others, it is more permissive and democratic. In either case the patient's image of the therapist as a person with specialized knowledge, conferring healing powers upon him, is of fundamental importance. In the psychotherapeutic sessions the patient shares his feelings and his experiences with one whose capacities he respects and whose understanding, acceptance, and support are of great value to him.

Methods of psychotherapy are of two general types—reparative and reconstructive—though admittedly this is a broad and oversimplified division. Reparative psychotherapy seeks to overcome symptoms and to deal with problems which the patient recognizes to some extent. Reconstructive psychotherapy seeks to alter the patient, to make him alert to faulty patterns of thought and feeling and behavior, which he does not appreciate or of which he is consciously ignorant. Reparative psychotherapy uses techniques of reassurance, support, understanding, and guidance, ranging from general counseling to more complicated procedures based upon the therapist's knowledge of psychodynamics and his ability to understand the nucleus of the patient's problem. Reconstructive psychotherapy is dynamic, explorative, exposing the patient to evidences of the real nature of his problems, and of the way they developed. One of the goals of such treatment is to promote insight into one's own conscious and unconscious life. Armed with this understanding, one should be able to make better decisions and to deal with future stresses in a more constructive fashion.

REPARATIVE PSYCHOTHERAPY

Reparative psychotherapy does not involve a cooperative search by the patient and therapist for the deep roots of actual dynamic problems. It seeks rather to reinforce existing assets, to strengthen existing defenses, and to lessen the intensity of troublesome symptoms. The therapist may use such means as dogmatic assurance, persuasion, suggestion, and direction, or he may find it useful to bring about some change in the patient's environmental situation. However, it is not a question of ordinary advice and encouragement and support. Thorough training and adequate experience and skill are required in the practice of psychotherapy. The work is based on scientific knowledge of the human personality, its development, its driving forces, its mechanisms of defense. In the series of interviews which the therapist undertakes with the patient, he forms and refines his appraisal of the manner of person he is dealing with. The patient's early life and development, his physical and emotional growth, the configurations of his school days, his adolescence, his more mature years, his work and environment, his previous physical and emotional health, his family and social relationships are the focus of the first interviews. Data emerging from the patient's biography, verified in as many ways as possible, indicate to the therapist general significant tendencies, suggest what the genesis of the symptoms may be, and the directions in which it may be possible to relieve them. The therapist's decisions are not based on haphazard personal impressions but on objective assessment. The help he is able to give the patient without striving for fundamental psychic changes may, indeed, be considerable. The havoc wrought by fear, anxiety, and guilt, or that produced by situational stress, can often be averted or mended by the skilled psychotherapist. Not infrequently this can be done without confronting the patient with much, if any, of the material which the therapist has judged to be significant on the basis of the life history and the trends of the psychotherapeutic relationship.

Persuasion

One of the hardy perennials of reparative psychotherapy is persuasion. Though it actually is a suppressive method, "binding up" and covering over the distressing effects of inner conflict rather than resolving the basic issues, it still has a few eloquent advocates. It was one of the basic ingredients of the moral treatment of a century and a half ago. The therapist uses reasoned argument and moralizing discussion in an effort to create, transpose, or strengthen certain inhibitions, or to get rid of some which are handicapping the patient unnecessarily. He indicates to the patient the manner in which faulty intellectual and emotional attitudes may develop as reactions to certain difficulties. The emphasis is on the voluntary, rather than the involuntary, on the avoidable, rather than the unavoidable. By dint of reasoned argument and the authority with which the patient vests him, the therapist seeks to persuade the patient that his symptoms will disappear. An instance might be the following:

> A matriarch complains to the physician of various physical symptoms and at the same time notifies him of the difficulties she is having with her family. After necessary examinations and failure to find a physical basis for the symptoms, the physician turns to the psychological aspects of the woman's problem and in the course of several sessions he is able to find out what she is doing that is aggravating her problems. Then, reinforced by the strength of his authority, he attempts to persuade her to give up or modify her excessive demands on her family's time and patience and suggests more realistic and satisfying lines of self-fulfillment. In this manner he tries to persuade her to a more positive outlook which will diminish her fears and relieve the tensions which are at the root of her symptoms.

This approach is often effective, but since the actual dynamic factors have not been dealt with, symptoms are simply suppressed. They may reappear under stress in the same or in different guises. Persuasion as a psychotherapeutic technique tends to overestimate the power of reason in attacking the products of mental disorder arising from irrational forces.

Suggestion

The power of suggestion has been recognized since the dim and distant past. As indicated in the discussion of hypnosis,[1] its scientific potentialities were definitely recognized late in the nineteenth century and there was finally a consensus that hypnosis depended on the suggestibility of the subject. Thereafter, suggestive therapeutics commanded the attention of numerous European workers. Modern hypnotic procedures stem in direct line from this activity. Apart from hypnosis, there are numerous methods of psychotherapy which revolve around suggestion. In all, the purpose is to implant or to induce the idea, by subtle and often indirect

[1] See pp. 206 ff.

means, that the symptoms or complaints for which the patient is seeking help are susceptible of relief and are, in fact, being relieved. The physician makes use of his professional authority, at the same time maintaining an attitude of assurance, understanding, and sympathy. Confident in the omniscience of the physician, the patient feels encouraged, less critical, less anxious and tense, comes to believe that recovery is possible. In some patients the eventual benefits are substantial. The following is an example of a case in which suggestion was used:

> A manual laborer had injured himself slightly at work and developed a hysterical paralysis of the right arm. Although he was due to be pensioned in another year, the company physician wanted him discharged, with forfeiture of his pension, if he did not get over his "nonsense." The psychiatrist enlisted the aid of two other physicians. They performed an elaborate physical examination of the patient and discussed the findings in tones which were low, but audible to the patient. Using impressive medical terminology, they agreed that he had an "inertia syndrome," a serious but reversible condition characterized by initial paralysis of an arm, followed by gradually increasing ability to use the shoulder, arm, and fingers, and leaving a residual endurable stiffness of the wrist (to satisfy the neurotic needs that had led to the paralysis). At daily examinations the doctors found matters progressing exactly as they had predicted, and expressed great enthusiasm and gratification. The patient returned to work with a stiff wrist and was retired at the end of the year with his pension.[2]

The best results from psychotherapy in the form of direct suggestion are in cases of recent and situational origin, when there are no deep-seated personality disturbances. The technique is often useful with children, with persons of limited intelligence, and with immature hysterical personalities. Suggestion does not favor the development of insight. It sup-

[2] Erickson, M. H., "Special Techniques of Brief Hypnotherapy," *Journal of Clinical and Experimental Hypnosis*, 2:109–29 (April 1954).

presses the symptoms and does not remove their cause. The underlying problems and needs that evoked the symptoms remain, and recurrence is not unlikely in future stress situations. The effects of suggestion should therefore be bolstered by re-educational techniques and, if necessary, by environmental manipulation to reduce the areas of stress.

Support

Supportive psychotherapy uses such simple techniques as reassurance, reasoning, use of authority, permissive attitudes, encouragement, explanation, advice, and the manipulation of environment in order to reduce anxiety and tension, but it does not attempt to deal with the basic reasons for the ills. Its aim is to help the patient strengthen his ability to face and deal with his real problems in a real situation. The therapist strives to shore up whatever socially acceptable defenses the patient has and to cultivate new defenses related to the old. If possible, he will help the patient acquire at least some understanding of himself and achieve some emotional maturity, but it is not a question of working for any radical personality change. This type of thing is done every day by the physician who encounters people who complain of nervousness, having no friends, disliking people, feeling that no one likes them, and adding to all of it a number of physical symptoms. Upon failure to find evidence of physical disease after necessary careful examination, the physician tries to assay the patient's most promising assets and encourage him to pursue them. He also will attempt to discover what has been frustrating the individual's desires. More often than not the causative factors rest in rejection or domination in childhood in the home or in the school or other surroundings. These efforts to accentuate the patient's good qualities and to manipulate the environment in their favor are often effectual if the neurosis is not too severe or long-lasting.

The patient cannot be allowed to become overly dependent upon the therapist, for regression to a passive attitude is harmful and constitutes an obstruction to improvement.

The patient has to be encouraged to deal with his problems himself in the framework of the therapist's support and understanding. Supportive psychotherapy cannot be too successful if the subject is unable to escape from harsh, environmental pressures.

RECONSTRUCTIVE PSYCHOTHERAPY

Reconstructive psychotherapy aims at an adaptive personality change, the creation of a new awareness in the patient of the real nature of his problems and of his methods of dealing with them. The aim is not the suppression of symptoms, but insight into them. Therapy of this kind is more uncomfortable for the patient because he must carry a much larger part of his own burden and work harder to disengage himself, perhaps over a much longer period of time.

Reconstructive psychotherapy includes procedures of different types, some being more penetrating and more radical than others. Psychoanalysis and distributive analysis are prototypes of deep, insight-oriented psychotherapy. The schools of Jung and Adler also aim at insight and awareness as the basis of change.

It is the assumption of both psychoanalysts and the practitioners of distributive analysis that emotional or personality disability stems from significant psychological experiences, that present attitudes and reactions to life experiences reflect those of the past, and that it is necessary to determine as precisely as possible what went into the making of the personality. It is assumed also that psychological processes are dynamic. From these basic assumptions the psychoanalysts and distributive analysts (or, as they are sometimes called, the psychobiologists) set off in different directions. The former regard factors of infantile conflict as absolutely crucial and look to the unconscious for the key to their nature. The latter take into account every period of life in analyzing personality, and in their therapy operate at the level of conscious discussion.

Psychoanalysis

We have discussed psychoanalysis at length in Chapter III, so there is no need to repeat the whole account of it here. It might be profitable, however, for the sake of comparison to note again that psychoanalysis, as the most revealing type of psychotherapy, probes deep into the unconscious via the interpretation of dreams, of transference relationships, of the products of free associations and resistances, etc., in an attempt to liberate the patient from long-buried, unconscious conflicts which are generating distressing disorders in his present life. Although it is not, in its classic form, applicable to all forms of mental illness, and although it is too time-consuming to be practicable in many cases, the insights offered out of the context of psychoanalytic research have been of immense benefit to practitioners of all other forms of psychotherapy.

Distributive Analysis

Distributive analysis is the therapeutic technique pioneered by Adolf Meyer from his concepts of psychobiology. Psychobiology conceives the individual as a whole biological unit with a history of development from birth onwards through various stages and situations. Personality, therefore, can be understood only in the light of the individual's whole history—what experiences he has passed through, how he has reacted, etc. Thus when a patient begins therapy with a distributive analyst, a thorough life study in long section is demanded as a prerequisite, with all important events noted and with a full consideration of all physical and hereditary factors. This casts considerable light from the beginning on the background of the patient's disorganized habits. In the exploratory phase of the therapy, a comparatively wide selection of areas for investigation is made, depending on the patient's complaints, symptoms, and attitudes, and the problems recognized by the therapist. In psychotherapeutic discussions, the patient examines the various factors, situations, and reactions which may have been of dynamic importance in the making of his difficulties, analyzing his problem in terms of his personal assets and liabilities. Then, with the help of the analyst, he constructs a synthesis out of what he has learned, stressing his assets and allowing for his liabilities, making formulations which will be helpful to him in his attempt to remedy the unfavorable emotional reactions and patterns of behavior which were the basis of his troubles.

In distributive analysis, there is no attempt to have the patient relive early experiences. The important point is that he understand their present meaning and relationships. To this purpose, his attention is directed more to actual situations and circumstances than to unconscious attitudes and mechanisms, and all this is done at a largely conscious level in face-to-face discussions with the therapist. Throughout these interviews, the physician maintains an interested, receptive, non-critical attitude and is careful not to overwhelm the patient with interpretations.

From the point of view of psychobiology, mental illness is a reaction to life's stresses. The psychotherapeutic discussion should give the patient an appreciation of the significance of his emotional crises in the development of his symptoms. To a degree the therapist becomes an educator. He helps the patient restyle conscious attitudes which have been warped by destructive feelings and motivations and assists him in developing a constructive philosophy of life.

It is important in considering this type of therapy to choose patients with sufficient intelligence and personality assets to participate in analysis and synthesis. The most useful areas of application for this approach are the psychoneuroses, the affective disturbances of reactive origin, the mild paranoid and immaturity reactions, and psychosomatic disorders. The approach is believed by many clinicians to be more suitable than the more formal types of psychoanalysis in the treatment of psychotic patients. There are practitioners of distributive analysis who feel that unconscious processes should not be neglected and who, therefore, make use of word association tests, Rorschach data, dreams, and even free associations to help them arrive at satisfactory points of reference.

DEVIANTS FROM THE FREUDIAN METHOD

Alfred Adler and Individual Psychology

Included among the reconstructive psychotherapies aiming at deep reformation of personality structure are several schools or systems which stem from Freud. One of Freud's early disciples, Alfred Adler, rejected some of the Freudian canons and introduced his own theory of psychotherapy under the title of individual psychology. For Adler, the drive to power rather than the sexual drive was the basic element in emotional life, and the difficulties of patients were related to faulty methods of implementing this power drive rather than to vicissitudes in the development of the libido. But while the drive for dominance and security is basic in psychic life, all individuals naturally begin life in an actual state of dependency and inferiority. This places them directly in a stress situation, and if they cannot resolve it, they develop basic feelings of inferiority, insecurity, and inadequacy—the famous inferiority complex. In reaction to these unpleasant emotional states, the individual may strike out in various forms of overcompensation, to correct his real or fancied inadequacies with exaggerated reactions in the opposite direction.

In Adlerian psychotherapy, the patient's life is explored for evidences of the struggle between feelings of inferiority and their overcompensations, and for signs of the repeated failures to achieve a sense of competence which led to refuge in illness. The therapist seeks to convince the patient by the evidence of his own behavior that his symptoms are really his way of winning the power struggle, and that they are not efficient devices. The main techniques of this method are interpretation and re-education. The patient's behavior and conscious thought are analyzed in terms of the drive for power, and his symptoms are explained to him as expressions of feelings he will not admit. In re-educating the patient, the therapist looks for the desirable tendencies and encourages them, aiming at helping the patient to develop the right social approach and a normal community feeling with his fellows. An example of Adler's style of attack is seen in the following case:

A man had a neurotic fear of marriage to his betrothed. Investigation showed that the salient feature of this man's life was the death of his parents when he was five years old. In his life in an orphanage he adapted by becoming docile and striving to please. Through his servility he came to occupy the role of the orphanage's most trusted servant. Later in life he succeeded well in business, making capital of the same servility which had served him so well as an orphan but, once he attained the position of dominance, he liked nothing better than abjectly servile attitudes on the part of his subordinates, a compensation he required to soothe his own repressed self-esteem. His basic style of life was to get to the top by servility, therefore, and to demand servile response, in turn, from his underlings. When the prospect of marriage appeared, he automatically put his system to use and adopted a servile and begging attitude toward his sweetheart, although it was a servility which would eventually demand recompense. The snag in the process was that this servility induced a number of neurotic symptoms, some of them very much like hallucinations and some of them making him hesitate about the marriage. His hesitancy had the effect of obliging the girl to become servile and begging, an end which his style of life was actually designed to attain but which in this instance might frustrate his desire to marry.

His symptoms were preventing him from undertaking this step. At this stage of his problem he consulted an analyst, who explained the nature of his style of life and the effects it was having, with the result that his symptoms disappeared and he was able to marry. The problem now was to restrain him from completely tyrannizing his wife.

Thus, the school of individual psychology looks to the patient's future, solving his problems by making him capable of reintegrating himself with his social milieu, in contrast with psychoanalysis, which looks to the patient's past and solves his problems by showing him their motivations in infantile experiences. The period of treatment in individual psychology is much shorter than that in psychoanalysis.

Some of Adler's concepts have had great impact on other schools of psychotherapy, including those geared to a cultural view of psychiatry and those stressing the basic human drives.

Carl Gustav Jung and Analytic Psychology

The founder of the school of analytic psychology, C. G. Jung, was another who parted company with Freud early in his career, largely because of the concept of libido. For Jung, libido is not limited to sexual energy, it is the whole creative energy of life, the *élan vital*. The mind is not only the deposit of past experiences, it is also the striving and forecasting of the future, with the aims and goals which represent the main directions of this life energy. Ideally, the individual should develop by the harmonious utilization of all his capacities and opportunities, and if some significant area is inhibited, stress and perhaps mental disorder will eventuate.

Like Freud, Jung stressed the unconscious elements of the mind, but for him, the unconscious was more than the repressed material from the individual's personal past. Even more important was the collective unconscious, the ways of thinking and feeling inherent in the minds of our ancient ancestors and passed down to us as an echo of prehistoric race attitudes. This psychological inheritance common to all mankind predetermines our modes of thought unconsciously, and shows up in our consciousness as archetypes, that is, as certain concrete symbolic images whose meaning is contained in our race's primordial experiences. Archetypes appear in many forms: persons—the Mother as all-compassionate; animals—the Snake as the enemy; geometrical figures—the Circle as wholeness or perfection. They do not appear frequently, and when they do, they are evidences of deep psychological tension, either by way of creative urge, or mystical insight, or, perhaps, as psychotic disorder. For the analyst, the archetypes which do appear reveal the fundamental repressed strivings of the soul.

From this orientation, Jung developed a psychotherapy said to be particularly valuable with adult patients, especially those who suffer from a meaninglessness in life. Jungians are flexible in their methods, using common sense advice, or confession and abreaction, or reductive analysis of the Freudian type, as the case may demand. The interaction between patient and therapist is important. The physician interprets thoughts, feelings, and behavior, and also dreams, for these are often indications of what is wrong, and of what the patient is unconsciously bent on doing about it. Word-association tests and picture drawing are employed to supply clues to repressed material and fantasy life. The patient is brought to recognize how the attitudes responsible for his symptoms developed, and how to live out his life more fully according to his deeper, innate tendencies. Even eccentric traits of personality are developed, for whatever value they contain, rather than destroyed.

One of the aims of analytic psychology is to show the patient that his tendencies are those of all mankind. Another emphasis is on spiritual freedom, and the satisfaction of spiritual yearning is held to be indispensable for the full unfolding of the individual's potentialities.

DYNAMIC-CULTURE ANALYSIS

Karen Horney and Harry Stack Sullivan are the foremost exponents of the dynamic-cultural school of psychoanalysis. The emphasis here is on environmental and cultural factors and interpersonal relationships in the genesis of psychiatric disturbances.

Karen Horney

Psychotherapy as practiced by Karen Horney and her followers is based on the view that basic anxiety is the standard condition of social life, the result of conflict between human beings. The neurotic symptom is a device of the character itself to safeguard its feeling of security. Hence the *manner* in which the patient protects his psychological needs is of much greater importance than anything else. Psychotherapy must therefore be concentrated upon the drives which presently motivate a patient, not on the infantile nature of neurotic symptoms. The safety devices which have grown into the character of the patient have an unconscious meaning which must be recognized.

Horney's treatment involves the demonstration to the patient of his use of neurotic devices to maintain security in his social world. The analyst assumes an active approach. Instead of reconstructing the causes of the symptoms, he demonstrates the consequences of the neurotic trend. The current conflict is brought into view and the reasons for the neurotic strife are clarified. An effort is made to mobilize the will power in constructive action. As in Adlerian psychology, aggression and the drive for power and prestige are brought into focus. The cultural influences shaping these drives are shown to be of basic importance in contributing to the neurotic's choice of safety devices.

The therapeutic relationship is crucial in dynamic-cultural analysis. It stresses a humanized atmosphere and a personal philosophy, including that of the therapist. The character structure of the patient has to be remolded to enable him to adjust to social pressures and relations which have aroused anxiety in the past.

Harry Stack Sullivan

Sullivan considered interpersonal relations, rather than instinctual processes, to be of primary importance in therapy. For him it was the early relationships with significant people which were crucial in the genesis of neurotic and psychotic symptoms. Therefore, it is incumbent upon the therapist, in psychotherapy, to enter into the private world of the patient's personal relationships, to effect a togetherness with the patient which will afford him a corrective experience in virtue of which he may be able to overcome his neurotic condition. The therapeutic situation is thus essentially a personal relationship. The physician becomes a participant observer, communicating not only by words but also by gestures and by the emotional impact of his presence. As he effects a close personal bond with the patient, he can show, by firm direction and education as well as by the interpersonal relationship he has formed, how the patient has evolved faulty ways of maintaining his security and self-esteem in his relations with other people, and how he can make the transition from his neurotic devices to social satisfaction in living. Such a therapy obviously emphasizes sociological events, present-day contacts, and current interpersonal relationships, rather than biologic events, past experiences, and infantile sexuality.

The concepts of Sullivan, relating neurosis formation to social living, have contributed useful insights to psychotherapy. For instance, with his emphasis on interpersonal relationships in the therapeutic situation, the problem of countertransference has become more apparent, i.e. that the emotional attachments of the patients are met by emotional responses from the therapist. He has also shown the importance of non-verbal expression on the therapist's part.

Briefer Methods of Exploratory Psychotherapy.

It is understandable that attempts would be made to develop briefer methods of interpretive psychotherapy, but, unfortunately, satisfactory methods are not yet brief enough to permit the clinician to treat the large numbers of people who are in need of his help. Some of these methods combine selected features of psychoanalytic, psychobiological, and supportive methods. Brief exploratory methods cut through material which seems comparatively irrelevant in order to reach presumably important material with the least loss of time and effort. Selected for exploration are areas of the patient's life which are most germane to his problems and symptoms. Therapy is focused upon these areas until they have been dealt with and constructive changes are set in motion. Among the variations are fewer sessions, interruption of treatment when excessive emotional dependency on the analyst threatens, manipulation of the transference through choice of interpretations, and, in general, greater flexibility. In these brief exploratory psychotherapies the therapist relies on his experience and judgment in selecting areas contributing to the patient's difficulties.

Many techniques have been evolved to adapt deep psychotherapy to shorter and less expensive schedules. Wilhelm Stekel, one of Freud's early associates, prefixed a time limitation for therapy, usually three or four months, and then took an active role in the therapeutic sessions; for example, he interpreted resistances at once, as soon as they were encountered. Franz Alexander, one of the foremost American analysts, recommended a direct approach to the emotional complexes which seemed most closely connected with symptoms, and limited the goal of treatment to the cessation of symptoms. Felix Deutsch of Boston concentrated on the psychological conflicts underlying specific symptoms, focusing attention on the actual complaint as the patient expressed it, and confronting the patient with the materials of his past life which seemed directly related to his problem rather than attempting to solve the problem by the interpretation of unconscious materials.

Narcosynthesis

Narcosynthesis is a form of psychotherapy which makes use of partial anesthesia with ether or with barbiturates to elicit repressed traumatic material. With this technique the patient is relaxed but not asleep, and the censorship processes of the personality are lifted enough for the repressed material to emerge. The effect is achieved relatively quickly. This method is advantageous in patients subjected to severe recent traumatic experiences and unable to handle the impulses and anxiety consequent upon them. The strong abreaction is often markedly beneficial. As the memory of the traumatic event returns, the patient lives through it again with the entire emotional appanage. Interpretation is facilitated by this method. Acute anxiety states, early traumatic neuroses, and conversion hysterias often respond well to narcosynthesis. The degree to which emotional resistance can be overcome varies. It has been noted, particularly in civilian life, that patients are not likely to disclose, under drugs or under hypnosis, material which they have consciously determined not to disclose.

Ventilation

Ventilation is an expressive type of therapy in which the patient talks out his problems in a tolerant, empathic setting. The physician interrupts only for the purpose of keeping the discussion going in meaningful channels. Doubts, impulses, conscious anxieties, family problems, and feelings of guilt may be helpfully ventilated. The opportunity to admit to these difficulties or to express resentments is a source of relief. Joint discussion of present conflicts and past life situations, as they seem to relate to emotional or psychosomatic symptoms, is undertaken, if possible. The effects of the ventilating process are reinforced by superficial psychotherapy based on knowledge of psychodynamics.

Abreaction

Abreactive psychotherapy permits the patient to relive the stressful situation which contributed to his symptoms. The abreaction, i.e. discharge of repressed emotions associated with the recall of a repressed memory, is often advantageous when the patient is suffering from a high degree of emotional tension. It may serve the purpose of making the patient less sensitive to a psychological conflict. The emotional reactions discharged are usually grief, rage, or fear.

These and other abbreviated techniques have made the insights provided by psychoanalysis available to an increasing number of patients. Their use was promoted during World War II when many psychiatric casualties were treated by psychiatrists who had received analytic training. Narcosynthesis proved effective in combat areas and behind the battle lines, to help the soldier-patient abreact the emotional trauma of war. Ventilation and abreactive techniques were also used without resorting to sedatives, and the same processes can be made to operate in hypnotherapy.

Group Psychotherapy

In group psychotherapies, a number of patients are gathered together periodically, usually under the direction of a skilled therapist, and in a friendly and communal atmosphere they talk out or work out their mutual problems, powerfully aided and sustained by the personal feelings engendered in the group. Though introduced about fifty years ago, these methods were sparingly used until World War II. Since that time they have become a major field of psychotherapy. The use of group methods is included in both hospital and outpatient programs in a wide range of diagnostic groups, including psychoses, psychoneuroses, emotional disorders of children, situational reactions, and behavior disorders.

Group psychotherapy should not be viewed as an alternative to individual psychotherapy, but rather as a supplement. However, there are certain types of patients for whom group psychotherapy seems to have advantages over individual therapy, among them patients who resist the individual approach because of negative attitudes toward all parental or authority figures or because individual psychotherapy is for some reason too threatening. In the group setting such patients may find the acceptance and support necessary for examining their problems. In some instances this opens the way to individual psychotherapy. In others the benefits derived from the group experience may be enough. Often selected for group therapy are patients with destructive family relations, lack of sibling experience, or unfavorable sibling experience, and generalized social maladjustment. When it appears likely that maladjustments stem from inadequate or unwholesome group situations during the formative periods of life, group therapy is a logical attack. Patients of rather backward intelligence may benefit from group therapy more than those of superior intelligence. Generally, children are helped by the group experience.

The structure of the group depends largely on the needs of the members. Certain basic principles must operate; among them are mutual acceptance of all members selected, avoidance of unnecessary restrictions, and permissiveness toward verbal expression and critical evaluation of group interaction. To be most effective, group members should be fairly homogeneous as to age, sex, and presenting problems.

In group therapy all of the participants become therapists

of sorts. The group itself offers advantages—the continual emotional interplay provides sources of stimulation in abundance, and group support tends to diminish individual anxiety. It is noteworthy that suggestibility and emotional contagion, which are found in therapeutic groups as well as others, wane as the group members grow in emotional maturity. The growth of individual independence and a more rational relationship to the group is often visible.

Group therapy varies in form with the particular skills of the therapist, the problems he is dealing with, and the aims of treatment. There are directive and non-directive methods of approach, with varying emphases in each. *Non-directive* techniques include analytic or free-association therapies, the leader being an analytically trained therapist. Such analytical group psychotherapy and group analysis is often used for psychoneurotic and mildly psychotic adults and adolescents. *Directive* group psychotherapy combines clinical methods and a didactic process. It embraces a number of techniques: so-called group interview psychotherapy, which can be applied to most age groups and a variety of psychiatric conditions; interview-inspirational group therapy, for most age groups and diagnoses; and social relationship groups, for seriously disturbed and aggressive children who require environmental manipulation.

For children between the ages of seven and fourteen the group psychotherapy preferred is of the activity type. If the problems are serious, group activity may be combined with group interviews. For preschool children, the method of choice is play group psychotherapy.

In clinical group therapy there is a preference for the round-table setting. As a rule the sexes meet separately. Group size varies but, in the experience of many workers, small groups are most desirable. Some have suggested seven as the magic number. In any event, the group should be large enough to permit a sufficient amount of interaction, yet not so large that some members are neglected. Whether groups should be entirely homogeneous is a matter of dispute. It is felt by some observers that too great an identification of interest can lead to group resistance. However, the group does not coalesce if the membership is too heterogeneous. Patients who disrupt, dominate, or exploit others and who stimulate pathological processes in them are usually considered to be improper subjects for inclusion in group therapy.

All groups seem to pass through certain stages of development: a stage of group unification, a stage of group interaction, and a final stage of understanding. Factors of mutual support and reliance lead to the molding of group spirit and identity. Emotional ventilation may serve to relieve tensions. Education in the group in the therapeutic setting dispels certain distortions about personal problems and relieves the fear and anxiety of some patients.

It is thus apparent that group therapy permits the operation of certain mechanisms not found in individual psychotherapy. There is a catalytic effect, each member activating the others, so that matters may advance more rapidly. By processes of identification and universalization patients discover that other people have problems like their own, that others have forbidden thoughts or the same reprehensible impulses. This discovery does much to reduce anxiety and guilt and to enhance self-esteem.

Members of small groups, particularly, may be able to see in the group an expression of their own unconscious motives, so that gradually they may be able to gain an insight into their difficulties, although not generally as deep an insight as would be attained in individual psychotherapy. This, however, is not necessarily a drawback. In some cases the mobilization of certain defenses may be an adequate goal. Thus in some psychotic patients the group processes encourage the repression of unconscious fantasies which manifest themselves as delusions, and as the psychotic mechanisms are enfeebled, the more normal ego elements take over. Group therapy is also finding a useful application in the treatment of senile patients in some institutions. The group process appears to increase alertness, dispel confusion, and improve memory and orientation, and often has a favorable effect on incontinence.

Statistics on the results of group psychotherapy vary. However, in many quarters the results obtained compare favorably with those of individual psychotherapy.

PSYCHODRAMA AS A FORM OF PSYCHOTHERAPY

Psychodrama is a form of group psychotherapy in which the patients act out their emotional problems in a stage setting with a more or less unwritten script. The pioneer of the technique, J. L. Moreno, states that the purpose is one of spontaneous improvisation. The drama deals with the private personality of the patient and with his emotional catharsis, with the persons within his milieu, and with the roles in which he and they have interacted in the past, in the present, and possibly in the future. The work is usually organized in a therapeutic theater. Self-presentation may be done in collaboration with a partner or partners, either real or substitutes. It may be done in the form of soliloquy. It may be done on a non-semantic level via pantomime, dance music, or haphazard vocalization, as the spirit moves. Catharsis takes place in the course of the psychodrama.

In addition to psychodrama focused on the individual for the active evocation of private worlds and ideologies, there is a so-called sociodrama which focuses on the group and aims at the active structuration of social worlds and collective ideologies. There is another form referred to as physiodrama, which focuses on the soma and combines physical culture and psychodrama. Similarly, hypnodrama combines hypnosis and psychodrama.

Moreno writes of his methods:

Because we cannot reach into the mind and see what the individual perceives and feels, psychodrama tries, with the cooperation of the patient, to transfer the mind "outside" of the individual and objectify it within a tangible, controllable universe. . . . The psychodramatic method rests upon the hypothesis that, in order to provide patients, singly or in groups, with a new opportunity for a psychodynamic and sociocultural reintegration, "therapeutic cultures in miniature" are required, in lieu of or in extension of unsatisfactory natural habitats.[3]

Certainly psychodrama is one of the most original and creative contributions which has been made to psychotherapy, and today it is used extensively in many parts of the world.

EXISTENTIAL ANALYSIS

A recent important development in the field of psychiatry is so-called existential analysis. It stems from the system of philosophy known as existentialism,[4] which is largely of European origin. Existential psychiatry seeks to understand man as a being who is always in the process of emerging, of becoming. It does not dispute the validity of the study of dynamics, of drives and forces in the human personality, but submits that these can be understood only in the context of ontology, the science of being and of the existence of the given individual, also known as *Dasein*. This individual existence, which is of crucial importance in existentialism, is what the individual is making of himself, how he is unfolding, what he is moving toward. Most men, who live out their lives unreflectively, are not aware that this is a problem to solve. The sensitive man, however, who faces himself and is faithful in trying to find his own meaning, sooner or later comes to the existential crisis. He discovers that deep anxiety is an unavoidable element of his life, an ontological characteristic of man, rooted in his very existence. This ontologic anxiety is the experience of the threat of non-being,

[3] Moreno, J. L., "Psychodrama," *American Handbook of Psychiatry*, ed. S. Arieti (New York: Basic Books), Vol. 2, p. 1395.

[4] Existentialism refers to certain philosophical attitudes and doctrines concerning man and his existence. There is no single existentialist philosophy. In general, existentialists claim that existence cannot become an object of thought. Existence is immediate experience; it is at once being and becoming. Existential analysis seeks to understand the psychiatric patient not only in terms of dynamisms and patterns of behavior, but also from the standpoint of his mode of being, of his own world-design, and of his simultaneous relations with and to other people and other objects.

of ceasing to exist at any time. It is a shaking experience, and yet a necessary one, for without it existence does not take on vitality and immediacy. Another source of anxiety in the midst of man's existence is guilt. One of the problems of the psychiatrist is to make the individual aware of the difference between real, existential guilt, which is the effect of not being true to oneself, and irrational guilt feelings derived from irrational authority.

Being-in-the-world is another major concept of this system, "world" being the structure of meaningful relationships in which the person exists and which to some extent he designs himself. World contains three ingredients: the *Umwelt*, which is the biological environment; the *Mitwelt*, that which involves one's fellow men; and the *Eigenwelt*, the self-world, that is, the meaning the real world holds for the individual. Consequently, in designing his world, the human being has a wide range of choices.

Daseinanalyse formulates its central task in terms of understanding the patient as a being and as a being-in-the-world. Thus, it is the responsibility of the psychiatrist to help the patient recognize and experience his own existence. Therapists who use the existential viewpoint belong to different schools of practice. As a group they do not consider themselves divorced from the body of orthodox psychoanalytic theory and method, but insist that it is the attitude of the therapist towards the human being that is of greatest importance. Psychotherapy can be successful only if the patient is enabled to fulfill his *Dasein*, to experience his existence as real. Only in this way is it possible for him to experience his own potentialities and to act upon them. Existential analysis looks behind the symptoms of the patient for the specific modes of existence which determine the symptoms. The therapist assumes the task of guiding the patient from his uncharted existence into new ways along which existence may proceed in orderly sequence.

Existential psychiatry is, in a sense, a protest against oversimplification and against technical preoccupation in scientific thought. It is a revolt against the compartmentalization of the human being. Thus, we have been reminded by Rollo

May that the concept of the unconscious loses none of its validity if it is based firmly on an analysis of "the total, ultimately indivisible existence of the human being."

HYPNOSIS

Hypnosis can be described as a state of partial impairment of conscious awareness in which the subject is readily susceptible to suggestions and direction from the hypnotist. It is probably justifiable to consider it separately in this chapter, not only because of its important historical role, but also because of the widespread interest it presently commands. Since World War II the phenomenon has seemed to evoke more interest than it had since the days of Charcot and Bernheim near the close of the last century. There is no doubt at all but that it is an effective agent, but when it is used to treat symptoms, it is simply palliative; the underlying condition remains. Despite this seemingly carping statement, things which appear magical can be accomplished by it, as patients are anesthetized for surgical or obstetrical procedures, induced to cut down on alcohol and tobacco intake, or to have various dramatic symptoms relieved.

The checkered career of this procedure is already known to us in part. The Austrian Anton Mesmer is accepted as its father and founder, though it is probable that many of the ancient religious healing systems of the Persians and Hindus used it in some form. On some occasions their healing efforts resulted in trancelike states for both healer and subject. Mesmer believed that the universe was permeated with a mysterious "magnetic" fluid, which was concentrated in his own person, and by this power he could influence his subjects through the medium of magnetic contacts and passes, as he moved majestically among them in a well-prepared setting. It should not be thought that his sphere of influence was only among the credulous and the ignorant, however. He drew his clientele in Vienna from all walks of life and it is said that he healed a number of important people, including one highly placed scientist who professed to have been "cured of paralysis."

Claims of anything savoring of the occult would, of course, be bound to stir up controversy, and that they did, resulting in Mesmer's precipitate departure for Paris. In Paris, Mesmer opened his clinic and in it constructed a "bacquet" made up of mirrors and iron rods, and, as he passed among his patients, they became "magnetized" and entered various "crises," some of a bizarre nature. Never one to hide his light under a bushel, Mesmer soon found himself the subject and object of an investigation instigated by the Académie des Sciences in 1784. The investigating committee, incidentally, was composed of a number of high-powered individuals, some of whose names will be readily recognized: Benjamin Franklin, Lavoisier, and Guillotin, the last-mentioned the inventor of that efficient instrument which bears his name and which, in some instances, has been considered a therapeutic device. Without going into too great detail, it may be said that, despite the condemnation by the committee in question, which characterized Mesmer as a charlatan, interest in the cause which he espoused grew, and, while one group of his followers teetered along the edge of illness, another, more professionally inclined, undertook a serious study of hypnotism in order to try to determine its possible use as a treatment procedure in medicine.

In the middle of the nineteenth century, James Braid, an English surgeon, braved the scorn and wrath of his medical colleagues and, after examining the phenomenon of animal magnetism carefully, decided that there was nothing particularly mysterious about it, but rather that it was a purely subjective phenomenon. It was he who renamed the so-called "animal magnetism" or "Mesmerism" hypnotism, after Hypnos, the Grecian god of sleep, and let it be known openly that profound physical and psychological effects could be realized from its use. Despite the efforts of Braid and some of his colleagues, however, an unsavory odor clung to the procedure. One physician lost his university post for espousing its cause. It was not until the latter part of the nineteenth century that a committee of investigation appointed by the deputy governor of Bengal reported favorably upon the results of a series of surgical operations performed successfully under hypnosis. After this the reports of investigating groups in the British Isles, including the committee set up by the British Medical Association in 1891, regularly brought in favorable judgments on the phenomenon.

Meanwhile, in France a great interest in the subject was aroused, and two groups of physicians, one under Liébault at Nancy and the other under Charcot at the Salpêtrière, began their now famous studies upon hypnosis. As seen by us today in retrospect, the phenomenon was the forerunner of modern dynamic psychiatry. It was hypnosis which forecast the end of the entirely materialistic approach to psychiatric problems by clinicians and investigators and turned men's minds from exclusive attention to pathological changes in the brain in mental disorder.

The group at Paris under Charcot considered hypnosis a pathologic phenomenon akin to hysteria, while those at Nancy under Liébault considered it a normal manifestation. Bernheim, after visiting and being impressed by this latter group, gathered the data which led to the publication of the first truly scientific work on the subject of "suggestion."

Though this important work was done in France, the effect which ultimately turned out to be of the greatest significance was produced in Austria. In 1882 the Viennese physician, Joseph Breuer, told his countryman Sigmund Freud the history of a patient he had treated, in which hypnosis had been a powerful agent. Interested, Freud collaborated with Breuer in work which was eventually published as *Studies on Hysteria*. When Breuer abandoned further researches in this line, Freud went ahead by himself, and eventually, developing the technique of free association, "discovered" psychoanalysis. Freud soon abandoned hypnotism itself altogether.

What Is Hypnosis?

The theories behind hypnosis are like those behind shock therapy—they vary depending upon the observer. Wherever there are a number of hypotheses regarding a medical procedure, it is safest to say that no one really knows the correct answer. There are several categories of theories which might be used, although one would be hard put to defend any of them. It was Charcot's basic contention that the hypnotic state was an artificially produced hysterical phenomenon. This theory is no longer held because of increased knowledge of a dynamic nature regarding hysterical phenomena. Psychologic and neurologic theories, which speak in terms of the inhibition of ganglion cells and the suspension of higher cortical functions, likewise fail to be completely satisfying.

Psychologically hypnosis has been and still is considered by many as a circuitous form of suggestibility, the ability to be hypnotized resting in the amount of faith in the prestige and ability of the hypnotist. It is estimated that 25 per cent of the general population is readily hypnotizable, but what makes one a good subject and another person a poor one has not yet been explained satisfactorily. Psychoanalytic schools have leaned heavily upon the idea that the important factor is the relationship between the patient and the hypnotist and believe that much depends upon the transference. Freud, incidentally, compared falling in love to hypnosis and found that the relationships between both pairs of individuals involved were comparable in many ways. At present none of the varied explanations of the phenomenon is entirely satisfactory, though one is heavily inclined to lean upon the psychologic approach in ordinary observation. Of two things we are certain: that the hypnotic state does not transcend man's natural powers; and that, unfortunately, the technique of the procedure can be learned in about thirty minutes.

At present numerous practitioners and dentists are seeking instruction and training in the techniques of hypnosis, and several pilot courses are being offered in medical schools. The American Medical Association has entered the picture by organizing a Committee on Hypnosis in its Council on Mental Health. Lectures, seminars, and demonstration periods have been organized, and serious efforts are being made to remove the procedure from all hippodrome trappings and keep it under medical surveillance. Hypnosis is an adjunct to other therapeutic techniques, and much more than a simple knowledge of its induction procedure is required if patients are to be safeguarded.

That the procedure can be dangerous is attested to by numerous incidents, some of them ending with subjects requiring psychiatric hospitalization. Just as anyone who would remove tonsils should know how to tie off the great vessels in the neck in case of dire necessity, so also anyone who would hypnotize another should know how to handle any psychiatric emergency which might eventuate during or after the process. The removal of symptoms, no matter how annoying they may be, can in itself be dangerous, for, if the symptom indicates serious pathology underneath, this requires investigation, and the person should not be relieved of the symptom until a diagnosis has been made. Also, it should be remarked that patients develop symptoms for good reasons, and their abrupt removal might leave a patient stripped of defenses and open to severe emotional upset.

The instances of serious eventualities in patients who were hypnotized and who should not have been are too numerous in medical literature to recount here. The British Medical Association Commission, while noting that these dangers have been exaggerated in some quarters, nevertheless recognizes that they do exist, particularly when hypnosis is used without proper consideration on persons "predisposed constitutionally or by the effects of disease to severe psychoneurotic reactions or antisocial behavior." The commission of crimes involving even danger to life is not entirely to be ruled out.[5] Meldman, an American, in a discussion of the dangers of personality decompensation after the treatment of symptoms by hypnosis, retails the history of an industrialist who was "cured" of his fear of flying by hypnotic suggestion but who had to be hospitalized at the end of the "trip" because he became agitated and hallucinated.[6] The necessity of determining the emotional status of the person who is to undergo hypnosis is obvious. The fact that this procedure should never

[5] British Medical Journal, April 23, 1955.
[6] Meldman, F., M.S., "Personality Decompensation After Hypnotic Symptom Suppression," Journal of the American Medical Association, May 28, 1960.

be used for entertainment or "mystifying" purposes is even more obvious.

As to the moral aspects of hypnosis, a question frequently asked by superiors of hospitals and others who are faced with permitting the procedure in their establishments, it can be said confidently that, when medically indicated and done by a competent therapist, it is morally unobjectionable. The interests of everyone are better served, of course, and all are protected if a third person is present when female patients are being treated by male therapists.

VIII

DRUGS, SOMATIC THERAPIES, REHABILITATION

. . . Pluck from the memory a rooted sorrow,
Raze out the written troubles of the brain,
And with some sweet oblivious antidote . . .

Macbeth

DRUGS

New Drugs—Their Use and Abuse

Though man throughout his history has searched for drugs to assuage his discomforts and his agonies, he seems never to have completely made up his mind how he really feels about them. Associated with his search there inevitably has been a wealth of magic and a close connection between drug treatment and healing by suggestion, as layman and physician alike have vacillated between belief in the almost magic efficacy of drugs and—at the other end of the scale—a conviction that they are useless. On the one hand man undertakes the quest for a life-giving elixir or "some sweet oblivious antidote," and then, upon learning that in addition "the patient must minister to himself," he, like Macbeth, bids the physicians "throw physic to the dogs," for he will none of it. As time moves on, it is found that each new pharmaceutical discovery promises more than it delivers, and each new generation of physicians watches disconsolately the waning power of a medication earlier endowed with great promise.

Within our memory numerous life-saving drugs have been introduced into medicine. It is impossible to dispute the power of these drugs over some of man's most implacable enemies, among them certain infectious diseases of the central nervous system. But, as new drugs appear, man's illnesses change; new strains of bacteria develop which prove resistant to wonder drugs, and physicians must regretfully return to older measures until another discovery is made. Apropos of this, perhaps the realistic view expressed by William Parr in 1863 should be given greater credence:

> The infectious diseases replace each other, and when one is rooted out it is apt to be replaced by others which ravage the human race indifferently whenever the conditions of health are wanting. They have this property in common with weeds and other forms of life, as one species recedes another advances.[1]

Though psychiatry developed to a great extent apart from the main stream of medicine, psychiatrists nevertheless did emulate their confreres in being periodically obsessed with drugs. In the days of the ancients, hellebore was widely used to dispel madness. Today we use chlorpromazine, and sometimes reserpine, the first of the new tranquilizers to appear, though actually reserpine is not new at all. The virtues of its progenitor, rauwolfia root, in mental illness were recognized in India long before the West was aware of it. The sedative properties of opium or morphine have been known for ages, and, despite their dangers, they were used in hospitals for mental diseases until the last few decades, when new somniferous chemicals came into vogue.

The psychiatrists of a century ago, incidentally, also provided a ration of alcohol in the daily diet of their hospital patients, a pleasant little custom which, needless to say, is no longer in vogue. Around the same time the depressant effect of bromide on the central nervous system was identified, and this became a basic medication both for general sedation and for epilepsy. By 1928 bromide was the fifth of all drugs in order of frequency of prescription in the United States. With the subsequent demonstration of intoxication hazards associated with its long-continued administration, bromide fell into disrepute, although it still remained a constituent of some patent remedies. While various other drugs appeared upon

[1] Quoted by René J. Dubos, "Medical Utopias," *Daedalus,* Summer 1959.

the scene and were used more or less judiciously, there was little or no reason to expect, in the thirties and forties of this century, that further help would be forthcoming from pharmacologic agents in psychiatric practice. Then the unexpected happened—a number of new tranquilizing and stimulating drugs burst upon the scene in rapid succession, and for the first time in its history psychiatry had potent chemical agents available for its use.

The Sequence of Events

Despite the great impact of these new drugs upon the practice of psychiatry and on mental health services in general, we are still in the pioneering stage in regard to their usage. A lot more research must be done and many more observations must be made over a long period of time before the place of these drugs can be realistically appraised. Any advance of this kind is fraught with danger, because overenthusiasm fosters errors of both judgment and evaluation. Sometimes damage is done before experience teaches us to be cautious and selective with drugs, with symptoms to be treated, and with the patients who present them. A new treatment in psychiatry is sometimes associated with the following sequence of events: First, there will be a profusion of preliminary reports on its use in all manner of conditions; results affirmative! These results are publicized widely; new reports out-do each other; a new miracle drug is born and there is all-around rejoicing. Then, after a year or so, the discordant observations begin to appear in the journals, some of them indicating that the treatment is no good; others that it does more harm than good; others asserting that, while it is good, it is no better than some of the old methods; still others stating that results are inconsistent and that more work needs to be done. Pessimism tends to supplant optimism, and some practitioners dejectedly discontinue use of the method. Then, after assiduous checking and rechecking and modifications of the treatment regime, of dosage, and the period of administration, plus the use of supplementary procedures, some judicious investigators determine that there is a place for the treatment after all, but a limited one, of course. This is as it should have been in the first place, and the drug now gravitates to its proper place in the physician's armamentarium.

It is unfortunate that this sequence must be repeated regularly, for in the initial burst of enthusiasm the hopes of patients and their families are raised out of all proportion to the reality of the situation. Each burst of publicity about one of these "miracle drugs" results in the hospital physician's mail being inundated with clippings from the lay press, sent in by hopeful relatives, wondering why their loved ones are not receiving this substance. The reason may be either that the agent does not do what it is purported to do, or that, while it does some good, its use is accompanied by deleterious side effects, perhaps even some damage to an organ or organ system. Thus, every few years it becomes necessary to assert publicly that there never can be any single miraculous drug which will solve psychiatric problems. Human beings are complex; there are many converging avenues necessary for the treatment of their ills; and one cannot scrap all of the old wisdom in favor of the new in every situation. However, hope springs eternal—and bitter experience continues to ratify the knowing remark of the wise old clinician who advised his confreres to treat as many patients as possible with the new drugs in the first few months after their discovery, for it is then that they are most efficacious.

The Over-all Picture

It is almost impossible to estimate the extent of the use of tranquilizing agents in their myriad forms in this country today. Each drug company has its own brand, or several brands, and they are being used widely and in inordinate quantities. The heads of one government health agency have indicated that well over 50 per cent of their patients are receiving some form of tranquilizing medication. In some state hospitals and private clinics the percentage ratio is even higher. The United States is not alone in this. An investigator in Glasgow reported that, on an overall basis, 50 tons, the equivalent of 150 million tablets, of one mild tranquilizing agent were being used per year. Some estimates are much higher, but we have no means of authenticating them.

It would seem, therefore, that too many people are using some form of these tranquilizing agents and there is reason to fear that they are being used in the minor anxiety-producing situations of everyday life, where they are least efficacious. It is at the state hospital level that these drugs are making the greatest difference. They have done much to eliminate destructive and violent behavior and even to change completely the complexion of the disturbed wards of these institutions. Formerly, because of the large numbers of patients in state hospitals and the paucity of psychiatrists and auxiliary personnel to care for them, treatment was at a minimum and not much could be done with the chronic and overwhelming case load. Though good work was done with new admissions, especially after the introduction of the various shock therapies, patients who did not respond to treatment within a reasonable length of time tended to drift to the wards which housed the chronically ill patients and, like them, frequently became more and more encapsulated in their illness. With the advent of tranquilizing drugs it became possible to salvage many of these individuals, to improve their adjustment in the hospital, and, by making them more amenable to other therapeutic forces, to secure social recoveries in an encouraging number of cases. It is difficult, of course, to determine what has played the most important role in these improvements or recoveries—the new drugs or the changed atmosphere of the hospitals.

The milieu in which a sick patient finds himself, the therapeutic spirit that prevails around him, the interpersonal relationships between doctor and patient, the group forces at work in the surroundings—all of these have a marked influence upon what happens to a patient. The new drugs have certainly played an important role in initiating these improvements, for, as the doctors realized they had potent treatment substances in their hands, their hopes were renewed in being able to treat others effectively and, thus, they themselves were treated.

It is in hospitals in which, previously, much was to be desired by way of therapeutic atmosphere that the most remarkable results are being recorded for the new drugs.

Smaller institutions, private hospitals and other facilities where it was previously customary to provide some kind of active and personalized treatment for all patients, and private practitioners in psychiatry find that their results with drugs are much less spectacular. Nevertheless, at these levels also the importance of the new drugs is not to be minimized. The most skeptical clinical psychiatrists cannot fail to see that these medicaments facilitate the control of some of the most difficult symptoms of psychiatric patients in a manner heretofore not possible. Those clinicians who earlier had the distressing experience of watching patients go through periods of mania, while they stood by almost helplessly, can only compare the present with the past and recognize the new drugs as a blessing and a boon. Yet, while giving thanks for them, we also must keep in mind that these drugs do not correct the basic psychotic process in a permanent fashion. Their best use is as a supplement to other therapeutic procedures.

Categories of New Drugs

It would not be in place to discuss here the technical aspects or enumerate the brand names or chemical properties of the myriads of new drugs which are regularly being released by pharmaceutical companies for use in the treatment of emotional and mental disorders. Called by some "the ataractics," these drugs are now generally known under the major headings of *tranquilizers* and *anti-depressants*. Each preparation has its advocates in the treatment of psychiatric disorders, and most physicians have certain preferred remedies they swear by and believe to be more useful than others. The tranquilizers undoubtedly are helpful in the treatment of patients who are excited or agitated, but they are generally contraindicated in patients who show signs of depression.

The present crop of anti-depressant drugs as a group is quite new upon the scene. Though central nervous system stimulants have been known for some time, they usually have had enough unpleasant side effects to interfere with their continued usefulness. As in the case of the tranquilizers, a wide variety of these drugs is available for use. None of them is completely reliable and none can be depended upon entirely, should there be serious depression with suicidal tendencies. In these instances the doctor still would do well to rely upon electroshock treatment for his patient.

There is little doubt, either, but that the use of tranquilizing drugs is helping to change the pattern of mental health services. By their judicious administration more patients can be treated in the community and more patients can be discharged from psychiatric hospitals, utilizing maintenance doses of these drugs. It is not possible, however, to dispense with medical supervision while they are being used; therefore, increased responsibility must necessarily fall upon community facilities and upon local practitioners, if deleterious reactions are to be detected early.

Hospitals and Drugs

Despite their obvious advances, psychiatric hospitals dare not become too complacent about the changes the drugs have effected within them, nor should they place undue emphasis upon the too rapid emptying of beds. Likewise, any thought on the part of legislators that costs can be lowered or personnel rosters cut because effective treatment procedures are now available would most certainly be a serious mistake. What is more likely is that an increase in personnel will be required if patients are to receive the benefit of the new therapies which pharmacological research has made available.

It is sometimes claimed that psychiatric hospitals are now prone to depend too much upon drugs and chemical restraints, and, while there may be a grain of truth in this claim, it is probable that this tendency is much more pronounced in community medicine. Heroic measures are often required in the treatment of the severe psychiatric illnesses which necessitate hospitalization, and, administered under proper precautions, the wide usage of these new agents is justified. One must proceed much more carefully, however, in the milder forms of illness, which are encountered in everyday community practice. No one is entirely sure as yet whether or not these drugs have deleterious effects upon ideation, perception, or intellectual adaptation to daily problems; therefore, the doctor is justified in being cautious about them. We do have proof that these medicaments reinforce certain euphoriant effects, such as those of alcohol, and there have been instances also in which this combination lifted temporarily certain inhibitions of a moral order. Anxiety and insomnia may be alarm signals of a latent illness or of a serious psychological situation. Before taking the easy way out and prescribing tranquilizers to relieve them, the physician must carefully examine the underlying causes of the symptoms which bring the patient to him.

Thus, it is necessary for physician and families themselves to remain tranquil and not to swing to either the enthusiastic use or the complete avoidance of these new and patently worthwhile agents. Though it is difficult to resist the age-old sirenlike lure which drugs, pills, and potions have for the human race, all of these agents must be used with caution. New drugs have the power to impress patient and physician alike, and, strangely enough, when a positive response is expected, it sometimes appears.

Placebos

In medical practice there is a common, yet extraordinary, phenomenon known as the placebo response. "Placebo" is a word imported intact into the medical vocabulary from the Latin language, in which it means literally "I shall please." Curious things happen to foreign words adopted for common usage in other tongues. The "I shall please" now finds itself a noun, and, by careless English syntax, also an adjective. A placebo is a substance administered by the doctor, whose aim it is to please the patient and thereby help him. It is quite devoid of pharmaceutical properties; it can be an inert pill or an innocuous injection, which logically should have no effect on symptoms arising from disturbed physiology or an ailing organ. Nevertheless, when a placebo is administered, a physiological response does occur—the placebo response—and symptoms may subside. Even more oddly, they may sometimes grow worse. How can this be explained? It is not necessarily a matter of suggestion, though suggestion is important in some cases. It depends, rather, on the meaning the placebo has for the patient. One theory holds that there is a connection between organs and the interpretive areas of the brain, so that virtually all organs and organ systems are capable of responding to placebos.[2] The patient does not imagine that he feels better; he really does feel better. As an example of positive response, Stewart Wolf cites the case of a patient with chronic asthma, which had been refractory to every sort of therapeutic procedure until a new drug was tried and the patient experienced dramatic relief. After some months the pills were running out and another batch was ordered from the drug company. It was then discovered that the drug company had sent an inert substance, not the drug, in the first place.

The existence of the placebo response points up the difficulties which always attend the evaluation of new drugs. The physician must always try to distinguish the placebo response from the therapeutic response, lest he make premature claims which later bring disappointment. One must always keep in mind the great psychological importance of the doctor's visit and of the fact that he gives something to the patient for a purpose, and this feature must be weighed carefully in estimating the real efficacy of the tranquilizing and anti-depressant drugs on the market today.

A word should also be said about the current tendency to use these drugs carelessly to meet ordinary, day-to-day stresses. Just because new drugs are helpful in managing certain psychotic patients, it does not follow that they can be given profitably in small dosage for the ordinary anxieties of life. People are prone to believe, because they have read it somewhere, that anxiety and fear are dangerous and require medical attention. They are less aware that some degree of anxiety is a normal biological reaction which serves a protective purpose.

It is unfortunate that there has been so much publicity connected with new pharmaceutical agents which are purported

[2] Wolf, S., "The Evaluation of Therapeutic Agents with Special Reference to the Tranquilizing Drugs," *American Psychiatric Association Mental Hospital Service, Monograph Series #2* (Washington, D.C., January 1957), p. 15.

to tranquilize or euphorize safely and effectively. Such publicity finds a receptive eye and ear in a culture which consistently runs in high gear and does not suffer stress or inconvenience gladly. For drug companies to have produced useful tranquilizing drugs for the use of psychiatrists has been a noteworthy contribution. However, the rush for tranquilizers, as the result of the often ephemeral longing for complete "peace of mind," is by no means laudatory, and the commercial interests have some responsibility for the increased consumption of such pills at the present time. Fortunately, the large drug companies in this country are reputable, even if understandably competitive, and it has been the general observation that their research efforts are conscientious and vast and that they make serious efforts to correctly appraise their products.

Not too long ago an article surveying this entire problem appeared in the *British Medical Journal* under the appropriate title "The Trade in Tranquility."[3] The authors' experiences were not altogether happy ones. Sometimes, they noted, new drugs go on the market before adequate clinical testing has been done. Also, when the news is finally bruited about that a certain drug does not, after all, accomplish what was claimed for it, in some instances there has emerged in a twinkling a new drug which will surely do the trick. Often such a new drug is just a variant of an existing drug. The authors speak for many who hope that "the development of a complete or absolute tranquilizer is an impossibility, since the removal of fear, guilt, and anxiety under all circumstances would render man less than human." And they make the excellent point, too, that it might be wiser to try to alter the conditions of life to render the perfect tranquilizer unnecessary, "for it will certainly be long in coming and may well be forever unattainable."

Habit and Addiction

There is another facet to the usage of drugs which should cause more concern. Strictly speaking, there is no such thing

[3] Laurence, D. R. and Pond, D. A., "The Trade in Tranquility," *British Medical Journal*, 1:700–02 (March 22, 1958).

as a non-habit-forming drug. People can get in the habit of taking any kind of medicament. There are certain personalities who are prone to addiction, i.e. a compulsive overuse of a drug. The drug to which they become addicted usually has high emotional significance for them and it may, in fact, represent the doctor upon whom they are so dependent. Any sedative, hypnotic, or tranquilizing drug could become habit-forming for some people.

The problem is not necessarily that of physical dependence. It is the problem of a psychological dependence on the use of the drug. The virtuous tonics, which grandmother and our maiden aunts used to depend upon and sometimes became habituated to, usually gave them both a physical and psychological lift, for they often contained just enough alcohol to make them pleasantly and decorously "squiffed." Any drug which has depressant effects on the central nervous system is likely to be habit-forming; the same is true of drugs with potent central stimulating effects. There are, for example, the stimulating drugs known as the amphetamines. It is well known that under some circumstances a dependence on these drugs may develop and result in psychotic symptoms which clear up upon withdrawal of the drug. The intensity of the euphoric response to amphetamines in normal subjects has been documented by investigators.[4] In normal subjects, and to a lesser degree in chronically ill patients, amphetamine surpassed morphine, heroin, pentobarbital, and a placebo in its ability to produce a pleasurable state.

It is important, then, that all tranquilizing and stimulating drugs be given under most careful medical supervision; one cannot urge this enough. Use should be made only of those drugs which are the least harmful and the best tolerated by the individual and which do not precipitate distressing psychological and physiological symptoms when they must be withdrawn or curtailed. It has been pointed out that so many drugs are given a succession of new trade names and so many are attached to sometimes old and worthless remedies, that

[4] Lasagna, L., *et al.*, "Drug Induced Mood Changes in Man . . . ," *Journal of the American Medical Association*, Vol. 157, No. 12, pp. 1006–20 (March 19, 1955).

the result can only be confusion and possibly an increase in the frequency of drug intoxication.[5] The importance of correct dosage cannot be overemphasized either, since even patients who have similar symptoms have dissimilar organisms and constitutions and react differently to the same doses of a drug.

SOMATIC THERAPIES

Insulin Shock Therapy

Rather unexpectedly and almost by accident an apparent "breakthrough" in the treatment of schizophrenia occurred in the early nineteen thirties in Vienna. While using insulin to relieve the withdrawal symptoms which morphine addicts undergo, Dr. Manfred Sakel noted an occasional beneficial effect of the insulin upon some symptoms which addicts exhibit in common with schizophrenics. He, therefore, began to treat schizophrenic patients, who were to be found in his wards in great numbers, in the same fashion. At first he tried to keep the patients from progressing into deep coma but, as he gained experience with schizophrenics, he found that they had to go into coma if they were to benefit. Thus, Sakel worked out a method of deep coma therapy which is still in use in some hospitals, though admittedly in greatly curtailed fashion. The patient goes into deep coma as the result of injection of insulin and, after a long series of treatment, improves. No one knows actually how or why this treatment works.

Briefly, the method consists in administering a single dose of insulin to fasting patients early in the morning, five days a week. The dosage of the drug is then steadily increased each day until the desired coma dosage is reached, after which the amount may be reduced. Daily adjustments of dosage are necessary, because, understandably, the sensitivity and capacity of each patient varies. Gradually the patient progresses

[5] Sargant, W., "Discussion on Sedation and Stimulation in Man," *Proceedings of the Royal Society of Medicine*, 51 (May 1958).

through various stages of drowsiness until coma is reached and, after a carefully controlled period of coma, glucose is administered by stomach tube or, if necessary, by the intravenous method in order to restore consciousness. After awakening, the patient is given a hearty breakfast and, upon leaving the treatment unit, he may resume his daily hospital activities, though he must be kept under observation lest his blood sugar again become low and he experience a so-called "secondary coma."

Understandably, the use of insulin treatment requires a skilled team of physicians and nurses, for there is always a small risk involved. The treatment is contraindicated in various heart, lung, and kidney disorders and in patients below the age of fifteen and over the age of forty-five. Delayed awakening or prolonged coma is one of the hazards of this form of therapy.

Results

The enthusiasm that greeted the introduction of this new treatment was justified. Prior to its advent psychiatrists had been at serious disadvantage in the treatment of schizophrenia, for there was little of a tangible nature that they could do. Initial reports indicated that 70 to 80 per cent of patients with early schizophrenic illnesses responded to insulin therapy. The rate of improvement was considerably lower (40 to 50 per cent) in patients who had been ill for more than a year. Even this latter improvement was an advance, however, and under the circumstances was considered to be particularly worthwhile. It was clear, however, that, as the illness became more chronic, insulin treatment was less and less effectual.

Follow-up studies over a period of years showed an unfortunate tendency among insulin-treated patients to relapse. In fact, informed observers believe that it is uncommon for the patients who made recoveries under this treatment to remain well for more than five years. The second course of treatment is usually less effective than the first, and the patient, if he responds, generally does so more slowly. Like all other methods of physical treatment, insulin therapy should be supplemented by psychotherapy.

Despite the contention of some psychiatrists that insulin treatment has no rival as an efficient therapy in schizophrenia, this form of treatment is rapidly giving way to drug therapy. Some hospitals have given up insulin treatment altogether, and this is understandable, for, even though the hazards are under fair control, the method is still expensive, highly complicated, and time-consuming when compared with other treatment measures.

Convulsive Shock Therapy

Three years after the discovery of insulin shock therapy the method of convulsive shock was introduced by Von Meduna[6] (1935), a Hungarian physician who later emigrated to this country. The treatment was given first by means of the drug camphor, and then by metrazol. Meduna originally suggested this method specifically for the treatment of schizophrenia, but experience soon showed that the best results were obtained in depressions and other affective disorders. In 1938 Cerletti and Bini inaugurated the use of the electroshock machine for the induction of convulsions by alternating current.[7] Their technique is still used extensively, though different types of machines using different types of current have also been introduced. As a further advance, in 1957 an inhalant, Indoklon, was recommended by J. C. Krantz and his co-workers for the induction of therapeutic convulsions.[8] If the early promise of Indoklon is substantiated by further experience, it may well take the place of electroshock. Patients seem to feel more comfortable under Indoklon treatment and they complain less of memory disability. All of these methods of treatment cause convulsions in the patients. For some unknown reason, many of the patients are helped and their symptoms disappear. Numerous theories were put forth to explain these actions, but the plain truth is that no one really

[6] Meduna, von, L. J., *Die Konvulsionstherapie der Schizophrenie* (Halle: Marhold, 1936).

[7] Cerletti, V., and Bini, L., "L'Elettroschock," *Arch. Gen. Neurol. Psychiat. Psecenal,* 19:226–68 (1938).

[8] Krantz, J. C., Truitt, E. G., Jr., Speers, L., and Levy, A. S. O., "New Pharmaco-convulsive Agent," *Science,* 125:353 (1957).

knows how the treatment works or why the patients improve.

Probably one of the most distressing things about this type of treatment is its name. Patients understandably develop all kinds of bizarre notions regarding what the treatment entails. Actually, under present-day methods the administration of drugs helps to allay fears and renders the patient somnolent and unaware of what is going on, and various muscle-relaxing drugs mitigate the convulsion and help to prevent fractures and dislocations. Some capable workers[9] object to these preliminary drug treatments, however, and believe that such expedients merely complicate the treatment, but other equally experienced physicians believe they should be utilized.

Convulsive treatments are usually given three times a week for periods that depend on the patient's response and the nature of his disorder. For depressed patients five to ten treatments may be adequate. For other disorders, showing slow but unmistakable improvement under convulsive therapy, the course may have to be extended to twenty-five or thirty sessions, followed, if necessary, by so-called maintenance treatment, which means treatment once a week, once a month, or whatever is indicated. Again, as might be expected, all manner of modifications of method, dosage, timing, etc. of the treatment have been tried. Unlike insulin shock, the treatment can be administered in outpatient departments of hospitals and in the offices of psychiatrists in private practice. The social implications of this are obvious, for in this manner the patients may remain in the community rather than have to be admitted to psychiatric hospitals. By the same token, however, the ease of administration of convulsive therapy also exposes it to abuses, and this must be guarded against with extreme care.

This therapy is of most value in the treatment of depressions, especially in involutional melancholia and in the depressive phase of manic-depressive psychosis. When depression is associated with other disorders, the patient may also be re-

[9] Kalinowsky, L. B., "Convulsive Shock Treatment," *American Handbook of Psychiatry*, ed. S. Arieti (New York: Basic Books), Vol. II (1959), pp. 1499–1520.

lieved by the treatment. Its use in schizophrenia is more restricted. However, in acute and subacute schizophrenic states, convulsive therapy often suppresses symptoms quickly, and relapse may be avoided by continuing the treatment until twenty or more shocks have been administered.

For the last several years, under the impact of the tranquilizing drugs and improved programs of psychotherapy and hospital treatment, there has been a declining trend in the use of convulsions for schizophrenia. The more recent discovery of useful anti-depressant drugs has even cut down somewhat on their use in depressions, though only a few venture to predict that drugs will supplant electroshock in the foreseeable future. The rapid, almost specific, effect of convulsive therapy in relieving depressions cannot be lightly dismissed. However, one does observe a growing movement to combine anti-depressant medication and electroshock therapy, so that less of the latter is necessary.

It is common belief at present that psychotherapy of a supportive type is of great value when used along with convulsive therapy. Though there are some contraindications to the use of the convulsive treatment, only occasionally is pre-existing physical disease thought to be one of them, particularly if the need for electric shock be definitely indicated. As is true throughout medical practice, each individual case must be weighed carefully and all risks properly evaluated.

Psychosurgery

The operation known as lobotomy consists in severing some of the connections between that part of the brain called the thalamus and the frontal lobes of the brain. This method, admittedly stringent, was introduced into psychiatry on the basis that the thalamus is deeply concerned with emotion and that stimuli passing along the fibers from it to the frontal lobes are involved in the conscious experience of emotion. Severance of these fibers therefore alters affective responses, reduces anxiety, and weakens the emotional impact of delusions and other symptoms of psychiatric patients. In the quarter-century which has passed since Egas Moniz published his epoch-making monograph on prefrontal lobotomy,[10] the field of psychosurgery has been explored in many directions and attitudes toward it have varied widely.

The idea of attempting to relieve psychiatric patients by brain section did not appeal to many psychiatrists when it was first proposed, and it still does not to countless others. In this country the pioneer work of Freeman and Watts[11] in frontal lobotomy, begun in late 1936, was largely ignored until favorable reports began coming from England. Then an increasing number of psychiatrists became interested in the possibilities of psychosurgery. Resistance continued among those who felt that the infliction of brain damage to cope with "functional" illnesses was inadmissible and among psychoanalysts, who are skeptical of most physical treatments as a matter of principle.

The early work with lobotomy was done on psychotic subjects and there was much uncritical reporting. It was difficult to evaluate the full range of effects in psychotic patients, many of whom were seemingly "deteriorated" or comfortable in their illnesses. Deterioration, as we now know, cannot be reversed by lobotomy. Even among proper subjects there were inevitable failures and relapses. There were also fatalities connected with psychosurgery, both immediate and late, the late fatalities occurring mostly in patients who were subjected to the more radical operations.

Disillusionment with this treatment was enhanced by observation of psychoneurotic subjects following lobotomy. Here the adverse effects upon important personality functions became readily apparent. Apathy and inertia were not uncommon results of this kind of surgery; bladder incontinence was also frequent. Character deterioration was often observed; some few patients became rude and profane, or gluttonous; many suffered a disorientation, especially as to who they were. Converts to psychosurgery turned abruptly away in

[10] Moniz, E., *Tentatives operatoires dans le traitement de certaines psychoses* (Paris: Masson, 1936).

[11] Freeman, W., "Psychosurgery," *American Handbook of Psychiatry*, ed. S. Arieti (New York: Basic Books, 1959), Vol. II, pp. 1525–40.

great numbers. Others, still convinced of the potential value of the approach, hoped that a better operation could be devised which would eliminate the dangers and the undesired side effects.

In the second decade of psychosurgery various limited operations on the frontal lobe were done, some of them appearing promising. But by this time many psychiatrists had become thoroughly disenchanted and, with the advent of powerful new drugs, the number of surgical interventions dropped remarkably, even in mental hospitals which had been partial to psychosurgery for patients with chronic psychoses. There is general agreement now that extensive lobotomy procedures are no longer justified in psychiatry.

In addition to the use of restricted operations, there has been another major change in psychosurgery: the selection of patients. Of late, conditions figuring especially prominently in psychosurgical operations are obsessive tension states, psychosomatic illnesses, and intractable pain. Schizophrenic patients who have not deteriorated much may be helped by surgery and show the least harmful side effects, but the number of other psychotic patients subjected to psychosurgery has shown a marked decline. More patients with anxiety, agitation, and depression are being given this treatment now, for better or for worse, and in England, it is used for certain depressions, especially in elderly people whose condition has not responded to electric shock. It needs to be said, however, that no matter how limited the lobotomy procedure may be, it is bound to have some impact upon the personality of the patient, no matter how mild, and all should know that the ideal operation has not yet been developed.

There remains in psychiatry a healthy reserve about psychosurgery, but, until an alternative way is forthcoming, it cannot be assigned to oblivion. In selected patients, refractory to other treatment methods, disabled by their illness and likely to remain so, the psychiatrist must do what he can to alleviate suffering. The general state of affairs has been recently summed up by Lothar B. Kalinowsky and Paul H. Hoch in their comprehensive book *Somatic Treatments in Psychiatry* (1961). This is, in part, what they have to say:

It is fair to say that psychosurgery is not the treatment of choice in any particular disease entity. Each case, whatever the diagnosis, must be decided on its own merits. The more treatment procedures are available in psychiatry, the less need will there be for such drastic methods as a brain operation. However, there are still many chronic psychiatric patients in whom no other treatment has brought sufficient relief. In these cases psychosurgery must be given serious consideration and will yield many satisfactory results unobtainable with other methods.[12]

REHABILITATION—EMOTIONAL ASPECTS

There is a new, active, valuable, and somewhat all-inclusive branch of medicine attracting attention at the present time because, through its efforts, people who otherwise might be condemned to life-long invalidism are being returned to health and a usefulness which restores their self-respect. Known as "rehabilitation," the discipline treats those who suffer permanent limitations because of chronic illness or crippling injury. Since in these areas the emotional outlook of the patients is of prime importance, for both good and ill, the contribution psychiatry makes is weighty and specific, and therefore the subject should be mentioned here.

Psychiatry and rehabilitation not only overlap in the areas they treat, they have much in common in their fundamental conceptions. They work both in the framework of the therapeutic environment and the therapeutic team and thus in the context of group dynamics. More important, they both subscribe to the philosophy that what they are dealing with is not a passive amorphous being to be manipulated willy-nilly, but an individual who lives, feels, thinks, struggles, and expends his own energy in defending himself against a threat to his integrity. Psychiatry and rehabilitation both maintain that it is vital to rehabilitate man as man, no matter how badly disabled he may be or how seriously restricted his activities. Both disciplines are striving to return to society a "compleat person," skilled, and perhaps newly skilled, in important techniques and especially in the art of living.

Any physical anomaly, however benign, and whether constitutional or acquired, can be the source of serious disturbances in the life of an individual. A nose, the contour of which offends only the owner, may be as formidable an obstacle to adjustment as a major amputation. The problems of rehabilitation are, therefore, extensive and extremely complex. They arise not only in the wake of accidents and crippling disease, but also with acute and chronic physical and mental illnesses and, very importantly, with the attrition of years. The rehabilitation of the aging individual is at present one of the most meaningful fields of modern medicine. The psychiatrist is deeply concerned with all these problems, and his orientation is beginning to influence, if not reshape, contemporary medicine itself.

Medicine is finding that, to fulfill its obligations in a changing culture and shifting pattern of diseases, it is not enough to apply the insights and techniques of pure science. It is equally important to treat the patient against the background of his environment and in the light of the personal and social meaning of the illness. Illness represents a serious threat to the patient as a self-sufficient, intact individual, and hidden forces operating within him may have much to do with its course and outcome. These influences cannot be ignored in any treatment program for any illness or any handicap; they spell the difference between success and failure in our efforts. It is upon these influences that the psychiatric insight has its greatest bearing and makes its most telling contribution.

Rehabilitation may be as inclusive or as limited in meaning as the concept of the user. It may suggest an effort to make the best of grim adversity, even if this means adjustment at a lower level, or it may suggest a new and better integration of all personal forces. The former is easier to achieve, of course, but it is the duty of physicians to make the goal a more positive one. If it is at all possible, he should refuse to settle for less than a "compleat person," no matter how disabled, adjusted securely in a society which, after all, has room for many combinations of skill, capacity, and motivation.

As the doctor sets out for this goal, he must be cognizant of psychodynamics, of the way in which the human personality is formed, and of the mental mechanisms and the defenses that determine behavior. Such knowledge enables him to work more purposefully in rehabilitation. It is the role of the psychiatrist in rehabilitation not only to treat patients who require his special skills, but to serve as a consultant to the rehabilitation team and to clarify those influences which in general and in particular prolong convalescence and, indeed, make this a never ending phenomenon. Unfortunately, there is no blueprint to be followed for dealing with or avoiding the psychological hazards of disablement. Each patient is unique, molded by his past history, colored by his environment, imbued with goals and values as varied as they are complex. But there are certain guides to understanding how and why the individual reacts to stress in a particular way, and if these are utilized early enough and consistently enough, the task of the rehabilitation team can be facilitated.

It was formerly believed that various disabilities brought a fairly consistent pattern of psychological reaction in their wake. The tuberculosis patient was said to be euphoric (i.e. elated); the deaf person, inclined to paranoid reactions; the one whose disease was located below the diaphragm, vulnerable to depression. It is now recognized, however, that the psychological reactions of patients to any type of illness depend largely on their previous personality makeup. The same is true of reactions to trauma. Some individuals recover quickly, a few develop serious emotional difficulties, and there is a wide range of reactions between these two extremes. The degree of emotional disturbance is by no means directly related to the intensity of the trauma; this fact is proven every day. It is related, however, to the meaning of the trauma to the person concerned. There may well be patterns of defeat in the personalities of patients which delay physical reablement and social readjustments for a long period, and even indefinitely.

Human motivation is a curious process, for it is based on unconscious, as well as conscious, needs. It is therefore not a simple thing to motivate a patient to work towards his own recovery, although certainly an atmosphere of optimism and high morale in the therapeutic team helps enormously. The situation is complicated, however, by basic human needs: needs for love and attention, dependency strivings and struggles against them, feelings of hostility and feelings of guilt. These patterns are found in the development of every individual, and difficulties arise when they have been imperfectly resolved in the course of maturation. Sudden physical disaster, and even more insidious physical attrition, reactivate conflicts, threats, and anxieties of long ago. There may be at times a retreat to a more comfortable state contrived early in life to minimize anxiety and pain. The adverse psychological impact of disablement is in fact greatly enhanced when it actually or symbolically recapitulates conflicts of childhood. The individual tends to revert to immature methods of handling them and his rehabilitation problems are compounded.

The rehabilitation team must ever be alert to forces which impair motivation. The disabled individual may equate service from others with love and attention previously denied him. He may equate it with punishment of those who neglected him in the past. He may equate the helplessness it symbolizes with retribution for his own hostility and guilt. Just as the victim of sudden disablement must work through the inevitable depression he feels, so he must work through his dependency needs before he can go on to better things. In some instances a certain degree of dependency will be inescapable; then the patient cannot be entirely self-sufficient and he must be encouraged to accept this. He must also be encouraged, however, to develop new skills and interests. The real problem of rehabilitation consists in helping the patient realize and accept that the emotional rewards of fuller function are greater than any secondary gains derived from dependency.

Throughout the period of convalescence, dependency problems present themselves to the rehabilitation team again and again. Even patients who are making excellent progress will have occasional lapses in that direction, requesting help or assistance in tasks they have already mastered. Such patients need support and reassurance so that they can go on to learn new tasks. As difficult as the overtly dependent patient, and sometimes more so, is the patient who denies his disability and denies his dependency needs entirely. An unrealistic insistence on independence and self-sufficiency also leads to defeat. Underlying it may be a real need for support and a need to be punished for it. It is obvious that these patients require a program of activities within their capabilities in order for them to gain confidence. This will help shield them also from the mistakes they will make and the humiliation they will suffer if they are allowed to proceed as paragons of courage, if not of prudence. So it is that the permanently disabled patient must neither surrender to his handicap nor deny that it exists. Accepting the disabled self is the decisive step on the road to rehabilitation.

The difficulties of accepting this new self must never be minimized. Within the "self-image" there is what is called the "body image." Everyone has one of his own and it subtends his conception of his own personality and his relations with others. This image has been built up from infancy and it contains many irrational and symbolic associations from infancy and childhood. These associations linger in the deeper recesses of the mind; they contribute to exaggerated emotional reactions to injury and losses of parts of the body, and to excessive fear or depression with minor disabilities. Hence, in addition to making an adjustment to certain real limitations and adaptations imposed by the disability, the patient must work through to a revision of his body image. This is a process which may kindle old conflicts and painful associations, and the individual may revert for a time to immature patterns of behavior. If this should happen, the rehabilitation worker's task is to work with the more mature aspects of the personality to prevent any chance of regression and, thus, to support the patient through the crisis.

The possibilities of rehabilitation of the psychiatric patient are enhanced by adequate liaison between doctors, nurses, and those who are with the patient most of the time. Psychiatric patients need attention around the clock, and the persons who are closest to the patients in the hospital are the nurses and aides. What these individuals do with patients influences the course of the latters' illnesses; therefore, in addition to careful training, nurses and aides need close liaison with the physicians and supervisors.

The psychiatrist is but one of the team of specialists and auxiliary workers active in the rehabilitation field. Although he must assume important diagnostic and therapeutic functions in the more difficult and complex cases, his role is predominantly advisory and educational. His contribution should grow with advances in his specialty, particularly in the area of social psychiatry as it opens up new possibilities for treatment and prevention. The task imposed upon everyone privileged to treat his fellow man is as unending as is the search for wisdom. Every insight attained reveals the existence of more questions to be answered, more mysteries to be revealed. Reality, including man's own, is inexhaustible. So, too, are the uses of adversity. Everyone must be prepared to make these servants, rather than masters.

IX

SOME EMOTIONAL REACTIONS
OF EVERYDAY LIFE

*Pestilence, on the road to Bagdad, was asked by the
leader of a caravan why he was making such haste. "To
take 5,000 lives," he replied. On his return he again
met the caravan and the leader said: "You lied to me;
you took not 5,000, but 50,000 lives." Pestilence replied:
"No, I took 5,000 and not one more. It was Fear who
killed the rest."*

Arabian Tale

It is an axiom of modern dynamic psychiatry that anyone
who hopes to understand and help others with their emotional problems must have some understanding and acceptance of himself. Only those who respect and are at peace
with themselves can be really respectful of others and capable of relating to them in a comfortable fashion. This
axiom holds, no matter whether the individual trying to help
is a family doctor, a psychiatrist, a psychologist, or a clergyman. St. Francis de Sales had pointed this out to us in a
simple fashion ages ago. "How can we reprove others
gently," he asks, "if we correct ourselves with disgust and un-
reasonableness? He who frets impatiently about his own im-
perfections will never correct them, for correction, if it is to
be of use, must come from a peaceful mind." The call, therefore, is for those of us who would understand and help others
to first understand and be kind to ourselves.

It is generally agreed that most of the emotional difficulties manifested by mental patients, no matter whether they
appear as neuroses or psychoses are similar to one another
in many ways and not dissimilar to the emotional problems
which all of us encounter in everyday life. It is only when

these problems become so complicated that they interfere with our daily routine or our relationships with others that they require psychiatric assistance. As we discuss some of the reactions which all of us exhibit at times in moderate degrees, it will become obvious that, if they were to become inordinate or habitual, we would be liable to more serious disorders. Emotional illness is a matter of degree of reaction, rather than a hard-and-fast, well-defined entity. The problems we will discuss in this chapter are not problems which in themselves bring people to the psychiatrist's door, but nevertheless they can be annoying problems, and the insights provided by psychiatric knowledge offer us means of handling them. Therefore they are proper materials for brief comment here. We will discuss anger and rage, hostility, bitterness, envy, and finally, prejudice.

Anger and Rage

Anger is a way of reacting when we are threatened and fearful, an emotional mobilization of our forces to fight off danger. It has its uses, biologically and psychologically, to arouse the individual to safeguard himself by repelling dangerous objects. But it is a primitive response, provoking marked bodily reaction and, usually, unpleasant feeling tones, and in complex situations it is a crude and unselective device. The aim of anger is to repel and destroy, and the effect of anger is to make us careless of consequences. This makes anger a hazardous tool to use, and often enough the danger rebounds on the individual who experiences it. If, for instance, his anger is aroused by a person he cannot afford to be angry with, it constitutes a threat to his own personal security, the threat of losing the love or respect of someone important to him. In this situation, anger becomes an anxiety-producing agent. Upon reflection, we can see that this would not be an uncommon experience in childhood. In early years many frustrations must be imposed on the mercurial moods and exuberant behavior of the child by those he most loves and whose love he would most fear to lose. When he reacts to the constraints with anger, as he often does, he must somehow dissemble or repress or overcome the emotion, or else suffer an attack of anxiety, and how he handles himself in these early crises will be a matter of grave moment for his developing personality.

If the head-on purpose of anger cannot be accomplished and the situation that provoked it continues unabated, then anger may proceed to rage. A great deal of energy is then discharged in useless random activity, such as throwing things about, or even destroying them. Rage is a somewhat symbolic discharge of anger; one cannot get at the dangerous person because he is either too significant or too powerful, so one vents the anger on substitutes. In the rage constellation, moreover, there is a tendency to advance toward hatred; instead of avoiding the object, one becomes bound to it in animosity. The person in the hate relationship becomes very necessary, sometimes even the most significant person in one's life, if he is not that already. We have all seen this and we wonder why a person who cannot get on with someone does not avoid him; instead he seems drawn to him and even to seek him out. In extreme cases there is a morbid preoccupation with the hated individual, but the only real interest displayed is connected with the damage that can be done to this person's prestige.

The history of persons who react in this fashion will reveal clues to their behavior. We find that rage was frequently prominent in their early family relationships and that profitable lessons for dealing with it were not imprinted during the period in which the child ordinarily learns to tame his aggressiveness. In these circumstances rage tends to become a powerful force within the personality. Subsequent experience outside the family—in school and in other situations—may prove corrective to some degree, as the individual learns how great a threat to himself his rage actually is. There may even be an overcorrection, if one may say so, with the individual resorting to other self-defeating mechanisms in an attempt to secure from others what he has not been able to get through rage. Nevertheless, once rage has become an integral part of the reaction pattern of the individual in early years, the tendency is not lost easily and desperate efforts may be required to inhibit it.

Some individuals develop ways of handling these feelings which do work to some extent. They become sensitive to the type of behavior in others to which they themselves are prone, but find it expedient to suppress. In their dealings with others they are on the *qui vive* for any behavior faintly reminiscent of anger; they adopt disapproving attitudes towards it; they scorn anybody who shows it. This makes them more comfortable, not only because they can feel superior, but also because they hope thereby to avoid entanglements with anger-prone individuals. On the other hand, they cripple themselves considerably. Their relationships with other people tend to be strained. The concealment of anger and the destructive impulses from which it arises is not easy. Other people sense these things and shy away. Hence the angry person does not succeed in his protective maneuvers. Moreover, he is not really interested in easygoing persons, and easygoing persons tend to avoid him. Willy-nilly he gravitates toward people like himself, and situations provocative of anger multiply. It has been said in this connection that, as intimacy thickens, injury also thickens.[1] The whole situation becomes a mutual struggle over who will do the most damage to the other. There is no constructive intimacy, despite the real needs of the individual for warmth and love, for which the impulses exist in the unconscious and sometimes express themselves inadvertently. One has the impression that the behavior of an angry person seems almost to indicate that he loves his implacable enemy. If he really were able to love him, however, and give up all attempts to damage him, his life would be much easier than it is likely to be otherwise.

Hostility

To hate is not in itself an evil thing; it is understandable that a man or woman will hate what is really evil. But in most of us, distressing as it may be, hatred is not reasonably defined and wisely directed; in most of us it exists at least in some degree as a hostility vaguely defined and amorphous,

[1] Sullivan, H. S., *Clinical Studies in Psychiatry* (New York: W. W. Norton & Co., 1956), p. 104.

compounded of indistinct resentments and aggressiveness, and even a little cruelty. It has in it the tendency to harm others or even one's self, and, oddly enough, it might even have an admixture of love in it. It can be detected in limitless forms—in the expression, "I love him but I would like to knock his block off"; in casual gossip, which ruins someone's reputation; in vindictiveness, plain and unadorned; or in its ultimate expression, brutality and murder.

Technically and psychiatrically speaking, hostility is more than mere unfriendliness; it is a tendency to hurt, to control, to win over, or destroy, and it can be conscious or unconscious. It arises, some believe, as a mechanism of adaptation, and it is passed not through genes, but through contact— like a communicable disease—from parents to children and thence to the environment.

It is the thwarting of the normal development of the child which sets off the first reactions of hostility. If his major motivating forces are allowed to develop within reason, there results a reasonably normal child; if he is thwarted consistently, the seeds of hostility are sown, along with a sense of personal inferiority. As he grows up, he may react to problems with blind resentment, mixed with a feeling of personal inadequacy, and if the situation is continuous and traumatic enough, he might eventually gravitate into alcoholism or mental illness. More frequently, however, one sees the person whose hostility is aroused only partially, as in the case of the son of the overly possessive mother. Here, though the boy usually gets on well with his peers, yet he is ridden with conscious or unconscious hostility toward his mother. He might even project this feeling to all women. Sometimes, even when as a man he is able to break the "silver cord" and take unto himself a wife, his hostility goes with him to his new habitat and the bride may find herself the target for hostility which she has not earned.

Many people suffer from unconscious hostility through no fault of their own. All of us have experienced it and have felt badly about it. The expression which typifies it is: "I never did like that person. Mind you, he never did anything to me, but I just don't like him." Now, should this feeling be projected to groups, a background for trouble is laid. Antagonistic labels on races, creeds, or skin color are evidences of this; they replace understanding and apparently do away with the necessity for it. Whole races or nations in this way serve as dumping grounds for the hostile feelings of a demagogue or his followers, particularly if the group's *raison d'être* is to be anti someone or something. Adherents can always be found to join forces with such causes, no matter how silly their purposes, and they bring all of the force of their unconscious hatreds and hostilities with them.

Though the underlying causes of hostility are in the disorders of childhood adjustment, the outcome in the adult makeup is determined not only by the intensity of the hostility, but also by the way in which it exhibits itself. Criminals handle hostility by taking it out directly, by acting it out, by lawlessness, by taking things into their own hands and thus indulging their hatred. We call neurotically hostile those who take their hostilities out on themselves. This group also includes some criminals, notably the kind that almost beg to be caught and punished. Lady Macbeth is a prototype, coldly planning murder, contemptuously counseling it, and then, aghast at what she has done, quaking with guilt and crying for punishment. Most embezzlers belong to this group. They intend to put the money back later; they convince themselves that they are not really stealing it; yet they delay its return so long that detection and arrest are inevitable.

Less obvious, but more neurotic, are those adults who, because of deprivation in childhood and failure to compensate for it, cannot possibly believe that they deserve love or esteem, and, when it looks as though someone really cares for them, they go out of their way to provoke a hostile incident. You have seen this often—people who have friends or beaux and repeatedly end up by quarreling with them. These individuals are recognized by their subtle reproaches and their suggestions to their friends that they are being let down, not understood—suggestions so vague that nothing can be done to improve the situation. These people travel from friend to friend, group to group, maybe even spouse to spouse, in search of love and happiness, never realizing that it is attainable only within themselves and that they are carrying their own built-in quarrels with them.

Other adults, crippled by failure to resolve such problems, become filled with chronic hostility which shows itself in various ways: one sacrifices a friend for a smart or cuttingly bright remark or to make himself look good in a group; another sells out his friends, parents, or maybe even his country for his own ambition. He must beat the other fellow out —not only keep up with, but outdo the Joneses—a continuous struggle for prestige and influence in his own distorted system of values. This group never realizes that the survival and happiness of society depend on how much one gives and not on how much one takes, and that there are satisfactory ways of handling one's hostile and inferiority feelings.

Hostility is present in some way in all mental disease and in most psychological disorders. Certainly it is also a contributing factor in some physical disorders, understandably so. We all know how carping, bickering, or criticism at the dinner table can ruin the appreciation, and even the digestion, of the best prime ribs of beef. We know how pulses beat faster, hearts pound, and blood pressures rise with anger. It surprised no one, therefore, when it was suggested that repressed hostility may be found to be a contributing factor in high blood pressure and in peptic ulcers. On the surface these individuals appear calm, but below their controlled exterior there is a hard tension. Hostility, defended against and suppressed, creates a great psychological burden.

The hostile person is distinguishable by his unhappiness. Sensing, but not knowing, the hostility within himself, he projects it upon others. Uncomfortable because of his own inferiority feelings, he makes others uncomfortable by pretending superiority. He is what the young folks would call "all mixed up," and he does not enjoy himself or others. The question which naturally arises is: "How can we alleviate hostility?" The greatest role, of course, could be played in the rearing of children. Since it is in childhood that hostility arises most often and is twisted into a pattern of life, it is here that ideally it could be markedly lessened, if not eliminated. The ideal situation, of course, would be to arrange for all children to be born only to parents who want them for themselves alone and are mature enough to love them with that love which permits each one to develop individually. Babies, however, even when they "trail clouds of glory," rarely come unaccompanied by a few problems. One problem for many people is in finding enough space and sustenance for these little animated appetites and some semblance of silence so that all may get some sleep. If these problems are seen as something the babies and children are to blame for, hostility toward them, with its resulting contagion, is inevitable. So, from the beginning, the problems of parenthood get involved in the life of the child himself.

Secondly, it is necessary for the parents at this time to consider their own maturity. Unless they can see this offspring as something outside themselves, they are going to have a hard time refraining from projecting upon him all sorts of frustrating dreams, anxieties, guilts, and resentments. On occasion one will encounter trouble in families because dad was a fullback on dear old something-or-other's great football team, which beat its rival in the last minute of play. His offspring, though he received a football for his eighth-month birthday, is not inclined toward football, and, even though he may be a perfectly fine boy who has real talent, his dad is liable to consider him a sissy. Unfortunately, also, life does not always wait until a child is mature before presenting him with mature responsibilities, as many an oldest child will testify.

Thirdly, there is the necessity of presenting the child with a behavior pattern that is cooperative, friendly, and understanding. This does not in any way mean a lack of discipline; there is a security in reasonable discipline for a child. There must be consistency and firmness in our expectations, but severity and cruelty are not discipline. The parent who screams that he or she will teach the child a lesson, as the youngster is whacked with whatever is handy, only teaches the child one thing—hostility. It is the fair, reasonable, reliable parent, with the steady voice, who teaches the child what it should know.

Lastly, the child needs to have some opportunity to perfect his skills and experiment with his capacities. In sum, in rearing children an attempt should be made to meet their basic needs for care, love, prestige, and fulfillment. This knowledge is not new; yet it constantly needs repetition, for it is frequently forgotten.

Emotional Tensions in Work Situations

Before proceeding to discuss other forms of unpleasantness, we might stop to note that many of the hazards of modern industrial activity reside, not in machines or in toxic environments, but in those who operate the machines and in what is metaphorically called "toxipsychology," i.e. the effects of toxic psychological attitudes. These hazards are brought to the job by both worker and executive, and they have to do with personality maladjustments, instability of mood, morbid drive and ambition, deep-seated inferiority feelings and insecurities, and family, financial, and related worries. The appraisal of the worker's job by his family, for instance, strongly influences his motivation and his job satisfaction. This is true of the executive also. Neither is any man "an island, entire of itself"; what happens to each one at home goes with him to the office, or to the workbench. There is a hidden human logic in the turmoil of feelings, thoughts, attitudes, and expectations underlying the sudden conflicts that arise in the course of each work situation to vex and astound all participants.

Work can be a great stabilizer for the human psyche. That is the reason why occupation or, better, constructive activity looms large in the therapeutic program of psychiatric hospitals. It is recognized that idleness promotes demoralization. In the great world outside, of course, work provides man with his livelihood, but work has more than bartering value. Work has important social implications. It is in some way the expression of the human person. It provides, or should provide, the satisfaction of fellowship and accomplishment; it is also the purveyor of prestige, or so it is generally regarded. One of the disadvantages of many modern industrial setups is that all too often work fails to provide the emotional satisfactions which men need in their occupation. Many jobs fail to offer an adequate outlet for man's instinctive energy, particularly his aggressive energy. Many tasks in their unending sameness strangle a man's creativity. Frequently in industrial quarrels the worker is striving more for job satisfaction than for strictly material advantages.

Monotony is not a tasty dish day after day. Yet, we all know how relative and subjective the feeling of monotony can be. On some days even an extremely varied professional job may seem unbearably pedestrian. And what may be monotonous for one person and completely undemanding may be stressful and threatening to another. So it is that worker and job, co-worker and supervisor, subordinate and superordinate form an interlocking system in which there can be much displacement and aggravation of personality and situational problems. Hostilities are easily displaced, and rancors are inflated to an enormous degree. It is well to remember that from 60 to 80 per cent of all dismissals in industry are due to personal and interpersonal maladjustments rather than to technical inadequacies.

Executives

If the worker in modern industry feels, justly or unjustly, that he is frustrated on many occasions, the executive is even worse off. Instead of one or a few people or situations to worry about, he has a profusion of them. Subordinates may err and conceal the error; they may quarrel and scheme with and against each other; workers strike or quit or build up grievances, or they work at a snail's pace, it seems, when it is most important to meet a deadline. And then there are the hazards of the outside competition. Equally as stressful, or more so, are the efforts the executive must make to keep his job, for at this level the possibilities of being fired are particularly high. A failure in human relations can be very costly. While the executive can delegate many of his functions to others, human relations he cannot delegate to any significant degree. Healthy human relations are vitally necessary to keep the company sound and in a good competitive position.

The head of a small business can be just as harried as one in a large company. Often his responsibility is complete, all the decisions are his, and errors are irretrievable. Alone he must face these problems, along with his conscience and his conflicts. Reasonable emotional stability is very important. It is important not only for business solvency, but also to protect one from anxiety and from psychosomatic disorder, for "the sorrow which has no vent in tears may make other organs weep."

Anxiety builds up in the face of unfinished business—past and present. It builds up in relation to events to come, when an important decision is to be made or awaited from another source. In the interim there is an inflation of time, a feeling of stress, and a spilling over of anxiety into other areas of activity. When the decision is internal and an important choice must be made, the same thing happens. Here a predisposed individual may develop a true anxiety state, or a depression, or physical symptoms. Sometimes, in fact, the only possible solution for unresolved conflicts is physical symptom formation.

The hazards which the executive brings with him to his office are in many instances more difficult for him to cope with than the ones he encounters there, and they are also more difficult for his subordinates. These are the hazards engrained in his personality as the result of defenses he has developed over the years. These unconscious forces play a signal role in all human behavior. A neurotic executive, however, can create a major problem throughout the entire organization. Even if his problem is not too serious, it can precipitate serious conflicts. Poor human relations at any supervisory level are costly, not only in terms of efficiency and production, but in the sense of contaminating other people, especially those with personality problems of their own. For an official to be badly maladjusted is worse than his having the measles. His compulsive drive or his aggressiveness, for example, may be responsible for high labor turnover or poor *esprit de corps* in his organization.

Some executives have an intuitive skill in human relations. Few are well informed in human relations theory. This is unfortunate, because great progress has been made in the field. It must be granted, however, that knowing theory and applying it are not the same thing. Personality difficulties often prevent the application. The verbal endorsement of better human relations by the top man, or his gracious acceptance of new policies, may mean nothing at all if he simply makes the gesture, but continues to make the same type of errors he made before.

No person is free from conflicts and there will always be areas of difficulty for everyone. But it is important to recognize that certain kinds of anxiety-driven behavior are especially bad in the business and industrial community. Overruling, bypassing, and undercutting are dangerous practices for the executive. There are various other destructive possibilities, of which the executive's thirst for approval and his drive to demonstrate superiority are the most obvious. Out of these come overagreeable behavior and laissez-faire supervision, on the one hand, and overauthoritative and aggressive attitudes on the other.

Unless the executive has arrived in the ranks of the lofty by accident of birth or longevity—because sometimes we attain position by our staying and outlasting qualities—he has probably done so by virtue of certain traits that mark him as a reasonably successful striver and leader. But the virtues of the man who strives are not the virtues of the man who has arrived. When he reaches the top, an executive has to make a new and even radical adjustment, and how well he succeeds in doing this will depend upon his emotional balance and his flexibility, things which should have been learned early in life. If he does not succeed, the strain on himself and on those he manages will soon be felt.[2]

Bitterness

We can now examine a few other less dramatic but equally unpleasant devices that some of us use at times in an endeavor to achieve security. Peevishness, bitterness, and sourness are a few examples. We find these reactions in normal

[2] See: Meltzer, H., "Personality Problems in Managerial Groups," *Indust. Med.*, 15:429 (1946); and Cohen, M. B., and Cohen, R. A., "Personality as a Factor in Administrative Decisions," *Psychiatry*, 14:47 (1951).

life and in the pathological, and by means of them people sometimes quietly and undramatically complicate their own lives and make the lives of those around them miserable. In *The Anatomy of Melancholy* it is written that St. Austin, while passing by a village in the territory of Milan, said: "I saw a poor beggar that had got his bellyful of meat and drink, jesting and merry. I sighed and said to my friend: 'Ah me, what a deal of trouble, madness, pain, and grief do we sustain to get that secure happiness that this beggar has!' And then the friend asked me: 'Truly, would I be as this beggar was?' And I needs must answer: 'No. I must choose to be as I am, tortured with cares and fears, but out of peevishness and not out of truth.'"

Peevishness, bitterness—these are our responses to the frustration of our expectations. When our desires are great, our hopes run high and our ambitions run strong. When we meet with failure, we rail and fight against those people and things we consider obstacles in our paths. One can see here the first glimpses of the background of prejudice. Some of us react in this fashion only occasionally, but with others it may be habitual, a way of responding to frustration that has been with us so long that we scarcely know when it began or what we really are bitter about.

St. Austin noted that his bitterness was not born of truth, but rather was a bid for sympathy, a cry of "woe is me." Like many of us, he enjoyed the burden he had taken upon himself, but also like many of us, he drew upon bitterness as a shield to defend himself from this self-knowledge. Every man thinks his burden is the heaviest, Seneca tells us, but Socrates looked deeper into the hearts of men. It was Socrates' suggestion that we all take our grievances and pile them in one single heap, in preparation for sharing them more equally. Then, he said, we would learn the truth—that each man prefers his own burden and would hasten to draw it back rather than accept the burden of another.

Bitterness is a feeling tone, and we know that the word springs originally from the reaction of our taste buds. Bitter, acrid, sour—these are the taste responses of disagreeable medicines: wormwood or aloes; and the way they pucker the lips and pinch the nostrils make their outstanding quality an apt metaphor for wryness of spirit.

Bitterness, sarcasm (which has its roots in bitterness), spite, and peevishness are born of bad experiences, real or fancied. Somewhere there has been a rejection—it might have been long ago, even in childhood, but it was deeply felt —and now there is the sense of being let down in business, in love, in politics, or in anything, and an unbroken chain connects with past grievances, as the individual expects to get a "bad deal." One speaks of the "bitter end" or of a "bitter old man," but bitterness is not limited to old age or to final stages. Young people may become bitter, and we have heard of the sullen bitterness of the "beatnik," his whole way of life stating silently: "I am a stranger and afraid in a world I never made."

When it impairs function, bitterness borders on the pathologic. The grumblers and the defeatists become their own enemies, as they thwart all chances of happiness and creativity with their complaints and laments. The bitter person does not forgive, and it takes a very little for him to gravitate into a destructive group. Sometimes it seems as though the individual arranges for his own defeats, and only occasionally can one get him to admit that his bitterness is not firmly founded. To admit to peevishness, it is usually also necessary to admit to an excess of fear or ambition, pride or desire. Though King Lear cried bitterly: "How sharper than a serpent's tooth it is to have a thankless child," when his aide tried to get him to admit that he had treated Cordelia badly, he fired him. This type of reaction is not unknown today.

The waspish character, also a bitter type, has a sharp tongue, and often enough a witty one, whose verbal stings keep people at a distance and protect him from an exposure of his basic insecurities. Suspicious persons and those who feel consistently put upon and abused belong in the same general category. They have felt hurt and resentful so often that they have come to expect a disagreeable life, and now, by a simple mental mechanism, they project all the fault and blame on others, so that they themselves can feel blameless and purchase an uneasy peace. It would be well for all of us to remember that suspicion is far more apt to be wrong than right, and unfair and unjust than fair. It is a first cousin to prejudice and persecution and an unhealthy weed that grows with them. Bacon tells us that "suspicions among thoughts are like bats among birds—they ever fly by twilight. They are to be repressed or, at least, well guarded, for they cloud the mind."

Envy and Jealousy, Psychiatrically Speaking

In our social order, just as in our business lives, a great many of the material and adventitious trappings of life are deemed to be "conferrers" of prestige. They also serve as props to security if one is impoverished in direct personal or spiritual satisfactions. Not to have these props means anxiety to some people. When another person possesses something that these individuals lack, they become acutely uncomfortable and envious. Marked envy is an index of personal insecurity. The secure person is not particularly bothered by the prestige marks of others nor by the discovery of ability greater than his own. Although envy is egoism in its most unpleasant form, people who are ruled by it have somehow secretly come to appraise themselves as actually inadequate in life. Some were children of whom too much was expected; they undoubtedly had gifts, but the gifts were not enough to satisfy their parents. Some had been given extravagant pictures of themselves when young, and when they failed to live up to these impossible and extravagant heights they came to the conclusion that they were inadequate.

In the wake of such experience the individual comes to overvalue various things which seem to carry prestige and approval in society, and the search for satisfaction in worthwhile pursuits is apt to fail badly. The individual can talk only in terms of how much he has, how much he needs to have. Other people find him dreary, to say the least. When the envious person is around people who have no evidences of power and prestige, as he sees them, he may be quite comfortable and congenial for a while. But eventually the charm begins to dissipate and the need for prestige marks reasserts itself, particularly as he notes signs, real or supposed, of his losing ground with these strangers.

The dynamism of envy, unfortunately, is frequent in our culture and makes for a lot of unhappiness. Naturally the envious person seizes not upon his own inadequacy, but upon the "injustice of it all." The derogation of others is a real aspect of our culture and is itself detrimental to the development of an adequate personality. One form this takes is the emphasis on "the good things of life," which in too many instances have come to mean things, gadgets, and material conveniences. Another is the lack of attention to the more important forces of human relationships and an inadequate respect for the human personality in the frantic quest for conformity.

Prejudice

All this discussion of personal insecurity, and the hostilities, bitternesses, envies, and jealousies it fosters has led us to a consideration now of an element in personal relations which, if it is not more injurious psychically to the unfortunate possessor, is surely a more insidious and pervasive agent of destruction in the general life of society. We are speaking of prejudice. In this country, the melting pot has done wonders for us all, but it has not yet reduced everything to one smooth and tranquil brew. There are always newcomers to go into the pot, and in each generation the newcomers are looked down upon as different and, hence, somehow inferior. They become the targets for hostilities which have grown up in those who preceded them to these shores. Their children are similarly stigmatized, at least for a considerable period of time, certainly long enough for them to develop the resentments and animosities proper to the experience of prejudice and discrimination. They grow up, though; they become citizens and voters; some of them get right up there with the best of their detractors. By that time there is someone else who is foreign, a threat to all perhaps, but especially to those who have most recently managed to make the grade.

Unpleasant as bitterness is to deal with, either in oneself

or in others, it nevertheless remains in great part rational and conscious. In this it is unlike prejudice. Bitterness stems from cause, exaggerated or misconstrued though that cause may be. Prejudice, however, is something else again. Bitterness is internalized; prejudice is externalized. Bitterness is subject to reason; prejudice, once it has taken hold, is not. The word "prejudice" stems from the Latin *praejudicium*, meaning originally a judgment based on previous decisions and experiences. Now it has come to mean a prejudging, a reckoning of the situation before the facts are in, a "before thinking" response with a large emotional component and without reference to data. Opinions which are rooted in prejudice are usually sustained with great violence. Prejudice is not an instinct. So far as we can discover, it has grown with civilization. An animal, faced with a strange being, is suspicious but curious. Man, civilized man, is frequently only suspicious.

"You've got to be carefully taught to hate and fear," runs a popular song and it expresses a simple truth. Prejudice is emotional learning inculcated at such an early age that it becomes part of the central core of the personality. All is strange to us when we first enter the world. Some things we are taught are "strange good," and these become the acceptable. Others we are taught are "strange bad" and to be avoided. But rarely do we learn these things by our own experience. When we try to think of what we know at first hand, we will discover we know very little. Most of what we know we have been taught through words. Prejudice is a virus that passes by word of mouth.

As H. G. Wells noted some years ago: "The power of most of the great prejudices that strain humanity lies deeper than the intellectual level." Another author tells us that reasoning against a prejudice is like fighting against a shadow—it exhausts the reasoner without affecting the prejudice. Argument cannot do the work of instruction any more than blows can take the place of sunlight.

Of course, not all prejudices are hostile. There are unreasoning predilections for some people and things, just as there are unreasoning distastes and fear of others. In children prejudices serve as protective devices. The young are incapable of judging; enough facts are not available to them. But just as we let them know that, as they grow in intelligence and good sense, we will permit them to roam beyond their playpens and their backyard fences, so should we also be capable of letting them know that some day they should explore the world beyond the prejudices we pass on to them for better or worse.

Prejudice can be grown out of, but it is not easy. To bring the light of reason to bear upon emotional reactions requires not only enlightenment, but also an environment which encourages rationality in such matters. Prejudice is resistant to contradictory evidence because so many times it is an integral part of the individual's orientation to the world he lives in. Also, although much racial and religious prejudice is little more than slavish conformity with prevailing attitudes, enough of it serves a self-gratifying purpose to make rational argument and exhortation against it completely unavailing. Highly prejudiced people are convinced that those against whom they are prejudiced seek some advantage, and they feel completely justified and even virtuous in their efforts to keep these groups at a disadvantage.

The loyalty to the cause one espouses is frequently militant to a degree and is tantamount to an antipathy to all others. "If you are not for us, you are against us." For some people the rejection of so-called "outgroups" is an insatiable need. Verbal rejection comes easily, erupting into all sorts of irrelevant contexts and tortured logic. The more spontaneous and irrelevant the argument, the stronger the hostility behind it. Soon afterward the stage is set for trouble; all that is needed now is a little more strain and the way will be easy, particularly if a rabble-rouser enters the cast of characters.

Prejudice serves to support the individual's way of life for numerous reasons. If he is burdened and undermined by insecurity, fears, guilts, early traumatic experiences, and other similar handicaps, his instinctive response to a new frustration is aggressive assertiveness. And sources of new frustrations abound. Personal deficiencies, a harsh home atmosphere, job dissatisfactions, the strain of competition in a society that puts a high premium on material success—all provide a fertile ground for frustrations. In periods of major social and economic change—wars, depressions, government crises, etc.—when there is a general atmosphere of heightened insecurity, when rumors and speculations are rife, and when unaccustomed restrictions are being imposed, some people instinctively look for scapegoats on whom they can vent their distress. In such times, pity the ethnic or religious or other minority group that has the reputation for being different.

Few people know the real reason for their antipathy towards other groups. The reasons many give are largely rationalizations (high-sounding methods of explaining things to themselves). They do not easily recognize the fact that their hostilities towards some groups are nothing more than outlets for unresolved aggression built up within themselves through a long series of chronic frustrations never adequately handled. If these people were patently sick, their effect on the community would be less dangerous, for their bizarre behavior would soon indicate to everyone the root of their aggressiveness. But as long as they can pass off their prejudices and paranoid ideas under the cloak of community service, they are listened to gravely, applauded and supported instead of being placed under treatment. Neither can they help themselves by the more sympathetic, outgoing qualities in their own personal makeup. They might indeed feel for a particular unfortunate individual in the group that lies under their condemnation, but the group hatred is more abstract and impersonal, and is not modifiable by individual friendships. Individuals can be taken as exceptions to the deplorable company the group is supposed to consist of; hence the inane statement often heard: "Some of my best friends are, etc. . . ."

There are various sources of prejudice. The type we have been describing so far is the type which grows out of free-floating hatred, which some people carry as part and parcel of their character, built up on a long series of bitter disappointments and frustrations in their personal relationships. They have been unable to form warm ties, or have been rejected by those to whom they have felt drawn, and the pain and humiliation in all this has produced a sense of wrong so all-pervading that the individual just has to hate someone.

Another source of prejudice is the anxiety we have mentioned above. Chronic anxiety alerts one to the possibility of danger from any direction. Feeling inadequate, the individual is fearful of life and even suspicious of those who seem more competent. But anxiety and inadequacy are things to be ashamed of. They have to be masked, or at least covered up by some emotion seemingly useful. So some of these anxiety-ridden people seize on the convenient objects of fear in the environment—the outgroups with their supposedly evil, menacing ways—to serve as scapegoats. Communist governments do this; whenever there is likelihood of internal trouble, they direct attention outside to distract the people and furnish a cause under which all can unite.

Though the main source of character-conditioned anxiety is the experience of early years, the adult years, too, are potent additional sources. There may be too few jobs for too many competitors, and the outgroup or groups are felt to be an unjustified threat. For the most part, the threat is not a genuine one at all. The marginal man is upset at any signs of ambition or progress on the part of a member of the outgroup. It is necessary to keep down these upstarts, and so feel more secure as well as superior. One has to feel superior to somebody.

The need for status, prestige, and self-esteem, therefore, is at the bottom of much of the prejudice we see all around us. Most people want to be more important than they are, and they hang on grimly to whatever shreds of status they may happen to have. This effort can bring about an almost automatic disparagement of others. It has been said that the easiest idea to sell anyone is that he is better than somebody else. This is reminiscent of E. M. Forster's *A Passage to India*, a classic novel on prejudice, in which several Englishmen are planning a party. The list of invited guests is growing long. Some Moslems and Hindus are included. One of the Englishmen remarks in consternation: "See here now, we must exclude someone from our gathering or we shall be left with nothing."

If we wished sincerely and deeply to employ them, we have the knowledge and the power to eliminate prejudice against other members of our own species. Experiments in offsetting the contagious prejudices of unreasoning parents by impartial information and knowledge have worked with simple ease in the few instances where they have been undertaken. But as fast as the prejudices have been lessened, various forces in our culture have operated to build them up again. Reason does not seem to be a powerful enough weapon in such a fight—emotion is demanded—and so, prejudice, bitterness, and mob-mindedness are encouraged.

"Mob-mindedness"—this term was used by Dr. Edward A. Strecker, a famous psychiatrist. A mob is a group which has beheaded individual personalities. As Strecker pointed out, we usually think of a mob as violent and destructive, a crowd as unruly, and a group as a dignified gathering. Definition by numerical strength is not the test, however; it is the dilution of rationality that is the test of mob-mindedness. No matter how large or small the group, if its components do not retain the full use of their rational faculties and perspectives, in the face of the temptation to go along with the more emotionally driven element, it is a mob. Most people, Strecker stated, live beyond their spiritual means, and the support of the emotions of others is often vitally important for them.

In crowds, we must remember, prejudice becomes active delusion, and bitterness becomes inverted to frame slogans that at first glance seem of a highly moral nature. Hitler's cry of *"lebensraum"* aroused a whole people to acts of brutality, for which they evaded responsibility by rationalization, and by high-sounding explanations of their purpose. The police state of Russia, with its dreadful regimentation of the individual, is sometimes accepted by people because of the benevolence of its slogans. Rationalization is such a simple and commonplace reality-evading device that only when it is employed by demagogues and mob leaders do we realize its pathological implications.

Unfortunately, we know less about tolerance than we do about prejudice and discrimination. It appears, however, that tolerant children are likely to come from tolerant homes, in which there is an understanding and a loving, rather than a depriving, atmosphere. Tolerant people tend to believe that we ourselves are responsible for our destiny. They do not care for values which are exclusionary. They pursue their way with a reasonable serenity. They are able to do so because they find security in the realistic handling of inner conflicts and social transactions. They take pleasure in variety and individuality. The development of mature and democratic personalities is largely a matter of the development of inner security, which is not at the mercy of intolerable threats of external or internal origin.

If, after wading about in all of this unpleasantness, we feel the need for a refreshing shower bath, we might remember that everyone has ups and downs, good days and bad days. Some days we remain tranquil and steady for a considerable period, but from time to time our state may change, perhaps suddenly, for better or worse. We may find ourselves "down in the mouth," moody, ill-tempered, worrying too much, or working without enthusiasm. These fluctuations are normal; like the changes of seasons, they create a healthy climate for our growth. A remark attributed to Ruskin is enlightening:

> I believe that the test of a truly great person is humility. I do not mean by humility doubts of his own ability. But really great men have a curious feeling that greatness is not in them, but through them, and they see something divine in every other man and are endlessly, foolishly and incredibly merciful.

If all of us could be "foolishly merciful," there would be very little bitterness or prejudice, and perhaps even fewer instances of neuroses and psychoses.

X

STUMBLING BLOCKS
AND MISUNDERSTANDINGS

Just so, the good or the evil is not in the vision but in the person who sees it and depends upon his profiting by it and his humility. Where there is humility no harm can possibly ensue even though the vision come from the devil. And where there is no humility there can be no profit even if the vision come from God.

St. Teresa of Avila[1]

From what we have seen thus far there has been little to justify fear or hostility to psychiatry as a discipline. Certainly through its efforts countless numbers of human beings have been rehabilitated and returned to society, who earlier might only have been relegated to institutions scarcely fit to house them. Though it has only partially succeeded in educating the public and securing its backing in its efforts and hopes, it has made notable advances in understanding the feelings and reactions of the mentally ill. It has emphasized and re-emphasized the great importance of early childhood impressions and their influence upon the later life of the individual. It has accented the great need for security and affection which every child requires, and it has emphasized this not only to parents but also to those in charge of institutions, schools, orphanages, and hospitals.

Before psychiatry produced its records, it was common belief that all that was needed by a child at home or in an institution was food, shelter, clothing, education, and moral guidance. Psychiatry had the temerity to state, however, that all of this can be given and yet the upbringing prove to be a

[1] *Book of the Foundations,* Ch. VIII, "The Complete Works of St. Teresa of Jesus," E. Alison Peers, 1946, Vol. III, p. 41.

miserable failure if warmth and affection are lacking. Creature comforts, discipline, and rectitude will produce conformism, but they cannot produce a healthful atmosphere if they are devoid of love and understanding.

Psychiatry, we have learned, is an empirical discipline and, as such, it is neutral with respect to religious ideas, no matter how religious its practitioners. It is not of its essence or within its scope to preach or teach any philosophy, creed, or moral code. In spite of this, however, it frequently, by means of its knowledge of emotions, helps individuals to better fulfill their religious duties, and it may even rescue them from superficial forms of religiosity and aid in developing a more genuine faith. It maintains that a person deeply enmeshed in neurosis and battered about by inhibitions, scruples, and compulsions can hardly be a capable functioning member of society nor lead a truly religious life. Seen in this light, psychiatry, far from being a danger to religious life, may even become a strong ally. As a medical specialty its task is to help sick people; it does not provide norms of behavior, but it does point out how certain actions and reactions lead to certain psychological impasses, and what must be done, therefore, to relieve the situation.

Admittedly, at times people have been prone to overrate the efficacy of psychiatry. They have also mixed their own ideas with the widely misconceived notion that all of man's life should be smooth and free of conflict and difficulty. This is a lay point of view. Conflicts are not symptoms and psychiatry is not a panacea; of itself, psychiatry cannot cure evils, whether they be personal or social, or assuage real guilt, nor does it pretend to do so. It does not presume to change various social ills, and the idea of a world ruled over or arranged by psychiatry is the sheerest nonsense.

In line with this present trend of thought, it should be emphatically stated that the psychiatrist neither persuades nor indoctrinates his patients, nor does he try to get patients to adopt his views. As Dr. Rudolf Allers states: "It cannot be the task of the psychotherapist to 'convert' his patients. However strong his convictions and however good his reasons for them, they have no place in the psychotherapeutic situation as such. If some belief of a more or less religious nature should prove necessary for the patient's return to normality and a satisfactory form of existence, a truly neutral formula must be found which is independent of the convictions of the psychiatrist and patient alike, that is, a definition of the 'minimum requirements' to be met."[2]

"Some people of strong and sharply defined religious convictions," he continues, "feel that to limit oneself to such minimum requirements would be an improper compromise. Anything less than the whole truth, as they see it, appears almost equivalent to falsehood, for if one knows the truth he has an obligation to proclaim it. Understandable as this viewpoint may be, it is both unfounded in theory and untenable in practice. These overzealous folk would do well to reflect on the words of St. Paul about the milk to be given to infants and the solid food suitable for adults. The minimum requirements should be such that they are acceptable to everyone, whatever his religious training and whatever his attitudes and prejudices."

The belief of some that psychiatry encourages laxity in morals by viewing immoral behavior as the effect of unconscious factors, instinctual constellations, and childhood experiences has been answered en route in this volume, but perhaps it would be well to repeat here the words of one of the nation's outstanding psychiatrists, Dr. Karl Menninger, on this score: "There is a common assumption that psychoanalysts favor sexual promiscuity and that they encourage people not to have any sense of guilt about it. This assumption is false, and its reiteration is a lie, a slander, a canard, and a misrepresentation of facts. Freud refuted this charge fifty years ago, and no honest, intelligent, informed person can allege it."[3] This statement should allay that fear for a while.

It is obvious by now that many misunderstandings of psychiatry are due to ignorance. That sharp reproaches may be

[2] Allers, R., Faith, Reason and Modern Psychiatry (New York: P. J. Kenedy & Co., 1955), p. 49.
[3] Menninger, K., "Religio Psychiatrici," chapter in book A Psychiatrist's World, the Selected Papers of Karl Menninger, Viking Press, N.Y., p. 782 (1959).

or may have been justified in some instances is certainly a possibility—nay, even a fact—but by the same token it is wrong to generalize from those instances. Father Dominic Bañes,[4] one of the advisers of St. Teresa of Avila, said: "When we see a very fine picture, we always value it, even if we know it has been painted by a very wicked man, and we should never allow the identity of the painter to hinder our devotion." Psychiatry—its nature, its procedures, and its aims—cannot be judged carelessly; more knowledge of its overall functions and accomplishments is required than most of its critics possess. Some of the more obvious misunderstandings which caused a great deal of difficulty in the past were concerned with such problems as determinism, guilt, and scruples, and they merit our consideration here.

Determinism

It is understandable that the early doctrines of Freudian psychoanalysis, at the time they were promulgated, were met with shocked surprise. Not only did these doctrines disturb the sensibilities and threaten the beliefs of a Victorian age populace, but they were put forth with that aggressive air and belligerence which sometimes accompanies the proclamations of advanced thinkers. "There is among some exponents of new ideas a noisome excess of enthusiasm which rarely fails to vex even the most amiable of men. Often there is also an aggressiveness which, in effect at least, is not unlike the threatening noises animals make to protect their young from real or imagined attack."[5]

It was inevitable, too, that these pronouncements would arouse a storm of protest and even ridicule, and, when they did, that the proponents would react by becoming defensive and isolating themselves. Whenever a minority group or the adherents of a specific doctrine withdraw, they develop a state-of-siege mentality. This serves to weld the adherents into a tighter unity and to promote vitality and self-reliance. It also usually spells the end of satisfactory communication

---

[4] Theologian at the University of Alcalá in or about 1567.

[5] Greenland, C., *Canadian Psychiatric Journal*, Vol. 6 (1961), No. 3, p. 133.

with others, particularly with those thought to be inimical to the doctrine. This train of events followed in the case of psychoanalysis. As its little coteries were formed, they separated themselves from their medical colleagues, and the breach which occurred a half-century ago has not completely closed even to this day. It is evidenced on the contemporary scene by the continued separation of psychoanalytic institutes from the mainstream of medical and university life. Until fairly recently this isolation, coupled with the suspicion and misunderstandings of those whose ideas are in opposition to the discipline, has had the effect of delaying clear, calm, logical discussion of the various doctrines about which there is controversy.

One of the doctrines which to all intents and purposes looked as if it would be productive of serious trouble was the doctrine of rigid determinism, which was considered to be a requisite for understanding the new science of psychoanalysis, even as it was said to be prerequisite for the understanding and appreciation of all science. This was indeed a serious stumbling block, for as some took it, it was that same concept which had been a source of conflict for ages. It held "first, that our actions change nothing in the events of life which were firmly established through causal connection, and second, that man is not free to dispose of his own will and choose between good and evil in his actions."[6]

The promulgation of this concept seemed to be a dangerous error. Here was a form of fatalism which apparently held that all of man's volitions were invariably determined by preexisting circumstances, and on the surface it appeared to make the concepts of moral obligation, responsibility, merit, striving, etc. illusory. Furthermore, a threat to legal responsibility and law and order was implied. It was feared that this deterministic doctrine would imply an "encouragement to irresponsibility, and that crimes will go unpunished and criminals unconvicted if the culprits can be successfully defended on the basis that they could not help doing what they

[6] Bleuler, E., "Die Naturwissenschaftlichen Grundlagen der Ethik," *Schweitzer Archiv. für Neurologie und Psychiatrie*, Vol. XXXVIII (1936), pp. 177–206.

did. They wonder how it can be decided which human acts are free and therefore punishable, and which acts are determined and therefore unpunishable."[7]

Apropos of this, it did seem as though Freud had categorically denied the existence of liberty when he said: "You have an illusion of psychic freedom within you which you do not wish to give up. I regret to say that on this point I find myself in sharpest opposition to your views."[8] And again: "Anyone thus breaking away from the determinism of natural phenomena at any single point has thrown over the whole scientific *Weltanschauung*."[9]

Paul Schilder, a brilliant follower of Freud, emphasized Freud's belief in the absolute determinism of psychic experiences and his refusal to see any freedom in the stream of consciousness. "Psychoanalysis," he said, "believes that whenever there is an inner psychic connection between two experiences there is also a causal connection . . . there is no difference between so-called psychic causability and physical causability."[10]

There were various other analysts who emphasized the same ideas, those of the Freudian school and those who had deviated from it. A. A. Brill, Freud's pioneer spokesman in America, felt he could give the concept a creditable ancestry by tracing it from the early Greeks, down through the Christian fathers to the modern philosophers, although some of the steps along the way are fairly disputable.[11]

Aaron J. Rosanoff, an American psychiatrist, expressed the view that the "phenomena of the will, like other natural phenomena, are subject to natural laws and are determined by antecedents for the most part beyond the control of individual responsibility. . . . The scientific point of view presupposes

[7] Knight, R. P., "Determinism, Freedom and Psychotherapy," *Psychiatry*, Vol. IX (1946), pp. 251–62.

[8] Freud, S., *Introductory Lectures in Psychoanalysis* (London: George Allen and Unwin, 1922).

[9] *Ibid.*

[10] Schilder, P., *Psychoanalysis, Man and Society* (New York: North, 1951).

[11] Brill, A. A., "Determinism in Psychiatry and Psychoanalysis," *American Journal of Psychiatry*, 95:597–620 (1938).

an irrevocable commitment to the concept of determinism in nature as an article of faith."[12]

All of this certainly seemed to be plain enough—determinism was the order of the day in psychoanalysis. There apparently was no place for the incidental, the casual, the fortuitous, and, viewed in one fashion, none for free will either. Whatever actions seemed to indicate free choice would be found on close inspection to be unconsciously determined; the causal factors were operative but the individual was not aware of them.

In reality, however, things were not that simple, even from the psychoanalytic point of view. All the while that the doctrine of rigid determinism was being preached, the analysts were busy trying by means of psychotherapy to achieve in their patients "a subjective sense of freedom—indeed a real freedom which is not merely an illusion."[13] Dr. Robert Knight asked the question: "From the viewpoint of the therapist, how can he be both a scientific psychologist, who recognizes the rigorous determinism in the operation of the causal factors which have made his patients what they are, and yet a psychotherapist, who expects them to change and is often able to help them change?"[14] Knight sees the paradox as more apparent than real.

These various chinks in what at first seemed to be the strong armor of psychic determinism should have given a hint that something was wrong and perhaps that the various opponents were not talking about the same thing. Brill, for instance, while he was assembling data to prove the necessity of determinism in this new doctrine and sometimes fitting the pieces of the mosaic together by procrustean methods, was at the same time indignant about some of the interpretations which were being made of the concept.[15] He was particularly wroth at the idea that anyone would introduce "the hackneyed arguments that believing in determinism

[12] Rosanoff, A., *Manual of Psychiatry* (7th ed.; New York: Wiley and Sons, 1938).

[13] Knight, *loc. cit.*

[14] *Ibid.*

[15] Brill, *op. cit.*, p. 608.

means one is not responsible for his acts, etc. I will simply say that neither Spinoza nor Freud nor Bleuler has ever expressed such ideas." He then quotes Bleuler, as spokesman for the others. "We need not be concerned," Bleuler tells us, "about the kind of causes that would express themselves in our impulses. It is essential only that we should will energetically, which [sic] must be demanded of the psyche by the determinist as much as and as emphatically as by the indeterminist. To accept such excuses as: 'I just happen to be that way'; 'I cannot act differently'; 'I have such an impulse'; or, 'My father was also that way,' is absolutely wrong" . . . such excuses, Bleuler found, were regularly "given by people of lazy or criminal temperament. . . . Hence, the right answer to people of that sort is that they really cannot know whether they are incapable of doing the right thing because they have never tried hard enough."

It is obviously a bit difficult to get this statement together with rigid determinism because, if things are strictly and invariably caused, how can the person change by trying harder? Freud also made comparable statements, which were hard to reconcile with strict determinism. "After all," he noted, "analysis does not set out to abolish the possibility of morbid reactions, but to give the patient's ego freedom to choose one way or the other."[16] Add to this the profound respect Freud had for reason, which he sought all his life to liberate from the fetters of the non-realistic fogs of a malfunctioning psychic apparatus, and we are left with the strong impression that he was not denying free will as the philosophers and theologians define it.

We are certainly facing here an interesting dilemma. Sometimes Freud explicitly insisted on psychic determinism and denied free will, and at other times he expressly spoke of human freedom, and all the time he labored in a context that supposed freedom to be not only attainable but highly desirable. Some analysts have emphasized the deterministic character of psychoanalytic doctrine, some have insisted it

[16] Freud, S., *The Ego and the Id* (London: The Hogarth Press, 1927).

in no way militates against human free will—the tension, in short, which Freud left in his system has not been clearly resolved by his successors. Whenever we meet a manifest dilemma of such proportions in a system of thought, we can be sure of one thing, that there are powerful arguments working on both sides of the question and producing a virtual impasse. And such is the case here. On the one hand are the requirements of scientific procedure; on the other, the evidences of common experience and the demands of human dignity. If determinism is not accepted as a postulate in scientific enquiry, evidence, perhaps of prime significance, is subject to being dismissed as capricious and fortuitous, to the ruin of scientific rigor. In psychological investigations in which the materials presented are so enormously complex and so often bizarre, the temptation to throw out pertinent facts is more real perhaps than in any other science, and psychology has in fact often suffered from this in the past. Freud was right in insisting that every single thought, emotion, mood, affect, idea, fantasy, etc. which appears in the minds of any man, normal or abnormal, must be accepted as caused by some preceding event, without which it cannot in any way be comprehended. To compromise this principle, which in Freud's hands was tremendously fruitful, would be to open psychology from the beginning to serious defects of omission or distortion.

But does this deny free will? Freud himself indicated the sense in which strict scientific determinism is compatible with the facts of human freedom. The most vigorous defenders of free will would not claim that an act of free will proceeds from nothing, that it has no antecedents which explain how it came to be. Free willing is not willing in a vacuum; every act of free will follows definite motivations, or else freely willed acts are meaningless. Therefore, looking at an act of free will *after it has occurred,* we can see why it occurred, we can see the motives which prompted it. Looking at an act of free will *before it occurs,* we cannot see whether or not it will occur, for while we see the motivations which are possible, we cannot predict which ones will be freely chosen. Freud describes this situation thus:

But at this point, we become aware of a state of things which also confronts us in many instances in which light has been thrown by psychoanalysis on a mental process. So long as we trace the developments from their final outcome backwards, the chain of events appears continuous, and we feel we have gained an insight which is completely satisfactory or even exhaustive. But if we proceed the reverse way, if we start from the premises inferred from analysis and try to follow these up to the final result, then we no longer get the impression of an inevitable sequence of events which could not have been otherwise determined. We notice at once that there might have been another result, and that we might have been just as well able to understand and explain the latter. The synthesis is thus not so satisfactory as the analysis, in other words, from a knowledge of the premises we could not have foretold the nature of the result. . . . Hence the chain of causation can always be recognized with certainty if we follow the line of analysis, whereas to predict it along the line of synthesis is impossible.[17]

Psychology is thus not like the other sciences, in which, when the causal sequence has been discovered, it applies both for explanation and prediction. In psychology, a causal sequence explains what has happened, but it cannot foretell what will happen in the next similar event, and the difference lies in freedom of choice.[18]

In effect, then, we may, and should, accept scientific determinism when studying psychological data, accepting the principle that every psychological phenomenon which occurs comes from a cause. Simultaneously, we can accept free will, asserting that before they have occurred, many psychological phenomena are subject to free disposition by the human agent. And this seems to solve the dilemma.

[17] Freud, S., "A Case of Homosexuality in a Woman," *Collected Papers*, Vol. 2, pp. 226–27.

[18] For a more complete study of this reconciliation of scientific determinism and free will, see Dr. Alden L. Fisher's "Freud and the Image of Man," *Proceedings of the American Catholic Philosophical Association* (1961), pp. 45–77.

There is no question but that the problem of freedom from a psychological viewpoint has been somewhat confused, and that pitched battles between overzealous psychologists and legalistic moralists did little to clarify matters. Père Noël Mailloux points out the problem stemming from the moralists' camp: "The close contact which existed between the psychological and moral sciences in their early phases of development had been lost and slowly the legalistic conception of morality prevailed. . . . The only condition on the part of the subject, which kept its importance, was the intellectual capacity to discriminate between good and evil, the awareness of what he was doing and the consent given to such behavior. . . . Unfortunately, we must state that the subjective conditions of the individual conscience remained almost entirely foreign to its consideration. . . . So long as such an attitude was maintained, the moralistic jurist had no use for psychology and could not avoid considering it as an unwelcome complication."[19]

If there has been one good result from the controversy over free will, it has been to focus attention back on the psychological aspects of moral problems. This is not a new point of view, but it is one which needs re-emphasis from time to time. Catholic doctrine has always held that in pathological situations the freedom of the human will may be diminished or even non-operative; a point, for instance, to which St. Thomas Aquinas repeatedly made reference in his great synthesis of moral theology. But this point of view was somewhat obscured during the seventeenth, eighteenth, and nineteenth centuries, when rationalistic systems of philosophy were in the ascendancy, and it fell to psychoanalysis, with its insistence on psychic determinism, to present the evidence from which a just balance could eventually be restored. Pope Pius XII gives a concise statement of this just balance: "Those psychic dynamisms may be in the soul in man; they are not, however, the soul nor the man. They are energies of considerable intensity, perhaps, but nature has entrusted their

[19] Mailloux, N., O.P., *Canadian Journal of Psychology*, Vol. 7 (1953), No. 1.

direction to the center post to the spiritual soul endowed with intellect and which is normally capable of governing these energies. That these energies may exercise pressure upon one activity does not necessarily signify that they compel it. To deprive the soul of its central place would be to deny an ontological and psychic reality. The question as to whether man is determined or free, then, is seen as superfluous, for he is both."

Guilt

The problem of guilt has been a stumbling block for some in their attitude toward psychiatry, for they persist in the belief that psychiatrists minimize guilt and remove patients' inhibitions so that they will not be concerned with infractions of the moral law.[20] This, of course, is far from the truth. With moral feelings of guilt due to sin in the theological sense, activated by the patient's conscience, the psychiatrist is not concerned. His concern is with unjustified or excessive guilt, neurotic guilt, which is the product of a harsh, punitive superego, and which is activated by unconscious causes.

Confronted with a discrepancy between the good and the morally right, which their consciences dictate, and their actual performance, of which they are ashamed, most normal people experience guilt or guilt feelings.[21] Ethical and moral

[20] "Unfortunately, the logical end term of much modern psychiatric theory is that there is no human responsibility—a false conclusion and one which reduces man to the level of Pavlov's dog. It is the aim of such theorists to abolish the feeling of guilt as something evil in itself"—et seq. Dom Peter Flood, O.S.B., B.A., M.D., M.C.H., J.C.L., in editor's foreword to Mental Hygiene and Christian Principles by Père Snoeck, S.J. (Cork: Mercier Press, Ltd.)

[21] Many misunderstandings have arisen between psychiatrists and psychologists and theologians because the former often say "guilt" when they mean "feelings of guilt" or "guilt sense." Guilt is an objective state, existing when the individual has broken a law or a moral imperative. Guilt sense is the awareness of a transgression and the feeling that the individual has about it. As Paul E. Meehl remarks in his "Treatment of Guilt Feelings" (published in Three Joint Symposia from the ACPA-APA Meetings of 1957, 1958, 1959, New York, American Catholic Psychological Association

standards of behavior are usually acquired as soon as a person develops enough to act more than instinctively and has sufficient awareness of himself to stand back and see his behavior as others see it. Granted normal intelligence, it seems impossible that he should not come to see that some ways of acting and thinking are better than others, and that he should feel "right" when he chooses the better way and "wrong" when he does not.

The capacity to experience guilt feelings develops comparatively early in the young child. The really young infant, of course, cannot feel guilt, only discomfort or comfort. He is hungry or uncomfortable for some reason and he expresses his discomfort by crying. Soon someone comes, performs what is necessary to restore his comfort, and he goes happily back to sleep. In time the child comes to associate this relief with the presence of another person and to recognize this person. With still further development, he comes to see himself as an individual, separate person, and this nurturing figure as another person, with feelings of her own. Sometimes she feels approving and loving and he feels secure and comfortable; sometimes she feels disapproving and less inclined to show love, and he feels anxious and uncomfortable. The child learns which actions bring approval and which bring disapproval, and for the sake of his own comfort avoids those actions which will evoke disapproval, at least while mother is watching. In addition to wanting to please his mother—and later his father—the child also wants to be like them. If he can do both at once, he gains twice. Thus, he may brush his teeth to be like mother and to please mother. These twin desires—to please and to be like—lead to the incorporation or the taking within the child of the parents' standards. Psychoanalysts use the term "superego" to connote the part of the self made up of the incorporated parental standards and concerned with examining the self and decid-

---

[1960]): "If a pastor is told by his parishioner that Dr. So-and-So is 'taking away my guilt,' the pastor understandably begins to wonder where Dr. So-and-So acquired the power of the keys, that he can absolve people from guilt by psychotherapy."

ing whether it is measuring up to these standards or falling short of them. They agree that the individual feels guilty and anxious when there is a discrepancy between the standards and actual behavior. They agree, too, that though the superego and moral conscience are not the same, one cannot deny that there is a close-knit connection between them.

The mature conscience appears when in the course of normal development the individual thinks and rethinks early incorporated standards, which he has learned in his home, his church, and his school, and of which he is becoming more fully aware. He considers them rationally and compares them with the standards of others, and tries to grasp their real meaning. He may alter some of his values. Finally he arrives at a set of standards of conduct and a set of values which he consciously accepts and wants to live up to. If he fails, he feels guilty; this is a normal guilt sense, of little concern to the psychiatrist. Unless it is extreme, it does not cause psychiatric symptoms. Among the characteristics of this sense of guilt are the facts that it is accompanied by feelings of remorse and regret, rather than self-hate, and that it is assuaged by expiation and reparation where possible, rather than by self-punishment. The person who has feelings of guilt of this kind wants forgiveness, not punishment.

To understand some of the pathological vicissitudes of the guilt sense which are properly the psychiatrist's concern, it is necessary to break down the concept of the superego and to see some of the different forms it may take. Paul Kramer speaks of three parts of the superego: the ego ideal, the benign superego, and the prohibiting superego.[22] The ego ideal, he says, represents what the person wants to be and derives from his childhood picture of his parents as he saw them or as he wanted them to be. The benign superego derives from the incorporated image of the loving and helpful parents. The prohibiting superego derives from the images of the hating and prohibiting parents. Normally these parts are united into a smoothly functioning whole, which

[22] Kramer, P., "Note on One of the Preoedipal Roots of the Superego," *J. Am. Psychoanalyt. A.,* 6:38–46 (January 1958).

supports the individual in his attempts to adjust himself to his own needs and the requirements of the external world.

It may happen, however, that the hating and punitive superego assumes prominence, while the benign superego is overshadowed. This development is the most frequent cause of the pathological guilt sense which is the concern of psychiatrists. It may come about when the parents are overstrict, overcritical, and unappreciative of the child's real achievements, punishing what is bad and letting what is good pass by without comment. As many psychiatrists have pointed out, this part of the superego may derive added strength from the child's own hostility toward the parents. Such hostility cannot be acknowledged, because the child who hates his parents must fear being abandoned by them and he needs them. Therefore he may project or attribute these feelings of hatred to his parents, and end up incorporating images of his parents which contain much more hatred than the actual parents felt. Since the young child also has feelings of omnipotence, the incorporated parents, with their added measure of hatred, may also seem to have a magic destructiveness.[23]

The subject of the formation of the superego, especially the hostile superego, is a complex one; the above explanation cannot cover all of its facets. It is generally agreed, however, that this type of superego is largely unconscious and utterly irrational in its demands. The individual feels its effects largely in the form of feelings of guiltiness, badness, and unworthiness, a need to be punished, and a host of neurotic symptoms.

We will not delve into the subject of the origin of neurosis

[23] Some authors identify the superego wholly with this hostile, punishing agency. Alexander A. Schneiders, in "Clinical Manifestations of Guilt" (published in *Three Joint Symposia from the ACPA-APA Meetings of 1957, 1958, 1959*, New York, American Catholic Psychological Association [1960]), pp. 7–18, says that the superego is derived from a sadistic parental image, whether the sadism was in the parents or was a projection of the child's own hostility. Gerhart Piers and Milton B. Singer say much the same thing in "Shame and Guilt; a Psychoanalytic and a Cultural Study" (Springfield, Ill.: Charles C. Thomas, 1953).

here, except to say that the presence in an individual of a hostile, punitive superego plays a large part in this disorder. Every person must find some way of meeting his instinctual needs, while meeting the demands of his superego and living in peace with his external surroundings. If the superego is too punitive, if it insists that the instincts are automatically wrong and that even the passing and unwelcome thought of a forbidden thing is terrible, if it makes inconsistent demands, then the individual is bound to repress some of his desires and ideas, to drive them out of consciousness altogether. The repressed material and the superego, both largely unconscious, war with each other, and the results of the battle in consciousness are: the neurotic symptoms which express the forbidden instincts; the denial of them; the punishment for them; and the guilt, shame, anxiety, and other noxious emotions, which represent the smoke rising from the field.

Because there has been some confusion and disagreement about the relationship of these noxious emotions, we will make an attempt to distinguish them here. As Gerhart Piers and Milton B. Singer point out,[24] *guilt* arises when there is a discrepancy between the moral demands of the superego and actual behavior. The ego ideal on the other hand is concerned with the total image a person presents to the world, including not only his moral and ethical behavior, but also many other qualities, such as wit, intelligence, athletic ability, etc.; a failure to live up to the demands of the ego ideal leads to *shame*. It is also possible in this conflictful world for the ego ideal and the ethical requirements of the superego to be in contradiction. A young man may have a superego which demands good behavior and an ego ideal, fostered by his youthful companions, which requires him to engage in questionable moral behavior. If he does the latter, he feels guilt; if he does not, he may be called "yellow" or "chicken" and is ashamed. A person whose standards are not established may alternate between guilt and shame.

Guilt is closely related to anxiety and fear. Fear is the emo-

[24] Piers and Singer, *op. cit.*

tional reaction to a threat to one's security and well-being. We learned earlier that in a state of fear the danger is outside the self. A similar feeling of apprehension, but more lasting in its effects, is called anxiety. This is felt when there is a danger from within—a threat that unacceptable impulses will erupt into consciousness and that the individual will then be subject to criticism from a hostile superego or guilt feelings. Guilt feelings are self-reproaches for what has happened within the person or without. An important part of anxiety is the warning that such painful feelings may occur.

Guilt is also related closely to self-hate, which is strongly felt in most mental disorders. The maladjusted person may give the impression to the layman that he feels only self-love, because he so often shows little real concern for others; but what he really shows is preoccupation with self, rather than self-love. His conflicts are so intense that he must be occupied with them and he has little energy left over for other people; but he is more often preoccupied with his supposed badness and inadequacy than with loving himself. What looks like self-love may be his defensive attempts to prove that he is not really so bad as all that. His feelings of self-hate are partly feelings of guilt from failure to live up to the impossible demands of the sadistic superego, partly feelings of inadequacy and shame resulting from failure to live up to the ego ideal, and partly the result of a variety of other factors.

As has already been suggested, the guilt sense, often unconscious, which derives from the workings of a sadistic superego is characterized largely by a need for punishment, rather than a need to make reparation and win back love.[25] The hostile superego demands severe and repeated punishment; to escape these demands the individual may commit a real crime, so as to incur real punishment, which will be more bearable and more comfortable than the vaguely un-

[25] "The superego never says: 'Go and sin no more.' It merely says: 'Wait until I get you next time,' or 'It is all right to be sorry, but you must pay for it time and time again until the end of your earthly days.'" Zilboorg, G., "The Sense of Guilt," *Proceedings of the Institute for the Clergy on Problems in Pastoral Psychiatry,* ed. A. A. Schneiders (New York: Fordham University Press, 1955), p. 21.

derstood inner torments. He will make sure that he is caught, once he has performed the illegal act; if the police somehow miss detecting him, he will go to them and confess. Unfortunately, this need for punishment is not akin to real remorse, which would lead to the cessation of guilt-provoking activity. On the contrary, the individual who has succeeded in punishing himself or in getting himself punished by society may feel that the score is now even and that he is justified in engaging in activities that would normally make him feel guilty.

We have probably all seen children who, egged on by an obscure sense of guilt, keep provoking their parents and getting worse and worse in their behavior, while the parents try to be gentle and understanding, until the parents finally explode and administer a sound spanking. The guilt is absolved, the air is cleared, and for a while all is well. However, the child who is disciplined too much by spankings may come to feel that it is quite all right for him to do anything so long as he submits to the spankings that he receives in retaliation.

There are many other manifestations of a pathological guilt sense, or need for punishment. They appear most clearly in the "criminals out of a sense of guilt," and in people who repeatedly hurt themselves in accidents. They are seen also in people who arrange their lives so that they can have no meaningful success or satisfaction, because they feel that they deserve to be punished and do not deserve to enjoy themselves.

In obsessive neuroses guilt feelings may be both expressed and avoided by constant washing of the hands or other compulsive rituals. In depression the guilt feelings and the punishment meted out by the superego are fully accepted and directed against the self. In psychosomatic disorders emotions which must be avoided or given no expression through words or through the musculature because of their guilt-provoking qualities find expression in changes of the blood vessels, mucous membranes, etc., and thus lead to somatic changes which automatically provide punishment for the subconsciously contemplated "crimes." Hysterical symptoms are an even clearer expression of guilt feelings. A woman with sexual impulses toward a certain man, for example, may develop a paralysis of the legs, which prevents her from walking toward the man, makes her ineligible for marriage in any event, and punishes her for her impulses, while keeping the whole problem out of awareness.

Apart from clinical syndromes, there are numerous specific mechanisms for dealing with guilt feelings. We have mentioned projection, the attributing of a guilt-producing impulse to someone else. People who are ridden by unconscious guilt feelings very often become aggressively self-righteous, constantly finding fault with others and becoming noted for their censoriousness. Other people, by pointed self-sacrifice and doing for others, try to induce guilt in others so that they will not have to feel it themselves. Someone once said of a certain woman: "She's the sort of woman who lives for others; you can tell the others by their hunted expression." Guilt feelings can also take the form of exaggerated scrupulousness over things that do not really matter.

Much of the task of the psychotherapist has to do with the uncovering of unconscious guilt feelings and bringing the causes of them into the open. He may demonstrate to the patient, if the patient denies them, by the nature of the patient's fantasies and dreams. On the one hand, the therapist must try to bring into awareness the impulses which are rejected as guilt-provoking, so that the patient can be conscious of just what his problem is, of what conflict demands a solution. On the other hand, he must work toward modifying the harshness and intolerance of the superego so that the patient, with new understanding, can work out a more rational solution for his problems. Some patients have "borrowed" unconscious guilt feelings; that is, they have identified with some person out of their past lives and assumed guilt belonging properly to that person. The therapist can be unusually successful in alleviating guilt feelings when this is the case.

Another type of reaction which therapists must deal with increasingly is the unconscious sense of guilt seen in a person who has intellectually repudiated the ethical system within which he was raised, but whose superego has not cooperated in this intellectual process. Such a person may, for example, be engaged in some immoral situation and aggressively claim that he sees nothing wrong in it, but still he suffers from heart or stomach disorders or other signs of an unconscious sense of guilt. He must be made aware of the real situation if these symptoms are to be removed.

Situations may be encountered in which the task of the psychiatrist is to encourage guilt feelings in the patient. There is a condition, fortunately somewhat rare in its purest forms, but widespread in its partial manifestations, called psychopathy. Psychopaths, as we noted earlier, live entirely to and for themselves, unable to feel any regard or concern for other people as people. They treat others as objects to be manipulated for their own purposes, without guilt or anxiety over their behavior. They are also unable to see the long-term results of their actions and any possible advantage to themselves in obeying laws and dealing honestly with others. They develop rationalizations to account for the fact that their lives are not actually very satisfying or successful, being interrupted as they are by jail sentences or abrupt but necessary changes of address. Psychotherapy with psychopaths is difficult, but to the extent that it can be successful, it depends on building up some kind of relationship with them, encouraging them to feel some kind of trust and affection for the therapist, and then encouraging some kind of guilt sense and anxiety on the basis of this relationship.

The therapist also may see the children of parents who believe that they should not discipline nor punish a child nor do anything to hamper his free self-expression, nor try to impose their standards on him. They believe vaguely that, if they always show love and support for the child, no matter what he does, he will grow up to be free of neurosis, happy, loving, and possessed of a reasonable set of standards for good behavior. His parents cannot help but feel anxious and disapproving about some things he does, however, no matter how hard they try to show constant and undeviating love. The child is now faced with parents who do not say what they feel and who give him no guidance as to how he can make himself truly loved and accepted, while they show him by their general tension, facial expressions, and manner of speaking that the situation is not as it should be. The child feels pervasive guilt feelings and anxiety that he cannot attach to specific actions, and grows more difficult and demanding as he searches for proofs of love. Eventually, perhaps as late as adulthood, he comes to a psychiatrist, suffering from guilt feelings, anxiety, problems of identity, and various other difficulties.

Some kind of guilt sense seems to be a part of the human condition. Once self-awareness appears and the capacity to judge the self, feelings of guilt must necessarily follow. The task of both the psychiatrist and the theologian is to separate the rational and mature guilt sense, which results from the neglect of some human responsibility or the commission of some act which is contrary to a moral or ethical norm, from the irrational, unconscious guilt sense, which produces symptoms of mental illness and may actually prevent the individual from acting in a responsible way, or may lead to acts which should be genuinely guilt-provoking but which are carried out without a sense of guilt. Therapy for the latter type of guilt feelings will not produce a hedonistic individual who never feels guilty or sees the occasion for it, but a mature, responsible person who is more truly capable of caring for his fellow men and feeling guilty when he injures them.

Scrupulosity

From these observations of the workings of the punitive superego, which is irrational and tyrannical, and with our knowledge of unconscious guilt, it is but a short step to the consideration of scrupulosity. The Latin word *scrupulus* means a pebble, which, like many small things, only becomes important when it gets stuck in a sensitive spot, lodged for instance, in the sandal of the traveler. The term is also applied to a small weight in apothecaries' measure, the fraction of an ounce which can move only a very sensitive balance. One can see how apt is this expression when it is applied to overly sensitive individuals, weighted down by troubles others can hardly discern.

The ordinary daily use of the term "scrupulous" also has healthy connotations, for it is connected with exacting fairness, a scrupulous honesty, etc. But in present-day psychiatry and in the pathology of moral life it is an unhealthy form of religiosity, a neurotic obsessiveness, and a morbid meticulousness. There are various types and degrees of obsessiveness and of scrupulosity. Mild obsessiveness in normal life, when it does not get out of hand, makes for the careful worker and the meticulous scientist, the perfectionist, as it were. When it gets beyond the bounds of normality, however, and in moral life tends to see sins where none exist and to multiply obligations which are not required and to confess peccadilloes repeatedly in order to allay anxiety, then it resembles a pathological obsessiveness.

In general, the scrupulous are emotionally immature, psychologically underdeveloped, isolated, narcissistic individuals, who have not solved their infantile complexes. It is thought that scrupulosity is connected with unconscious sexual or aggressive drives, repressed and unadmitted by the individual who harbors them. They would in fact be horrified to hear that they are aggressive and that they regard others with an ambivalence of love and hate. Their perfectionistic way of life is an attempt to compensate for their lack of personal affection. The image they form of God betrays their inner poverty. For the scrupulous, God is not the God of love, charity, and forgiveness. In their unconscious caricature of Him, He is a vengeful, rigid, watchful God, waiting to catch out some slight indiscretion in order to fling the victim into hell. It is obvious that this concept is simply a projection of their own cold, aggressive makeup.

The mildly scrupulous simply exhibit exaggerations of a normally meticulous, somewhat rigid, character. They do not suffer a serious complication unless some special circumstance precipitates it. In puberty or adolescence, they may run into rigid or fanatic teachings, and this may exacerbate their condition, or, later in life, some event which arouses strong guilt feelings may trigger their weakness. Usually, however, these individuals are able to continue their daily life without too much annoyance, and work and the security of the family group help to keep them on a reasonably even keel.

The more severely involved have definite evidence of obsessive-compulsive neuroses. It is in these individuals that careful scrutiny will demonstrate evidences of the difficulties in psychosexual development and unconscious aggressivity that we mentioned above. Although these phenomena are frequently encountered in penitents by the Catholic clergy, they are by no means the exclusive possession of Catholics and they can be found in all groups, religious, irreligious, and even anti-religious. The symptoms may differ superficially but the underlying pathology is the same.

Father Mailloux has this to say about these individuals: "They feel extremely disturbed when they disobey certain rules which they have established for themselves, rules which are extremely infantile or juvenile. Their concept of morality and of guilt is usually deeply deviated, extremely private, and has nothing to do with rational morality and the rational implementation of morality."[26] This description fits the compulsive neurotic unbeliever as it does the scrupulous believer. Karen Horney sees it rooted in a masterfully developed pride system, probably unconscious. She says: "There are indeed moral problems involved in the neurotic need for perfection, but they are not the ones with which the patient is apparently struggling, nor those which he pretends to have. The real moral issues lie in the insincerity, the haughtiness, the refined cruelty which are inseparable from the structure."[27]

One gets the feeling that most of these individuals, driven as they are, create false images of themselves and see themselves as angelic and martyrs and objects of great interest. These people are near the border lines of unreality and any undue emotional pressure might push them into the realm of illness. Their scrupulousness is a hostage to fortune, a protective device against mental disease.

The severe cases of this disorder are easily detectable. They have bizarre symptoms and are readily recognized as being psychotic. Any apparent religious coloring to their symptoms is simply fortuitous; the patients are basically ill and in need of care.

[26] Mailloux, N., O.P., St. John's Workshop Paper, 1956.
[27] Horney, K., New Ways in Psychoanalysis (New York: W. W. Norton & Co.), p. 231.

Though some of the definitions of these situations may sound critical, one does not get cross at these patients for being sick; rather one seeks to help them. Even though they prove to be annoying, they are like other people, no matter how bad they consider themselves. It is their severely hypermoral superego that accuses them much more readily than is reasonable. Dr. Leland Hinsie has an interesting observation upon this. "Ironically enough," he says, "unhappiness, psychosomatically expressed, is too often the cost of conscious decency. It is seldom that we encounter a psychoneurotic patient who has not lived with propriety, although overtures from the inner self temptingly beckon him along pathways of violation. This so-called mental patient suffers little compunction for what he has done, in fact, but he suffers immensely from what his unconscious self would have him do."[28]

This same point is also commented upon by Dr. John Donnelly:

Self-reproach and self-condemnation, which some people experience as a result of the recognition of unacceptable impulses within them, account for a great deal of unhappiness and depression. But it should be stressed that rarely is guilt arising out of moral offenses the cause of psychiatric illness. On the contrary, it is the conscientious person who is more liable to become depressed. I have heard reported statements of persons supposedly educated that only persons who have offended the moral code or who have done wrong things develop mental disorders. Such statements betray much about the individual expressing them and indicate the level to which their own personality development has proceeded.[29]

That these individuals would constantly return to the confessor for relief of their anxiety now becomes more understandable. By means of constant self-scrutiny and self-accusation they are able to atone for and ward off the punishment for aggressive or sexual acts before they are seriously

[28] Hinsie, L., *The Person in the Body.*
[29] Donnelly, J., "Feelings of Guilt," *Institute of Living Lecture Series,* No. 6 (1959).

punished. They are thus constructing a savings bank of pen-
ance against the hostile aggressive or sexual acts with which
their unconscious taunts them. The priest who encounters a
severe case of scrupulosity, Père Mailloux tells us, must try to
get the help of a good psychiatrist. He does not believe that
this problem can be handled in the confessional alone. "The
patient must not get the idea that the sacraments will cure
scrupulosity," he says. "The sacraments are there to give
grace, not to cure neurosis. They may pray to be cured, but
they must be told: 'This is an illness. Now you may pray for
this, as you may pray to be cured from any other illness.'"[30]

There is no need to go deeply into treatment procedures
here, for the care of these individuals is no easy task. The
mild cases can be handled by the confessor, for confession
deals with conscious failings and with matters of forgiveness
and direction. The more severe cases need to be referred for
psychotherapy, though the penitent will resent this and complain bitterly about being abandoned, unless the situation is
handled carefully. The confessor will have difficulty in handling the problem on a psychological level, for the penitent
will remain unconvinced that there is anything at all emotional involved in the situation. The more serious cases present no problem; they are in need of skilled psychiatric help
and they quickly exhibit this by their actions. It is obvious
that it is in this area that a wholesome cooperation on the part
of the clergyman and psychiatrist will redound to the benefit
of some individuals who are deeply and sorely distressed.

[30] Mailloux, *op. cit.*

XI

FAMILY DOCTOR, CLERGYMAN, AND EMOTIONAL STRESS

Let him [who is melancholy] . . . by all means open himself, submit himself to the advice of good Physicians, and Divines, which is a relief in uneasiness, . . . they may ease his afflicted mind, relieve his wounded soul, and take him out of the jaws of Hell itself.[1]

Robert Burton

It is common knowledge that the last several decades of this century have witnessed the greatest advances in the relief of human misery and the prevention and cure of diseases that the world has ever known. It is understood, too, that the physician of today is faced with a number of different complaints and different problems, for, as medicine has advanced and conquered old scourges, new health hazards have arisen to threaten the integrity of the population. Concomitant with all of this, however, is the fact that illness is a very personal thing, no matter what its manifestations may be. It strikes a man as a personal being and he exhibits one attitude or another to it, depending upon his place in human history.

Not only do attitudes differ, however; so do all complaints and symptoms. This is particularly true of the neuroses. The changes that we see embrace not only ideas that the doctor has about the patient and the illness; they also embrace the patient's own notions and his needs. People may more or less permit themselves to be dominated by their symptoms, or they may be oblivious to them to the point of disaster. It is this facet of human illness that the modern practitioner must

[1] Burton, R., *The Anatomy of Melancholy*, ed. Floyd Dell and Paul Jordan-Smith (New York: Tudor Publishing Co., 1951), p. 970.

keep ever before him as his practice burgeons with chronic diseases, geriatric problems, and emotional disorders which patients formerly lived with as best they could, or which they escaped because they did not live long enough to develop them. All of this is paradoxical. The more efficiently medicine operates, the heavier are the burdens placed upon it. The more effectively it eradicates disease, the more patients it has to deal with. The greater its contribution to the total health of the nation, the more it is open to criticism, and in the present day its critics are exceedingly vocal and numerous.

Changing Role of the Family Doctor

The family doctor began to fade out of the picture in the early decades of the twentieth century. His golden age had been relatively brief. It lasted but little more than half a century and paralleled the growth of scientific medicine that began around the mid-nineteenth century. Throughout that period the family doctor, like the psychiatrist, was handicapped by a lack of specific scientific and therapeutic knowledge in the many areas in which he had to work. As a consequence he developed a therapeutic role based upon a general conception and akin to the general idea of the moral treatment of the mentally ill which the psychiatrist developed in similar circumstances. He became a counselor, a supporter, and a confidant of the family. How well he did this may be seen by comparing the public valuation of the old family doctor, exemplified in song and story, with some of the hostile criticisms leveled at members of the medical profession today.

With the scientific temper of the early 1900s and the rapid increase in knowledge of the etiology of disease, it was inevitable that the doctor's attention would shift from families and people to diseases. This entailed the danger that people's identity might fade and they might come to be regarded simply as repositories for diseased organs. Then, as the increasing complexity of medical technology threatened to eclipse the resources of the practitioner, he found himself in danger of assuming the role of a medical floorwalker, who directed people to the right specialist or to that great and impersonal institution—the modern hospital—which was springing into being. Fortunately for all concerned, it soon became evident that patients should be viewed not only in the light of pure science, but also against the background of their environments and as contributors to their illnesses, as well as the subjects and objects of them. Along with this knowledge, the wisdom of having a family doctor as a trusted adviser again became apparent, and it is the family doctor who is again taking his place in the first line of defense against mental disorders.

As all of this was happening, the place of psychiatry as a basic medical science was becoming increasingly recognized. It was not a question of replacing good organic medicine by a strictly psychological approach, for one of the great advances of our civilization obviously has been the tremendous growth of organic medicine. It was simply to see that psychiatry offered a broadened dimension and another point of view to be added to the organic approach. When there is an awareness of the psychological and social factors in the patient's life which are influencing his illness, even a usually dull disease becomes an interesting one, and this new interest, which the patient inevitably perceives, serves to help in his treatment.

We have entered into a new era of comprehensive medicine, and this in itself has brought closer cooperation between family doctors and psychiatrists. Since the new tranquilizing drugs have been introduced, this type of cooperation is almost a necessity. The psychiatric patient has become ambulatory. He is going back to his own community, where someone must be prepared to help him with his problems, as well as with his maintenance treatment. The pharmacological approach to mental illness is all very well. Though it works marvels in some cases, it should never be forgotten that there is something else of importance. There is no substitute for tolerance, sympathy, and understanding on the part of the patient's physician or his community. The "healing touch" is a real thing, not a myth. It is part and parcel of the art of medicine. The doctor who has it cures his patients faster, because he is constrained to pay more attention to the individual's emotional needs.

Preventive Roles of the Family Doctor

With this point of view as a prologue, let us examine the various areas in which the family physician can make a real contribution to mental health. The battle for mental health has to be won in the community, and, as we observed earlier, the family practitioner is the key figure in that battle. A substantial range of reliable fact is already available to improve mental health, could we but apply it. We do know the causes of a large segment of the prevailing disorders, and for those still wrapped in obscurity we have developed useful treatments. Furthermore, prevention, as we know from the history of medicine, may sometimes be effected, even in the absence of definite etiological knowledge, when changes are made in the environment in which morbid processes are occurring. If we can increase the general resistance of the organism to assaults of various kinds, specific diseases are prevented. If we can institute treatment early rather than late, many difficult problems will be solved before they appear. If, failing in prevention, we can alleviate a residual disability, control symptoms, and make the patient feel better, even that is worthwhile. In other words, an attack on marginal problems would be enormously helpful, and this can be done best within the community, where the family physician's contribution looms large.

Prevention of mental disability is wrapped up with good medical care and the promotion of general health. It is closely related to the control of conditions which disturb or disrupt the organic base of personality. The most dramatic example of this is, of course, ordinary mental defect, which often is due to abnormal conditions or factors affecting the development of the child in the womb. Constant supervision of the mother's health from early pregnancy is, therefore, required from the standpoint of mental health, as well as that of physical integrity. The doctor must ever be mindful of the possible relationship between disorders of pregnancy and such later problems as cerebral palsy, epilepsy, hyperactivity, and reading disabilities. Infections of different kinds may be transmitted to the fetus from the mother. The same may be true of virus diseases; impressive evidence has accumulated that German measles in the first three months of pregnancy may be a prologue to mental deficiency and other defects in the child. This has even led to the suggestion that perhaps giving up quarantining children for this illness would lead to their attaining immunity before they grow up and marry. Some drugs prescribed for mothers are hazardous—the latest example being Thalidomide, the sedative which has been responsible for the birth of so many deformed infants. The so-called Rh incompatibility is another mental health hazard, and there is a positive correlation between toxemia and bleeding during pregnancy and the occurrence of mental impairment. Prenatal injury is one of the possible consequences of poor maternal nutrition. All these factors can eventuate in a wide variety of mental and physical disabilities.

The psychological aspects of these situations have not always been kept in mind in general medicine. Improved obstetrics, better use of protective services by all pregnant women, the prevention of prematurity, optimum care for the premature infant, all of these would necessarily cut appreciably into the mental deficiency segment of our mental health problems. Multiple pregnancy, complicated delivery procedures, and stressful obstetric situations demand increased alertness for possible complications. The importance of diagnosing cretinism during the first year must not be overlooked, in view of the good response to treatment at this time and the fact that later treatment will fail to overcome mental retardation. Certainly there should be joint pediatric and obstetric responsibility for fetus, infant, and child, so that a clearer view emerges of the mental (as well as physical) hazards of various complications from time of conception on, and of ways and means of preventing them. It is obvious that the family physician plays a critical part at this level of medical care.

The Environment

Improved mental health also involves the reduction of environmental hazards conducive to accidents, poisoning, and other insults which may damage the central nervous system. The question arises whether existing programs for the control of exposure to poisons and for control and sale of dangerous drugs are as intensive as they should be. The high incidence of morbidity in these situations suggests that improvement could be made. More attention might be given to adequate nutrition and adequate vitamin intake. Certainly this is true in elderly persons and people who are alcohol-prone. Pellagra psychoses are completely preventable; we know their etiology and yet cases continue to appear. More attention should be paid to infectious diseases which may directly damage the brain tissue. *Encephalitis lethargica,* (sleeping sickness), even if so mild that it easily escapes detection, may result in mental impairment when contracted in childhood, and in antisocial and irresponsible behavior when an adult is affected. Inoculations against contagious diseases in children are essential to lessen the incidence of inflammation of the coverings of the brain. Some of the formerly fatal cerebrospinal meningitides are now being restrained by antibiotics. Unfortunately, however, a virulent illness may leave a defective individual requiring long and perhaps unsuccessful rehabilitation. Early diagnosis and treatment of these infections is therefore essential.

In adult life a psychopathic development may occur after brain damage. If cerebral injury is at all extensive, it is likely to produce personality changes with neurasthenic, hysterical, or paranoid reactions, inadequate control of mood variations, and a general lack of initiative and energy. In the light of this, we need to strengthen those features of environmental sanitation work which reduce the incidence of head and brain damage.

Personality Development

From these areas in which good preventive work can be done, we now pass to the more complex field of personality development on which mental health or mental disorder grows. Certain basic propositions of psychiatry have important preventive implications, and this is being understood and applied more and more by the family physician. We believe that the dysfunction present in most people with emotional disorders stems from the inability to make satisfying relationships with other people, particularly with those whom they love. The impairment arises out of a failure to resolve powerful and conflicting instincts aroused by those who are loved —instincts of love and hate and their derivatives. In the individual unable to tolerate these contradictory affects, one or more of the warring elements are repressed, inhibited, or both; but the drive to action persists and may be experienced as tension, anxiety, and depression.

Such powerful and intolerable conflicts are special features of the experience of early life. It is during the first two or three years that the child is particularly prone to strong and contradictory impulses and is unable to bear the pressures; it is then that repression, inhibition, displacement, projection, and the various reaction formations are readily implemented. We assume that the child's experiences of satisfaction and frustration in relation to his parents have a determining influence on the strength and development of his impulses, on the development of the capacity to love and to internalize social and moral values. Psychiatry has convincing evidence of the need of young children for continuous affection, nurture, and care. A continuous relationship with a single nurturing figure seems to be an extremely important component of the experience leading to steps in psychic development between about the sixth month and two and one half or three years. In careful studies of cases in which mother and child are separated, John Bowlby of London has observed the following train of events: increased anxiety and dependency in the child, increased hatred of the mother, and a tendency to turn away altogether from love objects. Likewise, René Spitz has observed severe developmental retardation and deviant behavior in children assigned to the impersonal atmosphere of a foundling home during the first year of life, and Anna Freud has found that, when the mother-child relationship is broken up, the child's feelings are withdrawn from the environment altogether and centered on himself. She has stressed the child's need for a substitute object outside himself to vent the feelings he formerly had for the mother; and it has been her observation that the child behaves toward the substitute mother person in a manner appropriate to a much younger child, with considerable regression and an infantile, demanding type of love.

So it is that those responsible—and the family physician enters in here—should examine practices in their home communities to see whether they are prone to disrupt the mother-child relationship. Protection against emotional deprivation should be a basic policy in orphanages, residential homes for handicapped children, adoption and child-placing agencies, convalescent homes, and hospitals for children. One must consider the importance of small family-size groups for children during preschool and early school ages, with adequate and continuous care by one adult. Paralleling this, one should strive for shorter stays of children in hospitals, for the presence of the mother, if possible, or at least as often as possible, and for nursing care to be so arranged that one nurse looks after particular children. The problem of hospitalizing the mother of a young child for illness should be re-examined to see whether it would be feasible to provide housekeeping services for her while she remains under medical care at home. Her absence from the home in the child's early years causes more havoc than is realized. The importance of looking at an individual as a member of a family and of maintaining the family as a unit when possible should be recognized in all policies and activities of community health and welfare agencies. Finally, more should be done to extend medical and nursing care to children in their own homes and to focus on day centers and on day care, rather than on institutional care, for handicapped children.

The importance of preventing disturbances in emotional growth is also germane to mental health. Children must be protected from or helped in situations in which adjustment may be difficult. Too frequent changes of environment before the child has mastered preceding ones, the distraction of too many new people and their various standards of behavior, quick changes of habit routine, all interfere with orderly development. These and other principles of child growth and development should be incorporated into general mental health education. In the cases of children with physical disabilities, adaptation to the specific condition, without invalidism, is the best possible goal. The family needs help in understanding and accepting the child for what he can do, rather than for what he cannot do. Children who have been seriously ill or who have a residual handicap sometimes continue to dominate the concern of the parent at the expense of other children or the mate, with adverse effects on the mental health of the entire family.

The sense of shame and guilt regarding illness or defect in any member of the family can also be a destructive element. In some cases the burden of care of an old, ill, or defective member, improperly managed, will result in behavioral or emotional disorder in other members of the family, ranging from delinquency to psychosomatic disorders or worse, and this presents a pressing indication for support or assistance from health and social agencies. Certainly, there should be a close relationship between the community health agency and the family service agency in the interests of strengthening family mental health.

Early Evidences of Mental Disorders

It is axiomatic today that all illnesses have emotional and cultural overtones which affect recovery and adjustment during and after the illness. Attention to the anxiety incident to an illness at any phase of treatment brings obvious rewards, not the least of which is the prevention of mental disablement. The anxiety of the aged person in our society must never be forgotten. We observed earlier that some of what heretofore passed for senility was not an organic disorder at all. Rather it was culturally induced and was due to depression, isolation, and the confusion attendant upon loneliness. Activity and self-care not only aid in the care of the aged person, but actually delay physical deterioration and dependency. Nor should it be forgotten that simple nutritional and hormonal deficiency can result in symptoms of senility and that minor or chronic illnesses in old people, or even a change in environment, can activate symptoms of dementia.

The role of the practitioner in the early recognition of mental disorders is extremely important. The *adagio* of Erasmus still holds: "It is better to treat at the beginning than at the end." But, in addition to this, it needs to be said that, if recognition comes early enough, treatment may be given while the patient remains with his family or in the community and hospitalization may be delayed or avoided. Now that physical methods of treatment are capable of making such inroads into the psychiatric case load, this consideration becomes even more important.

The instances of major or minor psychiatric symptoms have been estimated to run as high as 60 per cent in the practice of many physicians in general practice. Florid cases of psychosis are usually readily recognizable, and the doctor endeavors to get them under psychiatric treatment and protective cover as promptly as possible. The more insidiously developing psychoses, however, may present considerable difficulty. This applies particularly to schizophrenic conditions, which often are masked for a long period by hypochondriacal complaints. Such cases offer a major challenge to the family doctor because of the improved outlook for adjustment of the early schizophrenic when the patient is submitted to adequate modern treatment. It is true that many chronic patients in our mental hospitals are being helped and are even achieving social remissions as the result of the powerful new drugs we have at our disposal. But the changes in our mental hospital statistics and the decline in residual cases of schizophrenia already noted are presumably also functions of early effective treatment.

In paranoid conditions there is an additional reason for accurate diagnosis and early hospitalization, namely the potential danger to society, should proper occasion arise and patients act out their delusions. Those cases in which compensatory grandiose delusions have not reached their full development and in which affective blunting has not occurred present some hazard. The more comfortable the patient feels with his delusions, the less dangerous he tends to be. Anything that decreases his satisfaction and security may precipitate an explosion.

Though we have discussed depressive and anxiety states rather thoroughly in an earlier chapter, we need to comment upon them here, for the picture of them as seen by the family doctor is completely different from the one the psychiatrist sees at a later stage of illness. The depressive states are a constant and increasing challenge to the practitioner, and there is much that he can do. In the early stages, before the patient begins to veer into frank depression, he may merely complain of a sense of indifference, an inability to feel the same toward his loved ones, or a lack of interest in pursuits he formerly enjoyed. Frequently, the growing depression is masked by physical symptoms. In addition to gastric disorders, backache, muscle spasm, and pain, which are not unusual complaints in these cases, there may be other more striking symptoms—compulsive eating, symptoms of heart disease, and the like. These various symptoms are generally defenses the patient is employing against the development of a psychotic state, and are relinquished as the psychosis takes deeper hold. In old people, there may be an intensification of bodily illness or accident-proneness, on the occasion, for instance, of the loss of someone close to them. Whatever the presenting symptoms might be, the incipient depression reveals itself by the underlying anxiety state. The patient's complaints are somewhat vague; his main complaints are those of tenseness, restlessness, irritability, fatigue, and insomnia. He may find his powers of memory and concentration impaired rather early, and his general effectiveness declines.

When the reaction to anxiety takes the form of hysteria or obsessive-compulsive behavior, or presents the picture of psychosomatic illness properly speaking, or has reached the point of psychosis, the problem is usually outside the province of the general practitioner. But mild or early cases of anxiety can be treated by simple psychotherapy on a conscious level or face-to-face discussion. Even encouraging the patient to talk and get things off his chest may give initial relief, but this has to be done by a physician who is sure that there is no serious organic illness present. It may be possible to provide symptomatic relief by the use of various medications that tone down the overactive autonomic system and alleviate tension. Since sleep increases tolerance for the stress and strain of daily life, the doctor should do what he can to relieve the patient's insomnia.

By helping the patient to understand what is wrong with him the general physician can do much to relieve anxiety states and prevent them from assuming serious proportions. His best work can be done in cases which are precipitated by some factor in the environment, at least partially recognized by the patient. In cases in which the patient is predisposed to anxiety because of lifelong insecurity and maladjustment, the chances that he can be helped by the practitioner are not too good.

Among psychiatric problems of unusual medical and social importance, that of alcoholism looms extremely large. It is the family physician who is consulted first in most instances, and his reactions to the situation set the tone for future handling of the problem. Unfortunately, the alcoholic rarely finds it expedient to seek medical advice early in his addiction; but, if he can be persuaded to do so by his intimates, he is much more apt to visit the family doctor than the psychiatrist. Excessive drinking is often based upon anxiety, and if this can be relieved the problem may be alleviated. The physician may even find such cases challenging, although he has often shied away from them in the past. The first step is first aid and the treatment of the impaired physical state. Sedation should be employed cautiously and selectively because of the possibility of drug dependence and addiction. A supportive approach is required, followed by constructive psychotherapy. It will do not good to lecture the patient or to intone to him the ominous results of drinking. He has had a surfeit of that before he got to the doctor's office. The possible contribution of Alcoholics Anonymous should not be overlooked. The work accomplished by this group has been one of the happiest developments in the field of alcoholism yet to occur.

In summary, to the usual psychiatric duties imposed upon

the family doctor, namely the handling of the mildly sick or their referral to proper facilities and the early recognition and disposal of the more severe psychiatric disorders, is added the general preventive task of attempting to eliminate conditions which are generally harmful to the patient's mental health. Neurotics are often found to be charming people—they merit assistance. Their greatest sin is that they consume too much of the doctor's time. They do, however, respond to preventive measures if these are made available. In the field of mental health the price which must be paid to achieve proper goals will be high, but it is worth it. Toward this end we can agree with Harold Lasswell, when he states that "one of our basic values has always been the realization of a commonwealth of free men in full possession of their wits."

The Clergyman—Counseling and Emotional Stress

This is indeed difficult terrain to embark upon and angels probably would fear to tread on it, but it needs careful consideration, for a recent national survey[2] established the fact that by far the largest number of our countrymen who seek help with their problems consult clergymen. Further, it indicated that by and large these people felt that they received more help than did those questioned who had consulted psychiatrists or psychologists. For the most part, the problems which people take to clergymen are different from those which are taken to psychiatrists, but the fact remains that the diverse problems presented to the clergyman for solution make him an important part of the nation's mental health effort and render it incumbent upon him to acquaint himself with a fair share of the knowledge which modern psychiatry and psychology have acquired concerning people under stress. Some clergymen have rejected this information, some have gone too far and are involved in a form of medical practice, but in general the largest number seek practical information that can be utilized in their pastoral duties.

Actually, people have taken their troubles to their pastors

[2] Gurin, G., Veroff, J., and Feld, S., *Americans View Their Mental Health* (New York: Basic Books), pp. 341–43.

long before psychiatrists were heard of, and, like the old family doctors, though the pastors' technical psychological knowledge was limited, their knowledge of people and families was great and they gave of themselves in a warm and helpful manner. When they did not respond thus, they drove some distressed people away from the church. This warmth and altruism often sufficed for the family troubles which were brought to the clergymen, and, besides, there was nothing else to do and no other place for people to go. This situation has changed now.

Early Indicators of Illness

The problems which are brought to pastors are often much more involved than those matters of conscience with which the clergyman is at home. More often than not they now concern some serious emotional, economic, or sociological problem and, unless the pastor has some knowledge of the vast amount of information which has been assembled in these spheres, his advice will be markedly lessened in value.

As we consider the various situations which we have discussed thus far in this volume, we realize that the pastor has a most important role to play in many of them. If he is consulted about a child who is having difficulty, the family will act upon his advice. If he merely makes reassuring suggestions without taking the trouble of looking into the problem, efforts to solve the problem will end then and there. If, however, he detects that there is the possibility of something serious in the offing, he would recommend consultation with a physician capable of assisting with the problem and in this manner would be found in the first line of defense against emotional and mental disorders. If there is difficulty in the family, more often than not he will be the first one consulted. He will see whether or not there is a possibility of solving the problem and holding the family together. If, on the other hand, he is inclined to minimize the danger, the situation may progress to the point where separation and divorce are in the offing, with the subsequent emotional upset, not only in those concerned, but in the children and the rest of the family. If it is a question of alcoholism in the family, it

is most likely that the one first consulted will be the clergyman. If he minimizes the situation, efforts to remedy it may
stop right there. Should he see the danger inherent in the
situation, however, and recommend medical or psychiatric
help, it undoubtedly will be sought. Hopefully, he will see
the futility of giving "the pledge" to a man whose anxiety is
so great that he has no possibility of keeping it and, thus,
drinks to forget that he broke it. Many of these individuals
need professional help or at least the ministrations of groups
akin to Alcoholics Anonymous.

Sick persons are to be found in every group. The manner
in which they exhibit their illnesses is manifold. Whether
they be angry, prejudiced, belligerent, alcoholic, paranoid,
or whatever else, they carry a heavy burden. It is not suggested that this burden be deposited upon the shoulders of
the clergyman, no matter how willing he may be. Rather,
it is suggested that he carefully assay the situation and de-
cide whether or not he can handle it and, if he cannot, then
help the patient to find someone who can. Few of these individuals are mentally ill, but many are under emotional
stress, and if they take their troubles to the family doctor or
pastor they have the right to expect that these professional
men will be prepared to advise them properly.

Though the clergyman's main orientation is not that of
mental hygiene, nevertheless every relationship that he has
with parishioners and outsiders can become either psychotherapeutic or psychonoxious. People become angry at physicians today, not because of a technological lag in their
knowledge, but because of the feeling of being pushed aside,
or thought little of, or of being treated slightingly. So, also,
people ordinarily do not leave their church for deep underlying theological differences of opinion; rather they leave because they feel they have been treated badly or have had
some quarrel with the clergy. Therefore, clergymen do play
a role in mental health, whether they like it or not. They
contribute to it; they receive from it. All of them have a won-
derful opportunity to be of assistance to people who are distressed, but who still may be described as normal and who
exhibit the tensions and anxieties of everyday living that ev-

eryone experiences. In dealing with such problems the clergy-man can give support, comfort, and practical advice about what to do and what not to do. Not infrequently, however, he runs into trouble with the person who, because of his conflicts, cannot follow the advice that is given him or follow the moral imperatives of his church. Such a person has in the past been tolerated in the hope of later improvement, but also, because of his failure, he has been all too often rejected. The clergyman has had trouble also with people who seemingly perform all the acts of a good Christian but, because of their unconscious hostilities, stir up trouble for themselves and others and come to him with problems which are completely misunderstood by themselves and generally blamed upon others. He has been troubled, too, by people with incomprehensible emotions. In short, he has been severely limited in dealing with neurotic difficulties because he has not understood their causes.

Father Gustav Weigel, S.J., who has the ability to summarize situations succinctly, says in this regard that long before psychiatry organized itself as a conscious discipline and framework, priests were hearing of these inner conflicts of men and women as no one else did. In their seminary days they were given outlines of cures for these complaints. "However," he says, "these curative aids rarely recognized the psychological nature of the disease and, when they did, the psychology used was woefully inadequate for the task at hand."[3]

New Approaches

This situation has been complicated further since the discovery, by Freud and others, that conscious mental functioning is only part of the workings of the mind, that neurotic difficulties can be caused by unconscious conflicts and wishes, and that behavior is a result of the interaction between conscious and unconscious mental functioning. The person who has a problem in doing what he should, or feeling right

[3] Weigel, G., S.J., "The Challenge of Peace," *Pastoral Psychology*, February 1959.

about what he does, can be helped by expert psychiatric exploration of the forces entering into his behavior—noxious emotions can be expressed and overcome or neutralized; unconscious attitudes can be transformed during the working out of the transference relationship, etc.

This discovery could not fail to produce its effects on the attitudes of many clergymen towards distressed members of their flocks. They could not help but see a new way of helping their black sheep and those lightly tinted, and visualizing a new responsibility toward them. They could not help but see a new way of assisting people who were experiencing neurotic suffering. Since they could not separate the concept of spiritual welfare from the concept of mental welfare, they have had to re-examine their responsibilities for the mental health of their people.

This re-evaluation of pastoral functions with regard to distressed parishioners has, unfortunately, in some instances led to the assumption by clergymen of psychiatric functions for which they are not prepared. With few exceptions the clergyman has not had training or experience in dealing with unconscious conflicts, the handling of transference phenomena, nor the recognition of countertransference mechanisms in himself. Therefore, he is ill-advised to enter the involved field of psychotherapy, for, even should he be able to identify unconscious conflicts, the question arises whether he will know how to handle them or how to present them to emotionally disturbed persons without arousing more anxiety or panic, or even precipitating a depression with its risk of suicide. This is a serious question; without the time, training, and experience in handling deep emotional problems, the clergyman cannot be a good psychotherapist. If he gives too much of himself in trying to be one, he may end up being neither a good clergyman nor a good psychiatrist. While, on the surface, remarks of this kind may give the impression that the psychiatrist is arrogating to himself a function which has long belonged to religious advisers, this of course is not the case. Anything within the realm of normality or in any way connected with the religious life definitely belongs in the sphere of pastoral counseling, but the more involved illnesses just as definitely do not, and there is always the risk that one may produce serious complications from poorly advised therapy. The late Agostino Gemelli, OFM, a priest-psychiatrist, was definite about this and he stated it unequivocally:

> Priests and religious should abstain from engaging in psychotherapy. Leave this responsibility to the doctors. They should heed the advice, not of the general practitioner, but of the doctor who is a psychiatrist and specialist in his field.[4]

Conrad Pepler, O.P., sees the situation in the same light:

> But unless a hierarchy of subordinate professions is preserved, the patient, instead of being made whole, is pulled to pieces. In this hierarchy . . . the priest must occupy the headship, as ministering to the soul from which life, both natural and supernatural, derives [its] whole being. But the priest must recognize the limits of his sphere to operate. He must beware of becoming a "know all," ready to advise on medical and psychological problems as well. Similarly the doctor and the psychologist must respect the spheres of the others. . . . Everyone knows of the lamentable results of the priest playing the psychologist or the doctor advising on religion.[5]

In the same fashion one might add here that any attempts on the part of the psychiatrist, directly or indirectly, to become involved in theological problems or to influence a patient's religious beliefs would be reprehensible. This is outside his field; he has no competence in it and should stay completely out of it.

As to the role of the psychotherapist, though we have already spoken of it, we can re-emphasize our beliefs here by the following statements by Dr. Paul E. Meehl, a skilled psychologist and a prominent Lutheran layman. The job of the psychotherapist, as he sees it, is "to heal neurotics," not to convert sinners or reform scoundrels. The goal of the psychotherapist, when he enters into a therapeutic relationship, is to restore the patient's psychological integrity. To put it

[4] Gemelli, A., OFM, *Psychoanalysis Today*, p. 53.
[5] Pepler, C., O.P., "Health and Holiness," editorial in *Blackfriars*, Vol. XXXI (1956), No. 360, p. 107.

crudely, the secular therapist's job is to help the neurotic sinner become a healthy one. A patient, Dr. Meehl says, does not go to a psychiatrist seeking to become more sanctified. Hence, "it is inappropriate behavior for the psychiatrist to enter into a missionary relationship with the patient. The therapist doesn't assume that he is going to make the patient good, although we all recognize that successful therapy for the disturbed person may make him a better person in a religious and ethical sense, even though the methods used to improve his bad behavior were essentially non-ethical, non-moral, and non-religious."[6]

It seems, therefore, that there must be a division of labor between the psychiatrist and the clergyman, just as there has been a division between the general practitioner or surgeon and the clergyman. (At one time healing was a religious function, but in only a few religious groups today do religious leaders object to having a doctor treat appendicitis.) It is necessary for both clergymen and psychiatrists to evaluate the contributions to the welfare of the whole person that they can make and to appreciate and respect the contributions made by the other group. The clergyman is still responsible for the care of souls. This means that he is ultimately responsible for the whole person. However, he should relegate specifically psychiatric problems to those who are best able to handle them.[7]

[6] Meehl, P. E., *What Then Is Man?* (St. Louis: Concordia Publishing House, 1959), p. 223 ff.

[7] Dr. Alexander A. Schneiders, in a panel discussion on "The Pastor as Counselor" (published in *Mental Health Aspects of Pastoral Counseling*, the proceedings of an institute held in Hartford, Conn., June 16–18, 1958, pp. 57–59), suggests that the pastoral counselor should concern himself with marital difficulties, vocational aspirations or confusions, premarital relationships, problems in sexual adjustment, problems in heterosexual relationships, moral problems (including scrupulosity), and problems of spiritual growth. He states that the pastoral counselor is not equipped to handle problems of homosexuality and compulsive masturbation, acute alcoholism, compulsive promiscuity, psychopathic tendencies, and the pathological disorders, including severe neurosis and psychosis.

Dr. Leslie D. Weatherhead, in *Psychology, Religion and Heal-*

What precisely does constitute collaboration between clergymen and psychiatrists? In general it means agreement on some fundamentals. It is acknowledged that the life of grace can be hindered and even rendered ineffective by the maladjustment of the individual to his natural life. The supernatural life of grace builds upon this natural life in order to transform and perfect it. If there is distortion or maladjustment, grace may be hindered or even wholly obstructed in its healing work.[8] "Here we pass wholly or in part from the spiritual sphere in which the clergyman's work lies and enter upon the sphere of therapeutic operation which properly belongs to psychology and the psychiatrist. Since man is a unity, made up as a person of body and soul, the two spheres are very closely connected and interpenetrate each other; but they are not identical. Priest and psychiatrist must work together, each keeping to his own sphere."[9]

On the specifically practical level this collaboration is being developed in several different forms beyond the informal individual confrontation, and particularly in mental hospitals in which the chaplain is expected to function as a part of the "team." Here, as in other collaborative efforts, however, the clergyman has a different function from that of the psychiatrist. "Just where does such a clergyman fit into the psychiatric team? Does the chaplain serve his function best by performing his role as a minister of God or as a disciple of Aesculapius? . . . Unless the chaplain takes complete medical and psychiatric training, he can never hope to be more than a pseudo-disciple of Aesculapius. . . . If the clergyman did take such training, he would become a psychiatrist as well

---

ing (New York: Abingdon Press, 1952), says that any man who really wants to devote his time to psychotherapy should take a degree in psychological medicine and regard the practice of this discipline as a Christian vocation. He does think it permissible for the clergyman to attempt some psychotherapy, under medical supervision if possible and being careful not to outrun his understanding, if it is a choice between that and the patient's getting no help at all. Editorial, *Life of the Spirit*, XII (1953), No. 136, p. 147.

[8] *Ibid.*
[9] *Ibid.*

as a clergyman and he could then wear his hat either fore or aft as he saw fit!"[10]

"It is our belief that the training of the chaplain should not be in the direction of diagnosis or of treatment, but oriented towards a recognition of where he must not trespass. Active cooperation does not mean that the clergyman should become a 'junior therapist' whose assignment is to be made by the psychiatrist. The chaplain certainly should receive enough psychiatric training to be dynamically oriented in his understanding of mental illness. He should be empathic and understanding, but his primary orientation should be spiritual and not psychiatric. The clergyman on the psychiatric team should, therefore, retain his supernatural orientation, while the natural orientation should be left to the medical specialist. . . . The chaplain's training in psychiatry is only to provide a background for his pastoral hospital practice."[11]

In his daily life in his parish, the clergyman does have an important and serious role to play in regard to emotional distress and mental disease, for, as we have noted, he is often the first one to whom specific problems are brought. No matter how he feels about it, he cannot ignore the existence of emotional problems. If he is hostile to psychiatry, as is, unfortunately, sometimes the case, or if he does not recognize the nature of the problem and send the person to someone who can do something effective about it, the problem will not only remain unsolved, but perhaps grow worse.

People have a right to expect, when they bring a problem to a clergyman, that they will get some kind of skilled attention, either directly from the clergyman himself, or through referral to some competent person. The first important thing for anyone to do is to listen sympathetically to the account of the situation. This act of listening may be therapeutic in itself. Just discussing problems with a sympathetic listener who has some authority very often lessens their impact. A

[10] Cavanagh, J. R., and Dinardo, R. A., "Beyond Peaceful Coexistence," read at annual convention, American Psychiatric Association, May 1958.
[11] Ibid.

person may leave his pastor feeling relieved and comforted, when all he has done is unburden himself of a mess of worries and painful emotions which he did not feel he could express to anyone else.

It may happen also that the person with the problem has not formulated it very clearly in his mind when asking for help. In presenting it to another person and answering the questions that he is asked, he may find that the problem becomes clearer; he may even see a solution that had not occurred to him earlier, when the problem was still confused and muddled. He may, in addition, work out some of his unconscious problems unconsciously. Let us take, for example, the person who has unconscious problems with authority, which are causing difficulties in his work situation. He may go to his pastor, who represents authority to him, expecting unconsciously to be met with hostility and condemnation, only to find sympathy, understanding, and offers of assistance. His attitude toward authority may change, so that his work situation improves, even though there has been no exploration of the unconscious aspects of his problem.

However, there are times when listening and the giving of such practical advice as occurs immediately to the clergyman are not enough, and yet the problems presented are not psychiatric ones and are not related to deeply rooted emotional conflicts. Here the clergyman has a legitimate function, bordering on that of psychiatry and existing in addition to his sacerdotal functions of advising in matters of belief and conscience. He may have to deal with existential problems— problems of meaning, values, and goals, and problems of anxiety over fate and death, non-neurotic guilt, doubt, and meaninglessness. He encounters everyday problems involving conflicts which are close to the surface, or problems involving the need for change in conscious or near-conscious attitudes or ways of living.[12] These problems are all in the

[12] Rabbi Jeshaia Schnitzer, in a panel discussion on "The Pastor as Counselor" (loc. cit., pp. 60–62), says: "Counseling embraces the everyday problems of marriage, children, education, sickness, and death. The problems of guilt and sin, the problems of love and hate, the problems of bereavement and loneliness are the concern of the pastor as counselor."

domain of the pastor of souls. There are multitudes of people with them and, certainly, they do not belong in the psychiatrist's hands, even if there were enough psychiatrists to treat them.

Pastoral Counseling

The clergyman normally deals with these problems of day-to-day living by applying religious insight to them. This is the process of pastoral counseling. Pastoral counseling is not the same thing as giving guidance and advice on the one hand, or psychotherapy on the other. It differs from advice in that it aims at a change in the person, brought about by new religious understanding, occurring in the context of a relationship with another person. It differs from psychotherapy in that it does not deal with truly unconscious conflicts, which are the concern of the psychiatrist.[13] Pastoral counseling starts when the parishioner brings to his clergyman some problem which has arisen during the stress of marriage, parenthood, work, etc. The counselor and the troubled person then enter into an emotional relationship, in which God is the third party. The counselor enters into the relationship with a warmth and acceptance which in no way implies acceptance of what the person has done or is doing, but rather an acceptance of the person as intrinsically worthwhile. (The

[13] The Rev. William C. Bier, S.J., in a panel discussion "The Pastor as Counselor," discussing "Techniques of Counseling," (*loc. cit.*, pp. 39–50) points out that "counseling is more than advice giving . . . counseling involves something more than the solution to an immediate problem. Counseling involves emotional experience and does not rely upon purely intellectual attitudes to furnish the raw material of the counseling process . . . counseling inevitably involves relationships between people . . . counseling, and with it pastoral counseling, stands midway between guidance on the one hand and psychotherapy on the other." In stressing the religious goals of pastoral counseling, Father Bier goes on to say: "Unless as a religious counselor you conceive of yourself as having counseling goals which are at least partially different from those of secular counselors, I find it difficult to see how you justify your existence as a separate kind of counselor. . . . The aim of the religious counselor . . . is not only to make his client more comfortable in his human relationships, but to bring him also to improve his relationship to God and to feel more at ease in it."

person being counseled is often self-critical enough; after all, he came for counseling. But his self-criticism is often destructive and unrealistic. After counseling he may be more intensely self-critical in a way which leads to improvement in his attitudes and behavior.) The counselor then acts as an auxiliary reasoning power, bringing his knowledge of the situation and the people involved to bear on the problem. In addition, he tries to lead the person being counseled to new religious insights, which can change his understanding of the problem and of himself. He may use techniques that he has learned from the mental health field, but only those which can help him reach the individual with his own pastoral resources. He does not use techniques related to intensive therapy. The goal of the process is to lead the person with the problem to more adequate goals and values and a better understanding of himself as he relates to others and to God.[14]

In the course of his pastoral functions, the clergyman may find that what seemed like a religious problem is really a psychological one. Intense "mystical" preoccupations may indicate the beginnings of schizophrenia. Even loss of faith, which might seem to be a purely religious problem, may have unconscious psychological roots. The clergyman cannot give religious solutions for problems which are not religious in origin. He needs to recognize the psychological dimensions of the problems that come to him, whether they present themselves as religious problems or problems in everyday living.

If the clergyman is to recognize deeply rooted psychological problems when he sees them, he needs some background and training in the field of psychology. This background he seeks not with the intention of becoming a therapist, but simply to aid in the evaluation of problems presented to him.

---

[14] Rabbi I. Fred Hollander, in a discussion of Father Bier's paper given at a panel discussion "The Pastor as Counselor," (loc. cit., pp. 51–53) confirms this idea. He says: "This technique [of pastoral counseling] . . . is best utilized for those problems which can be resolved by dealing primarily with their spiritual or transcendental aspect. The pastoral counselor's task is to explore the religious implication of the situation brought to him and then to help the individual approach his problem in its spiritual framework, and deal with it at that level."

Such evaluation may be facilitated by special courses in the seminary and by a period of time spent in mental hospitals. There is, of course, always the danger, if an individual—medical, clerical, or lay—obtains only a smattering of superficial knowledge and does not have much actual experience with emotional disorders, that he may be carried away by the little he has read and may see schizophrenic thought disorders in everyone who disagrees with him, or neurotic difficulty in everyone who expresses hostility. There is also the danger that the psychological novice will confuse basic psychoanalytic theory with clinical practice and think that he is seeing a neurotic whenever he recognizes a mental mechanism. As Father Weigel puts it, the clergyman wades into the psychological morasses, relying upon common sense, though he would not entrust his electric shaver to a repairman working upon the same principle.

Let us assume that the clergyman has sufficient background to identify more serious emotional disturbances. He may see the difficulty when he encounters the specific problem, or he may detect signs of it in his routine contacts with his parishioners. Because he maintains some psychological distance from his parishioners, he may see slowly developing personality changes in them and be aware that trouble is brewing, even before the family is fully aware that anything is wrong. (Indeed, he may have an advantage over the psychiatrist at this point. Because he knows the entire family, he may know before the psychiatrist does which member of the family is really sick.)

The pastor in these instances has the responsibility of seeing that his disturbed parishioner gets appropriate help. He needs to know what psychiatric facilities are available in the community, so that the parishioner will get into proper hands. He may even have to persuade the parishioner that psychiatric help is what is needed, for such help may not as yet have achieved the full confidence of the community. None of these tasks is easy, but they are rewarding. It is wise, of course, whenever possible, to take some responsible member of the patient's family into one's confidence and enlist his aid in endeavors to see that the patient is properly placed.

Patients who are depressed are liable to approach the pastor with ideas of great sinfulness or of having been abandoned by God. It is important that these people be properly handled, for suicide is always a possibility, the victim believing that the world, and especially his family, would be better off without him. It is the pastor who can assure the patient that seeing a psychiatrist and taking steps to get well will not be accompanied by a stigma. It is also the pastor or his deputy who can explain to patients and families just what psychotherapy is and how it works, and thus save the patient from the hope that his visit to the psychiatrist will result in a neatly worked out and packaged solution to his problems. Failing to take this precaution may result in the return to the rectory of a man even more disconsolate, saying: "I went to the doctor you suggested and he has not helped me at all." Properly instructed, he may know what to expect and even return to his pastor for further support and advice. The pastor may be especially useful to him during difficult periods of therapy, when unpleasant psychological attitudes are being uncovered and when a strong faith would stand him in good stead.

Everyone, of course, must ever be wary of manipulative patients who try to play clergymen and psychiatrists off against each other and carry tales to each which are calculated to cause dissension between them. During difficult periods in therapy these patients may complain to the pastor that, not only is the psychiatrist doing them no good, but in fact they are worse and they fear for the stability of their religious beliefs, as a direct result of psychiatric treatment. This more often than not is a neurotic trap, and if the patient can cause unrest between the clinician and the clergyman, then he has no need to face up to his difficult problems. "If these two experts can't agree, what can you expect of poor little me?" In the ill feeling generated between the two the patient feels justified in abandoning therapy. This possibility further points up the need for close understanding between clergymen and psychiatrists.

If the clergyman recognizes the presence of psychosis in its incipient or full-blown stages, his problems of dealing with parishioners and their families may be a bit more touchy.

Families sometimes have a tendency not to want to recognize the seriousness of some of the situations which are going on around them; they fear to do so, lest neighbors think ill of them. The pastor finds it incumbent upon himself to assay the situation and seek advice. If things are allowed to progress, a tragedy or a scandal may occur. On the other hand, if the patient can be kept out of the hospital without fear of unfortunate happenings, it would be unwise to insist upon hospitalization or to seem to be interfering. If hospitalization must be arranged, then the mediation of the clergyman is indeed welcome, for it often comes as a shock to the family.

Once patients are hospitalized, it is wrong to neglect them, feeling that they will get all of the care necessary in the institution. Visits of family doctors and clergymen are most desirable when the attending physician deems them advisable. Likewise, the family itself is in need of help during this time, for they will be going through a period of turmoil and will be bothered by a constantly recurring question: Have we done the right thing? Here the guidance of the clergyman and family physician is indeed important, for not only can they help the patient and the family under these circumstances, but they can also make the way of the patient easier and prepare him properly for that difficult event, his return to the community.

Ideally, the psychiatrist and the clergyman should be able to work in close cooperation. Both are concerned with aiding the person to function as an integrated, responsible whole. The psychiatrist is interested in mental health and maturity for their own sake. The clergyman is interested in the relationship of man to God, and sees that a man can reach mature theocentric attitudes more readily if he is fully liberated or redeemed from immaturity. Thus, they are working for coordinated goals, using different but complementary methods.

The troubled person can use the help of both the psychiatrist and the clergyman. We have seen that emotional disturbance is related to the difficulties and stresses that people encounter at various times in their lives. The inner resources that they bring to these stresses and the unconscious conflicts which keep them from meeting the stresses adequately must be carefully evaluated. All people have inner conflicts and self-destructive and hostile impulses. Whether these conflicts and unconscious forces lead to neurotic symptoms and misery or remain a minor factor in people's lives depends on how they are balanced by constructive relationships, positive values, strength-giving features in the environment, and the encouragement of the strong impulse towards health present in everyone. By giving the disturbed person religious insights, ideals, and hope, the clergyman may throw his weight on the side of the positive forces within the person and help him to transcend his difficulties.

Yet, not all difficulties need to be transcended. If one had a thorn in his foot, he would try to get it out, rather than walk on bravely in spite of the pain. In some instances a psychiatrist can straighten out an emotional difficulty with relative ease, as the doctor can remove the thorn. In most instances, however, the emotionally disturbed person needs to get from the psychiatrist some understanding of how and why he has become sick, what unrecognized things within himself need changing, and what unconscious forces prevent them from changing; and he needs also the inner strength and integrity that he can achieve through religious insight.

A truly collaborative relationship between the psychiatrist and the clergyman, desirable as it is, occurs only occasionally. It would be especially unfortunate if the relationship were to be further clouded because each tried to assume the role of the other. But such a collaborative relationship is an ideal worth striving for, even if it is never perfectly achieved. "The golden rule of the therapist should be: 'Teach your patient to become himself.' The golden rule of the spiritual advisor is the rule that St. John the Baptist established for himself in the third chapter of St. John's Gospel: *He* must increase and I must decrease."[15]

[15] Godin, P., "Therapeutic and Pastoral Work," *Life of the Spirit*, Vol. XII (1957), No. 136, p. 330.

XII

THE FUTURE

Mankind is entering one of the most beautiful spring-times the world has ever known, a spring marked by a great awakening and development in all fields of human life.

Pope Pius XII

Predictions concerning scientific endeavor are often hazardous, for at any time discoveries might be made which would markedly change existing ideas and reverse current directions. This is particularly true at present, for at the rate scientific advances are being reported, prescriptions regarding the future seem almost presumptuous. Portents of remarkable new developments are already visible and seem to indicate the nearness of an extraordinary awakening in all phases of intellectual and scientific life. These rich potentialities, however, are overshadowed by a threat. The promises inherent in our scientific advances, and even our survival, rest precariously on our ability to live in peace with our fellow men, and avert that final act of insanity which is symbolized by a mushroom cloud.

Unfortunately, no matter what the future may be, it will neither hold still for its portrait nor furnish a script of the drama it intends to enact. We may therefore either follow Horace's dictum and "cease to inquire what the future has in store," or we may attempt instead to prognosticate the future with that "delightful discontent which the hope of better things inspires." That we may not be entirely successful in our prognostications, as far as disease is concerned, is suggested by René Dubos. "There is overwhelming historical evidence," he says, "that the evolution of disease is influenced by many determining factors that at present are not and may never become amenable to social or medical control. The changes that spontaneously have occurred in the prevalence of various diseases during the past few centuries should serve as a warning that it is unwise to predict the future from the short perspective of the past decades."[1]

On the surface the evolution of mental disease is not as strikingly apparent as is that of the infectious diseases, for, in the mind of man, to be mentally ill has always been to be mentally ill. The clinician observes, however, that various forms of emotional illness come to the fore at different times and then seem to go into eclipse to return later in a different guise. Hysteria, we noted, is a case in point; evidences of it can be found as far back as the Battle of Marathon, the symptoms appearing, then disappearing down through the ages —now scarcely visible, and again so widespread as to constitute almost a psychic contagion. More than a few of our troops who displayed emotional symptoms in World War I tended toward hysterical manifestations, while the illnesses of World War II were singularly free of this taint and tended more toward the psychosomatic. The reasons for these fluctuations are hard to fathom, for mental illnesses, like all others, are influenced by many and diverse factors.

New Problems to Cope With

It is safe to predict that the emotional well-being of man will assume more and more importance in the light of various complicated and pressing new problems which lie before us. Automation, with the attendant leisure time it will bring; the battle for men's minds in our various encounters with communist states; the new adventures in rockets, atomic submarines, and space exploration are a few fascinating examples of the kind of problem which is emerging. As to the first-mentioned, there is already a clamor for a shorter work week, which will of necessity bring an enforced increase in leisure time. Desirable as this seems to be at first glance, it may not be an unmixed blessing. For many people, unprepared for the profitable use of additional free time, it could result in idleness and, with idleness comes the danger of malignant

[1] Dubos, R. J., "Medical Utopias," *Daedalus,* Summer 1959.

boredom, a serious threat to emotional stability. That this might pose a mental health problem is within the realm of possibility.

Another set of new problems with broad implications arises when men are placed in isolated situations, on long undersea journeys, in antarctic areas, and in outer space. In all of these situations there will be changes in man's relationship to his fellow man and in his relationship to his external environment. Men, having explored all of the horizontal frontiers on land and sea, are now preparing to explore the vertical frontiers, and in these they will find the pressures more rigorous and the requirements more demanding than in anything encountered thus far. In these situations, as in most things that he does, the importance of man's emotional stability will become strikingly apparent, for, no matter how technically perfect the apparatus might be in which he will undertake his flight into space, it is his emotional reactions in the end which will spell the difference between success and failure.

Things learned from psychology and psychiatry have already played important parts in the selection of the astronauts, and they will play increasingly important roles as the astronauts make longer flights and attempt to explore the moon and the planets. Space flight is so apparently an extension of jet flying that the military services have naturally served as reservoirs of candidates for this hazardous duty. The ability to engage in dangerous flying, however, depends not only upon technical aptitude but also upon such complex factors as motivation and emotional stability. Strangely enough—and this is the reason for discussing the subject here —the emotional pressures which interfere with the proper performance of flying duty *are more often due to family pressures and disturbed interpersonal relations than to the stress of the operation itself.*

Though the primary emotion experienced during space flight is in reaction to the danger itself, there are two other phenomena involved which have emotional connotations— sensory deprivation and isolation. While few of our readers will experience these phenomena, they are worth mentioning for what they imply.

The integrity of the human ego is critically dependent upon continuous meaningful contact with the outside world. As stimuli of various types are received via the sense organs, they travel through the various nerve pathways and connections to the higher centers of the brain, where the messages are sorted and evaluated. Although we can only speculate at this time, it seems that when these stimuli cease (sensory deprivation) the mind is "cut adrift" and brings forth its own productions, which may appear in the form of hallucinations.

We acquired some valuable information about the effects of isolation when Admiral Byrd cut himself off from his companions in Antarctica in 1934 and went to live alone in order to make climatic observations. Among the many remarkable things he wrote in his diary was the following:

> Something, I don't know what, is getting me down. This would not seem important if I could only put my finger on the trouble but I can't find any single thing to account for the mood. Yet, it has been here and tonight for the first time I must admit the problem of keeping my mind on an even keel is a serious one.

The long period of isolation was taking its toll.

We have learned even more about the effects of isolation since the time of Admiral Byrd's observations, but we need not go into detail about them here. We need only indicate that not only are we dependent upon our normal surroundings for our physical well-being, but we are even more dependent upon them for our mental health. Deprived of our accustomed surroundings and of our ordinary social and psychological roles, logical thought processes have a tendency to become hazy. If pressure or threats are exerted upon us at this time when we are vulnerable, we are liable to forget people and concepts which are dear to us. Our communist enemies have learned this lesson well and have used it to influence their prisoners.

And Old Lessons to Relearn

In the wake of the Korean War evidence came to light of the successful efforts by the communists to manipulate the minds of American prisoners of war. These men, abruptly removed from the securities and influences of one way of life and subjected to unusual pressures, apparently forgot the duties and loyalties expected of them as military men under all circumstances. The results were a shock to the American public. Many soldiers taken prisoner collaborated with the enemy in some way, from writing anti-American propaganda or informing on comrades, to making broadcasts to home and family which put the enemy in a good light. Some were apparently guilty of serious collaboration, such as committing disloyal acts, agreeing to spy or organize for the communists after the war, etc. Not everyone agrees on the extent of the deterioration of American prisoner morale, but it seems evident that a number of the soldiers were not prepared for the psychological rigors of prison life.

To further exacerbate the situation, not one American prisoner escaped and returned to his lines, though the first duty of a prisoner is to attempt to escape. Finally, more than 38 per cent of the men who were captured died in prison. In contrast with this breakdown in our morale, not one of the Turkish soldiers captured died in prison and none collaborated with the enemy or sold out his fellow prisoners.

The report of the reactions of the American collaborators dismayed the nation. If new and cunning psychological weapons were being used to bring pressure on prisoners of war, taking advantage of emotional immaturities and weaknesses in moral fibre, measures would have to be adopted to counter them. The susceptibility of psychological manipulation might trace back to character defects implanted in childhood, to defects in education, in preparation for hardship, to lack of patriotism and lack of religious belief, and to an almost complete lack of realization of the advantages of the political system under which they lived.

All of this points up a warning for the future regarding the preparation of the men who will defend the nation. If the "cold war" is to be our lot for some years to come, with eruptions of "hot war" in various localities, then the men who will represent the country need careful emotional and political screening and indoctrination in addition to careful physical and technical preparation for the pressures they will undergo. This is the reason for discussing this problem here. Psychological preparation for this type of duty is as necessary as is psychological preparation for space flight. The fate of the free world may depend upon it.

The Mental Hospital of the Future: Admissions

As we move to matters closer at hand and consider the future of the mental hospital, one of the first things which will require correction is the method by which patients are admitted to these institutions. Apparently, admission procedures in some parts of the United States are still traumatic, although arrest and a sojourn in jail for the mentally ill is becoming less common. Judges, however, still commit criminals to jail and the mentally ill to mental hospitals, and sometimes the implications of the court procedure are so traumatic that the hospital has little chance later of gaining the patient's confidence in order to treat him.

While it is only just that the patient's rights as a citizen be legally protected, it is also right and just that he be treated in a humane and dignified manner and in a way which will not hamper his recovery. Too many legal formalities can work against both of these purposes. No one seems to worry about this, however; people are too busy protecting patients from "venal psychiatrists," who, in their minds, are willing to clap anyone into mental hospitals indiscriminately.

In truth, the direct opposite is the case. Mental hospitals are usually so overcrowded that harassed doctors err on the other side and discharge patients sooner than their condition warrants. In addition, the present trend is to keep patients out of hospitals altogether, if this is possible. When people have the plague, smallpox, or other illnesses, doctors are permitted to handle their hospitalization, but not so in the instance of mental disease—here the law has stepped in. To make matters worse, each legislative session witnesses additional attempts to further complicate the mental disease picture by making it more legalistic. Actually, patients are well protected by the fact that responsible relatives can always remove them from mental hospitals, and they are further protected by the right of communication with their lawyer, doctor, and clergyman, with any judge, and by writ of *habeas corpus.* The new English Mental Health Act removes hospital admissions from most of their legal trappings, and British people may now enter mental hospitals as they do general hospitals, in dignified fashion.

The Philosophy of Mental Hospital Organization

Perhaps the greatest advance in recent years in mental hospital management has been the realization that the hospital organization itself is a factor in the cure or the continued illness of the patient. This realization is responsible for the so-called "open hospital." The phrase implies that either all, or the largest percentage, of ward doors are unlocked and that the patients are free to move to any part of the hospital or grounds or, with permission and when conditions permit, to leave the hospital grounds. Two misconceptions had led to the excessive legalism of admission and discharge from mental hospitals, and both of these were responsible in part for the closed confinement and custodial care in our institutions in the past. First, it was assumed automatically that every mental patient was irresponsible and had to be confined, and, second, it was assumed that all mental patients were potentially dangerous and that the places in which they were confined should have security features; hence, the barred windows and locked doors. Psychiatrists have known for a long time that neither of these ideas are true, and yet they were powerless to change public opinion in the face of these widespread unfortunate generalizations. It is not generally recognized as yet that only an extremely small minority of mentally sick people are prone to commit antisocial acts, a much smaller number, in fact, than the so-called normal offenders.

The "open hospital" movement began in Great Britain and has spread widely in this country. In the New York State hospital system two thirds of the patients are now in open wards.

This is a loose figure, for some of the hospitals are completely open and others only 30 or 40 per cent open as of this writing. The advantages of the open hospital are obvious, the most important being that the dignity of the individual is markedly enhanced. Now treated as individuals and with respect, it is found that most mentally ill patients can be trusted far more than was generally supposed. Patients are expected to control themselves and, under these circumstances, they become cooperative and are willing to do so. There is less regression and far less aggression, and it becomes more and more evident that much of the patients' aggressive behavior in the past was due to the conditions of their confinement rather than the illnesses from which they suffered. In the open hospital not only do the patients assume more responsibility for their behavior, but their relationships with hospital personnel improve, and this in itself is an aid to treatment.

The future must certainly see the end of the large, bleak, dysfunctional, monolithic structures which have housed many of the mentally ill in isolated hospitals. It is certain that the British will never again build a mental hospital larger than one thousand beds and, wherever possible, will divide existing institutions into several small autonomous units.

Efforts are being made to divide large hospitals in the United States; this is already under way in the New York State system and several others. As this idea spreads, it can only redound to the benefit of patients. The large hospitals in general are a bit unwieldy and do not lend themselves readily to therapeutic endeavor. One can scarcely hope to cure a patient by removing him from an abnormal home environment and placing him in an abnormal hospital environment.

One other thing which will be seen more frequently in the future will be the tendency to use the mental hospital, not as the one and only service available to psychiatric patients, but as *one* of the facilities available to them, depending on their needs and condition. This trend has been variously determined: First, community medicine is more alert to psychiatric problems, more disposed to handle those within its competency and to refer others to the appropriate sources of assistance at an opportune time. Second, there has been a rise in the number of psychiatrists in private practice in some of the large urban areas, where so many psychiatric problems are always found and where, in all probability, they are often engendered. With a more equitable distribution of these specialists, there should be further favorable impact upon the state hospital situation.

General Hospital Units

Of great importance is the rise in the number of psychiatric units in general hospitals. These units can become valuable adjuncts to the community mental health services, provided they are adapted to the singular needs of psychiatric patients instead of to the mores of the general hospital. This is not always the case. As was pointed out in the Third Report of the Expert Committee on Mental Health of the World Health Organization (1953), the psychiatric ward of the general hospital is at the present time too often expected to conform to the ward pattern of the rest of the hospital, with patients confined to bed and nurses engaged in activities that look like general nursing. Furthermore, general hospitals are prone to refuse admission to such wards of patients who are grossly disturbed or who appear to be poor risks. To this observation may be added another: Taking the most promising material—the acutely ill patient—the psychiatric ward in the general hospital sees that patients receive symptomatic treatment immediately and, with the abatement of symptoms, discharges these patients, though with no assurance that the recovery will continue. As a result, sooner or later some of these patients, along with other more chronic cases, are funneled into the community mental hospitals. The World Health Organization suggests that these problems might be avoided if the psychiatric staff of the community mental hospital were made responsible for the psychiatric wards in the general hospitals, so that the two activities could be integrated and neither operated to the detriment of the other. In this country this probably is not feasible at present, but a closer cooperation between the staff of the mental hospital and the psychiatrists in charge of the wards in the general hospital is certainly highly desirable.

The direction in which psychiatric thought and research is presently moving gives every indication that the mental hospital will have to extend the scope of its services. Before this can be done, a great deal of work will have to be accomplished. Learning to manipulate group forces will be a fundamental step in mental hospital improvement. Improvement will also come from the assumption of greater medical responsibility for the relief and control of irreversible disorders. Effective individualized treatment will have to be pursued, not only as early as possible, but also as continuously as possible.

In general, then, the mental hospital of the future will have to keep abreast of technological advances, while pursuing a judicious course between extremes. It should be a center of research in psychiatry and constantly alert to its opportunities to contribute to medical progress. Definite plans must be formulated now and aggressive work accomplished. Hospital administrators will in the future be constrained to abandon the rigidity of organization, so familiar in the past, which has been shown to hamper therapeutic effort.

Community Service

Nationwide there is a growing appreciation of the need for more community service clinics, guidance centers, and general hospital outpatient, as well as inpatient, facilities. Providing such services will necessarily do much to shorten the duration of severe mental illness. For many years psychiatry has emphasized the value of early diagnosis and early treatment. With further public education and with the provision of community facilities for early treatment and for rehabilitation following short-term hospital treatment, patients and families will be more inclined to seek help early rather than late. Despite the fact that with modern treatment methods even patients with long-standing illnesses are being helped, sometimes to the point of social remission, it is in the early stages of illness that the most effective treatment can be given with the best outlook for future stability. Brief hospitalization is desirable for reasons other than economy and lightening the load of the mental hospital; we have already touched upon some of them.

Gradually, as the size of the large state hospitals decreases, the upsurge in the small branch mental institutions, which, though they are annexes to the state hospital, are closely related to the local medical center, will increase. Such a mental hospital would be much like any other community hospital, and the community's acceptance and support would be more readily forthcoming. To such a branch or daughter hospital would accrue the advantages of the community's social agencies. Its close proximity to the local medical center would make unnecessary the expensive duplication of certain diagnostic, treatment, and surgical facilities and would exclude the dissipation of psychiatric effort on medical problems which ought to be handled by other physicians. Always, however, while these transitions are taking place, the patients who still remain in the state hospitals will have to be kept in mind and, in the newly found interest in daughter hospitals, those who remain in the old institutions must not be regarded as second-class citizens.

New Developments

One can safely predict the rise of day and night hospitals and the increased utilization of the so-called intermediate or halfway houses. The day care center is the logical development for mental hospitals after outpatient departments. Only when a patient cannot be handled on an outpatient level with the help of day care will it be necessary to resort to 24-hour hospitalization. These facilities should also be available to patients after discharge from the mental hospital. The policy of brief hospitalization cannot be expected to "pay off" unless the patient is able to maintain his gains in the community. It is essential, therefore, that he be prepared throughout the period of hospitalization for the problems he will meet when he recovers and, equally important, that the family and the community be prepared for the return of the convalescent individual. There is little use in giving the patient the advantage of the best in rehabilitation procedures if the family or the community will not receive him when he recovers. To slight the returning patient, to denigrate him, to render him unwelcome is to cause him to regress and even to prefer the mental hospital to the community which rejects him. Hence, the need for a variety of rehabilitation facilities in the community—halfway houses, foster home care, day and night hospitals, sheltered workshops, outpatient clinics, and, above all, people and places within the community where patients can turn for help when they need it.

In the future there necessarily will be greater provision for emergency psychiatric service in the community. Some of it may follow the pattern used in Amsterdam, where a psychiatrist is available twenty-four hours a day to go into the home of the family which calls for help, in order to supply whatever emotional assistance is needed or to determine whether or not hospital care is indicated. If it should be, then the doctor solicits the patient's cooperation to this end. A more extensive effort will probably be along lines already apparent—the provision of psychiatric emergency service in the community psychiatric clinic and the general hospital. This is obviously of prime importance. Treatment at the moment of crisis often pays off more than at any time thereafter, and it may even prevent a serious long-term illness. The psychiatric clinic should be made flexible enough to handle emergencies as they arise on a 24-hour basis, flexible enough also to permit follow-up care so that the patient-doctor relationship may be maintained, even if briefly and intermittently.

In one way this change of emphasis will be of help to the psychiatrist, for it will bring him closer to people at a time when medicine in general seems to be moving away from them. This is indeed important, for, as the social psychologists remind us, when the family doctor had only a home practice, he was beloved, adopted by the family, almost as a member—a trusted one—a veritable "Dutch uncle." When he moved out of the home and took more of his practice to his office, the relationship became a little more formal. Now that much of the medical practice is in the hospital, the patient's needs are cared for by a number of people. The practice of medicine thus has become fragmented, and with it the doctor-patient relationship has become fragmented also. This is part of the price the doctor has paid for his scientific advancement. All of this has taken its toll, and now it is common knowledge that the physician has dropped a notch in the affection of the people. He is no longer the beloved figure that he was; it is much easier to criticize him and, incidentally, in the future it may be much easier to regiment him.

Quite evidently, then, there is today a widespread effort to rise above the difficulties which always militated against the recovery of psychiatric patients, and in this lies hope for the future. Therapeutic advances have come rapidly in the last twenty-five years, and more can be expected. Undoubtedly biochemistry and pharmacology will contribute further of their leaven. All of these factors, together with other technological advances—the fruits of research—should contribute to the eventual decline of the population of large mental hospitals. Whether further understanding of the functional psychoses will be our good fortune, it is not possible to foresee. Though physical agents are available to control the symptoms in many instances, no physical cause for them has been uncovered, despite assiduous exploration of innumerable paths and bypaths. It is felt by many that a purely mental conception of these psychoses will yield the greatest harvest. In any event, we can look forward to clinical advances in both somatic and psychotherapeutic treatment, either of which or a combination of which should reduce the number of patients incarcerated. Hopefully, also, we will find a way to cut down the great human waste which abandonment of our older group to idleness and dependency brings in its wake.

The Future of Drug Therapy

It has been established that drugs are first-aid measures and that they do not really solve problems of emotional illness. Tranquility, in the last analysis, is achieved only through an emotional balance within the individual himself, and can be acquired neither from a drug nor from relief from the vicissitudes of everyday life. It is the person who is willing to accept the daily jolts and insecurities and to solve his problems who will attain a measure of tranquility.

There is a great temptation, in dealing with the vexing problems of the human mind, to seize upon anything that will facilitate treatment, provide a short cut, enable us to spread, however thinly, our meager resources in professional manpower and auxiliary personnel. Of all approaches, of course, drugs seem to be the most convenient, the least time-consuming, the most in line with medical practice itself, if one assumes that medical practice is largely concerned with introducing things into the human organism to relieve pain and combat intruding elements, or of removing something the organism itself has formed out of its own tissues or humors which is not to its benefit. We have tried these two expedients before in psychiatry. Today we are trying only one of them; we are introducing a variety of things into the organism in the attempt to relieve our patients. On the whole we are not removing organs; the days of purging and bleeding, of the removal of hypothetical foci of infection, in psychiatric practice are gone—we hope for good—though in view of the way history repeats itself, variants of these unfortunate and uncomfortable activities may come to the fore again. At the present time, however, all the psychiatrist desires to remove is psychological material, patterns and forces which he believes to be harmful to the patient. But that is another story.

It is natural, of course, for man to try to escape difficulties and to avoid unpleasantness, and it is not unusual for him to seek refuge in some *ersatz* which will help him forget that he is a limited creature. The medical profession, however, has an age-old admonition: abstain from whatever is deleterious and mischievous. The physicians of old recognized many important phenomena in the use of drugs which we keep rediscovering: that there is a time to medicate and a time to stay one's hand; that drug effects may be purely fortuitous; that the same drug in different patients, or in the same patient at different times, may have dissimilar and even contrary effects; that substances with apparently opposite properties may at times bring about the same results. To these perennial problems the physician must continue to address himself.

It is probable that one of the most immediate advances in drug therapy will be in the category of anti-depressant drugs, for it appears that the chemists will be able to increase the stimulating effects and reduce the side reactions of these agents. In the meantime, the tranquilizers will be improved and will find their greatest value in hospital psychiatric practice. No matter how much improved these drugs may eventually be, however, they will not be the final answer to treatment; that will still rest in the hands and the efforts of a wise, dedicated physician.

A former president of the American Medical Association said: "The people should learn that there are no final answers in medicine. The sensation of today may be forgotten tomorrow. Out of conflicts and opinions, through discussions and by careful experimentation, certain generally accepted truths emerge. They should know that medicine advances slowly and painfully toward the goal it always seeks but has not yet reached. They should learn again of the great advantages in attaching themselves to a personal physician and of trusting him and relying upon him to guide them through the maze of scientific wilderness, rather than entering this wilderness without a guide."[2] This is excellent advice, for it will prevent the individual from the injudicious use of new and untried nostrums. It has been said that the man who has himself for a doctor has a fool for a patient, and this axiom nowhere demonstrates itself as forcibly as it does in the use and abuse of drugs.

The Report of the Joint Commission on Mental Illness and Health

The Mental Health Study Act, passed by Congress in 1955, directed the Joint Commission on Mental Illness and Health, a group of experts from all segments of the psychiatric and psychologic disciplines, to analyze and evaluate the needs

[2] Martin, W., "The Art and Science of Medicine," *Texas Reports on Biology and Medicine*, Vol. 13, No. 4 (Winter 1955).

and resources of the mentally ill and make recommendations for a national mental health program. In its final report[3] this commission tried to arrive at a program that would approach adequacy in meeting the needs of the mentally ill and to develop a plan of action, for it recognized that the efforts made thus far had been neither intensive nor sustained. In addition to recommending that a larger proportion of total funds for mental health research should be invested in basic research, this group suggested that greater allocations of money should be made for venture or risk capital in support of persons and ideas in the mental health research area. They suggested also that the federal government should support the establishment of mental health research centers or institutes operated in collaboration with educational institutions or training centers, or even independently. In order to make better use of present knowledge and experience, several policy recommendations were made, and, though we have alluded to some of them in other parts of this work, we mention them again because of the importance of this report for the future of psychiatry, especially for the decade ahead. The plans envisaged in the report have led to its being called the Magna Carta of the mentally ill.

Recommendations

1) That the mental health professions should adopt and practice a broad, liberal philosophy of what constitutes treatment and who may do it within the framework of their hospitals, clinics, and other professional service agencies. They defined "who might do what" by way of treatment in reasonable detail, reserving the psychoses and various forms of medical and "depth psychological" therapy for accredited practitioners, and suggesting that others who undertake the more minor roles do so under the auspices of recognized mental health agencies.

2) That mental health professions need to launch a national manpower recruitment and training program, expand-

[3] "Digest of Action for Mental Health," *Final Report of Joint Commission on Mental Illness and Health,* released March 24, 1961.

ing upon and extending present efforts and seeking to stimulate the interest of American youth in mental health work as
a career.

3) They advocate that persons who are emotionally disturbed, i.e. those who are under psychological stress that they
cannot tolerate, should have skilled attention and helpful
counseling available to them *in their community*. This means
that they shall have expert care at the earliest beginnings of
their illnesses.

4) Immediate professional attention should be provided
in the community for persons at the onset of acutely disturbed,
socially disruptive, or personally catastrophic behavior—that
is, for persons undergoing a major breakdown.

5) It should be recognized that major mental illness is the
core problem and unfinished business of the mental health
movement, and that acutely ill patients should have first call
upon fully trained members of the mental health professions.
There is a need for expanding treatment of such patients in
all directions via community mental health clinics, general
hospitals, and mental hospitals as rapidly as personnel to
man these agencies becomes available.

Closely associated with this latter recommendation is the
one which suggests that small state hospitals of 1,000 beds or
less, and suitably located for regional service, should be converted as rapidly as possible into intensive treatment centers
for patients with major mental illnesses in the acute stage or
with a good prospect for improvement or recovery if the illness is more prolonged. All new state hospital construction
should be devoted to these smaller intensive treatment centers.

6) The commission advises that no further state hospitals
of more than 1,000 beds should be built; that not one patient
should be added to any existing mental hospital already
housing 1,000 or more patients; and that existing large state
hospitals be gradually and progressively converted into centers for the long-term combined care of persons with chronic
diseases, including mental illness. This conversion should be
undertaken within the next ten years.

7) The objective of modern treatment of persons with major mental illness is to enable the patient to maintain himself in the community in a normal manner. To do so it is necessary (a) to save the patient from the debilitating effects of institutionalization as much as possible; (b) if the patient requires hospitalization, to return him to home and community life as soon as possible; and (c) thereafter to maintain him in the community as long as possible. All after-care and rehabilitative methods and agencies should be integrated, among them the day hospital, foster family care, etc.

It is obvious that this program has vast connotations in both the professional and economic spheres. It is a bold, humane program, however, and its implementation is necessary if the mentally ill are to have their just due.

The New Era

The report of the Joint Commission thus enumerates some of the changes which we can envision; they are but part of the vast overall changes which lie before psychiatry and all of the sciences. In view of the infinity of things to be discovered, clarified, and understood on this earth, new questions always arise in the wake of each advance; never is a need supplied but another springs up to replace it. The new intellectual era on which we are embarked, with all of its promise and all of its danger, will affect every aspect of our lives—economic, social, medical, psychological, and spiritual. Each discipline will be searched for the segment it can contribute to an overall science of man which will enable him to realize all of his potentialities. But we will have to keep in mind the fact that, while we search for ever more specialized and rigorously proven knowledge, the whole man cannot be served by a viewpoint which in any way might tend to depersonalize him or to deprive his existence of its real meaning. And while we seek to solve our common problems, we will have to be wary of the temptations to find a facile peace in an overadjustment which attempts to fit all men into a common denominator as cooperative, submitting members of the herd. Our sciences will have to be wed to wisdom and common sense.

It is clear also to everyone who thinks about it that, as science continues to thrust forward more and more rapidly on ever widening fronts, our lives and all our institutions will be profoundly affected by the changes to come. Our political and economic forms, our social patterns, our academic institutions and media of communications will all be subjected to stress and remolding. We have tried to forecast some of the directions which the care and cure of the mentally ill will take. We have surveyed not only the new currents which are affecting modes of therapy and the organization of medical institutions, but also the new attitudes towards and new ways of thinking about mental illness itself. All along it has been near the heart of our purpose to address ourselves to the role that religion has to play in the events which are to come.

Religion cannot stand apart, concerned only with other-worldly hopes as mankind proceeds into new areas of worldly conquest. At the head of this chapter we cited the words of Pope Pius XII, optimistically looking ahead into the coming decades: "Mankind is entering one of the most beautiful springtimes the world has ever known, a spring marked by a great awakening and development in all fields of human life." The Pontiff was by no means willing to grant that this springtime would belong to the secularists alone. "The future belongs to believers and not to skeptics and doubters. The future belongs to those who love, not to those who hate."[4] For religious people who are perhaps overly concerned by the forms of the past he made himself equally clear: "No, there cannot be for the Church, whose steps God directs and accompanies through the ages, there cannot be for the human soul, who studies history in the spirit of Christ, any going back, but only desire to go forward toward the future and to mount upwards."[5] ". . . tradition is something entirely different from mere attachment to an irretrievable past. It is exactly the opposite of reaction against all healthy progress. . . . While progress means but the mere fact of marching

[4] "On the Problems and Dangers of Our Day," *The Catholic Mind*, June 1947.

[5] "Plea to Warring Nations," *The Catholic Mind*, May 13, 1942.

forward step by step, looking into an uncertain future, tradition conveys the idea of an uninterrupted march forward, which progresses serenely and in a vital manner in accordance with the laws of life."[6] In these and in many other similar words, the Pope aligned religion with the forward-moving, constructive forces of healthy progress in all the arts and sciences and envisioned religion as leading and guiding the whole movement.

In religion itself there are signs of new awakenings. Various influences are at work, reviewing and shaping the forms of religious endeavor; there is talk of unity and greater understanding between all religious groups; the laity are being charged with greater responsibilities. For us to keep abreast of all these changes requires preparation, for it will be incumbent on all, in accordance with the talents he has received, not only to teach what he knows but to strive to learn what he does not yet know.

Christian Humanism

In his presidential address to the American Psychiatric Association in 1957 one of the present authors stressed several points about the future orientation of psychiatry. First, there is the need for psychiatry to become a humanistic discipline, an essential part of the overall science of man. Second, psychiatry must avoid the belief that any one school of therapy and theory can provide all the answers to the questions which still perplex us. Third, the ideal of psychiatry should be to achieve wisdom over and above the circumscribed knowledge the science now affords.

Apparently there was some mild misunderstanding of this advice, probably because the word "humanism" was misunderstood. Dr. Michael F. Maloney tells us that the substantive "humanism," without qualification, has connoted since the eighteenth century an unrelieved secularism.[7] It is obvious, however, that the humanism which we advocated was not

[6] "On Tradition," *The London Tablet*, January 19, 1944.
[7] Maloney, M. F., "Christian Humanism—Past History and Current Relevance," *Spiritual Life*, Vol. 4, No. 4 (December 1958).

of this type, but rather was a "Christian humanism." The basic idea of this type of humanism was expressed well by Father Steinmetz: "Man must complete his nature by harmoniously developing all of his faculties and capabilities and so unify the complexity which he discovers within himself."[8] It has been the mark of the Christian humanist through the ages that he employs profane learning as a preface to sacred aspirations; "first the natural, then the supernatural, rightly understood, is a profound spiritual maxim."[9] This is a particularly important maxim, not only for psychiatrists, but for everyone in this present age. As Maloney uses the term, the Christian humanist is one who seeks to develop all his natural powers, but more specifically in this context, his intellectual powers, and develop them to the highest degree of which he is capable. Here is a goal for modern man to point to, but, as he aspires to perfection, this term is not to be understood as restricted solely to moral conduct. It has to be taken literally, as indicating the maximum of total actualization that can be attained. The responsibility of the educated Christian was never heavier than it is today. As Bacon pointed out, the power of man is commensurate with his knowledge, and he advised that we have our fuel prepared, for it is hard to tell when the spark will come that will set it afire.

The pursuit of wisdom will challenge the practitioner of psychiatry as well as his fellow men in the new era, and a dedication to excellence in the pursuit of new knowledge will have to be encouraged. It will be a difficult task to overcome some of the anti-intellectualism and pious rationalization that cover intellectual laziness, but using to the fullest extent our God-given intellects will be necessary if we are to fulfill our destinies.

If psychiatry is to advance and fulfill its function, the believer will have to learn assiduously the elusive and sensitive art of handling new ideas. Undoubtedly the greatest obstacle to our progress thus far in our search for new ideas is fear, a fear which can, on occasion, disguise itself as caution or

[8] Steinmetz, P. B., S.J., "The Frontier Days of the Human Spirit," *Spiritual Life*, Vol. 4, No. 4 (December 1958).
[9] *Ibid.*

prudence or even as courage. It is said frequently, rightly or wrongly, that the psychiatrist who has a religious background is fearful, protective, and hesitant to embark upon new adventures or accept new ideas. If this is true, then disaster lies ahead. Mind you, this is not to advocate the swallowing whole of any new or untried concept which is presented to us, nor is it to advocate a frenzy to maintain an *entente cordiale* between faith and any innovation which comes along, but it is our task to carefully examine and weigh all new ideas. Thomas F. O'Dea tells us:

> In a very real sense the Catholic has no choice as to whether he shall enter or remain aloof from the whole range of culture and knowledge. The world is God's handiwork and, since He has given man the capacity to do it, He must intend man to study it and to grow in the dominion of it, to push further back the horizon of what he can know about the macrocosm and the microcosm, hearing always the voice of Aquinas reminding him that every truth, without exception and whoever may utter it, is from the Holy Ghost.[10]

Emotional maturity is attained when one conducts himself in unselfish adult fashion and can be depended upon to perform in a manner commensurate with his age and education. Maturity is attained when one is able to face the unknown with some equanimity. The quest for knowledge necessarily involves risk, and risk will always be the object of admiration and fear. Yet, as we worship God and seek out His handiwork, we cannot always be assured of safety; rather we undertake adventure of the spirit.

The believer, whether he be psychiatrist or layman, cannot remain alienated from the intellectual life, nor can he retreat into his own safe formulae and remain aloof from what goes on around him. The Church is not provincial nor backward, and frequently the distorted view which is presented to the world by the fearful, purporting to be Christianity, is, according to O'Dea, due to the individual's lack of knowledge of the

[10] O'Dea, T. F., *American Catholic Dilemma* (New York: Sheed & Ward), p. 48.

subject and dependence upon his own social and economic background and prejudices.[11] If you would have proof of this, just think about the reception which new ideas received in the past as they were presented to the world, and think of the opposition to all of them that we mentioned. Remember that Aquinas was considered by some to be a dangerous innovator and an extremist, and remember, too, that there will always be batrachians who will croak idly by the stream.

One thing the believing psychiatrist must avoid entirely is any hint of defensiveness and negativism, which is so characteristic of those who maintian a state-of-siege mentality. To acquire the tag of "reactionary group," opposed to everything except verbalism and formalism, is particularly easy. One large medical society, rather unjustly, has acquired this reputation, and it reacts to its detriment. Any such attitude as this will limit our usefulness. Such defensiveness results from the refusal to face frankly and honestly the great potentialities of our growth in the psychological and the intellectual sense because of fear.

Some Needs for the Future

Father George H. Tavard observed that, though theology is, in the customary phrase, "Queen of the Sciences," this does not imply that she should stand aloof, like an unapproachable sovereign. On the contrary, she needs the services of all the sciences.[12] "Our present century," he says, "ought to be favorable to this brotherhood of faith and science. For the current emphasis on psychology and sociology has reversed interest in man as a field of investigation; and man is much closer an image of God than nature is. If the Church's mystical tradition has not been afraid of comparing divine love to human love, it would seem that the Christian understanding of man should not now fight shy of depth psychology. Psychoanalysts have emphasized aspects of the soul, of which mystical authors have long been aware. This field remains largely unexplored by modern Catholics. Yet, it obviously provides

11 *Ibid.*
12 Tavard, G. H., A.A., "The Intellect and the Spiritual Life," *Spiritual Life,* September 1959.

a standpoint from which a Christian, reading of the book of the soul, may be developed today."

Father Gustav Weigel assures us that the war had one good consequence: "It clearly indicated the sovereignty of psychiatry in its own field of endeavor."[13] "Other fields of human concern," he states, "are not imperiled by the autonomy of psychiatry, which is not imperialistic, but quite content to stay within its own bounds."

With these various assurances we can now face up to the more practical implications of the matters we have been discussing. Our overall purpose has been to present psychiatry to the interested reader in a way which will enable him to appreciate its dimensions so that he can respond intelligently whenever an issue with a psychiatric aspect presents itself. Our more specialized purpose has been to enlist the understanding and cooperation of all those who are engaged in religious activities, for it is our belief that issues with psychiatric aspects do present themselves to this group with exceptional frequency and cogency. As a consequence, a clear and sound judgment on psychiatry as a whole seems particularly important for those who deal with men's souls and spirits and should be provided for them during the time when they are forming their basic outlook on things. This means that psychiatry, at least in its general principles and broad outlines, should be introduced into the major seminaries, not to make professional psychiatrists out of the students there, but to give them a deep and solid orientation toward an area of science which will impinge closely on almost all the other areas they will study.

Furthermore, in order to meet the numerous demands which are made and will continue to be made upon psychiatry itself, there is an urgent need for additional special professorships to be set up in medical schools and universities throughout the country. These professorships should be held by men whose task it is to study and to integrate and to bring up to date the various bits of psychiatric knowledge which

[13] Weigel, G., S.J., "The Challenge of Peace," *Pastoral Psychology*, February 1959, p. 29.

are being gleaned from our researches. They should try to collate information from philosophy, theology, sociology, and anthropology. The individuals who occupy these particular chairs should not be overwhelmed with heavy teaching schedules, nor should they have to rely on private practices in order to support themselves or their families. Rather, the tasks of these men should be those of scholars, collators, and coordinators. Necessarily, these chairs will have to be endowed, for the individual should be paid enough to render it unnecessary for him to be concerned about outside interests. Where are these funds to come from? From benefactors. Funds are collected for other projects which do not hold nearly as much promise. It is only now that we are arriving at the point where we can appeal for benefactions of this kind.

Finally, it is obvious to us that there is a great dignity in the calling of the modern scientist. It is his task to unfold the wonders of nature; whether on earth or in space, he can only find what God has put there, and God is neither a tinkerer nor a small-volt engineer. What He has done is vast, and the scientists have only begun to fathom its depths. Therefore, courage, humility, and the search for truth must be the order of the day for all who are concerned, be they religious or lay.

EPILOGUE

Since this volume was finished and was on press, many of the things predicted in the last chapter have come to pass. Certainly their beginnings became visible with the delivery of the message of the President of the United States to the Congress on February 5, 1963. The message concerned itself with mental illness and mental retardation and in it he made an appeal for an all-out attack upon both scourges. In speaking of them he said:

> This situation has been tolerated far too long. It has troubled our national conscience—but only as a problem unpleasant to mention, easy to postpone and despairing of solution. The federal government, despite the nationwide impact of the problem, has largely left the solution up to the states. The states have depended upon custodial hospitals and homes. Many such hospitals and homes have been shamefully understaffed, overcrowded, unpleasant institutions from which death too often provided the only firm hope of release.

> The time has come for a bold new approach. New medical, scientific and social tools are in sight and now available . . .

Since the delivery of this message the Congress has reacted by proposing bills to build comprehensive mental health centers and to help the communities pay for the personnel to staff them, and various other encouraging signs and events have occurred. It is devoutly to be hoped that this excellent beginning will forecast a new era for the mentally ill and the mentally retarded.

GLOSSARY

Note: Many of these terms are explained in the text but are added here for the sake of easy reference.

ABREACTION. A phenomenon characterized by an intense emotional outburst occasioned by the recall of some stressful experience which had been hitherto repressed from consciousness. Abreaction often has a therapeutic effect since painful emotions are released and the person can gain insight into the experience and learn to tolerate it.

AFFECT. Emotion; a quality of feeling; a feeling tone.

AMBIVALENCE. A mixed attitude or orientation towards some person or thing, e.g. love and hate towards one person. One or both aspects of this mixed attitude may be wholly or partly unconscious.

AMNESIA. A pathologic loss of memory. Unlike simple forgetting, amnesia is a condition in which the recollection of a period of past experiences is obstructed by an organic injury or emotional conflict.

ANOXEMIA. Lack of oxygen in the blood.

ANXIETY. An emotional state of fearfulness or uneasiness. Psychiatrically, anxiety is used to designate those fears whose source is from within the psychic makeup of the individual, e.g. fear of one's own sexual impulses, and is largely unknown or unrecognized. Anxiety is considered pathologic when it is intense enough to interfere with effective and satisfying living. Anxiety is a general characteristic of the neuroses.

Acknowledgment is made of *A Psychiatric Glossary*, American Psychiatric Association, as the source of description of some of these terms.

AUTISM *(autistic thinking)*. A mode of thinking which is motivated by the desire to gratify unfulfilled urges rather than by the need to understand reality as it is. Objective facts are ignored or distorted in favor of wish fulfillment.

AUTOEROTICISM. Securing or attempting to secure sensual gratification from oneself. A characteristic of an early stage of emotional development.

AUTONOMIC NERVOUS SYSTEM. That part of the nervous system which controls basic life-preserving functions such as breathing, heart rate, and digestion. It is not subject to voluntary control and operates unconsciously.

CATATONIA. A type of schizophrenia characterized by immobility with muscular rigidity or inflexibility. Alternating periods of physical hyperactivity and excitability may occur, and generally there is marked inaccessibility to ordinary methods of communication. *See also* SCHIZOPHRENIA.

CATHARSIS. Healthful release of ideas and feelings by talking out of repressed ideas, accompanied by suitable emotional reaction.

CENSOR. In psychoanalytic theory, a part of the unconscious self (i.e. the superego and parts of the ego) which functions as a guardian to prevent the emergence of repressed material into consciousness.

COMPLEX. A group of ideas and images which have become closely associated in the mind, and which have a strong common emotional tone. The complex may be wholly or partly unconscious, and can significantly influence attitudes and behavior.

CONDENSATION. A spontaneous psychologic process often present in dreams in which two or more concepts and/or images are fused into a single symbol representing the several components.

CONVERSION. A psychological process operating unconsciously by which psychic conflicts, which would otherwise give rise to anxiety, are instead given symbolic expression in a variety of somatic symptoms. Example: paralysis of a limb which prevents its use for aggressive purposes.

DEFENSE MECHANISM. Specific psychological processes, operating unconsciously, which act in such a way as to resolve emotional conflicts and avert anxiety. Some common defense mechanisms are: repression, compensation, conversion, displacement, dissociation, identification, introjection, projection, rationalization, reaction formation, regression, and symbolization.

DELUSION. A false belief out of keeping with the individual's level of knowledge and his cultural group. The belief is maintained against logical argument and despite objective contradictory evidence. Common delusions include:

Delusions of grandeur. Exaggerated ideas of one's importance or identity.

Delusions of persecution. Ideas that one has been singled out for persecution. *See also* PARANOIA.

Delusions of reference. Incorrect assumption that certain casual or unrelated remarks or the behavior of others apply to oneself.

A delusional system is a set of false beliefs more or less logically consistent with each other, although the totality is out of touch with reality.

DEMENTIA. Term formerly denoting madness; now used to indicate loss of intellectual power due to organic disease.

DEMENTIA PRAECOX. Obsolescent term for schizophrenia.

DEPRESSION. Psychiatrically, a morbid sadness, dejection, or melancholy; to be differentiated from grief, which is realistic and proportionate to what has been lost. A depression may vary in depth from neurosis to psychosis.

DISORIENTATION. Loss of appreciation of relationship of self to time, place, and other persons.

DISPLACEMENT. A mental mechanism, operating unconsciously, in which an emotion is transferred or "displaced" from the object which originally aroused it to some substitute object which is for some reason more acceptable.

DISSOCIATION. A defense mechanism which involves unconscious and automatic separation or splitting up of psychic processes. For example, the emotional significance and affect may be separated from an idea, situation, or object, or a part of mental experience may be blocked off, as in selective amnesia.

DISTRIBUTIVE ANALYSIS. Guided and directed investigation and analysis of the patient's entire past, especially stressing his assets and liabilities, leading to a constructive synthesis; therapy used by the school of Adolf Meyer.

DYNAMIC. Having the nature of movement, force, energy.

DYNAMICS. The study of the development of emotional and behavioral patterns; the mechanisms of the development of emotional reactions, especially intrapsychic defense mechanisms.

DYNAMIC PSYCHIATRY. Psychiatry oriented toward the study of emotional processes, intrapsychic forces and structures, their origins and modes of growth and change, of progress and regression. As distinguished from descriptive psychiatry, which is oriented more towards a static and descriptive study of clinical patterns, symptoms, and classifications.

EGO. Refers to the conscious self, the "I." In Freudian theory the part of the personality which deals consciously with reality and controls active behavior. The ego's function is to find ways to satisfy the instinctual impulses arising from the id without transgressing the restrictions imposed by the superego, while at the same time it operates within the framework of opportunity and limitation set by external reality.

EGOCENTRIC. Self-centered; all or most ideas centered about oneself.

EMPATHY. An objective and insightful awareness of the feelings, emotions, and behavior of another person, and their meaning and significance. To be distinguished from sympathy, which is non-objective and usually non-critically emotional.

EPILEPSY. A disorder characterized by periodic motor or sensory seizures or their equivalents, and sometimes accompanied by a loss of consciousness, or by certain equivalent manifestations.

EPINEPHRINE. Active principle of the medullary portion of the adrenal glands—prepared synthetically.

ETIOLOGY. The causes which underlie and determine an event or thing; the science of these causes.

EUPHORIA. An exaggerated feeling of physical and emotional well-being which is out of proportion to the apparent causes; usually of psychologic origin, but also seen in organic brain disease and toxic states.

FANTASY. A sequence of imaginary events and mental images. Fantasy is normal in children, but in adults excessive fantasy may indicate an attempt to avoid emotional conflicts by providing substitute satisfaction.

FORENSIC PSYCHIATRY. Legal psychiatry.

FREE ASSOCIATION. The spontaneous flow of interconnected ideas and images through the mind which occurs when voluntary control and direction of thought are relaxed. In psychoanalytic therapy the patient reports the contents brought to mind by free association fully and unreservedly.

GUILT. The state of one who has violated a law; a special kind of anxiety which is caused by the perception of a failure to live up to an ideal or the consciousness of the transgression of a norm of conduct. A major concern of psychiatry is to distinguish the reasonable sense of guilt from excessive or irrational guilt feelings.

HALLUCINATION. An apparent but false sense perception occurring in the absence of an objective stimulus. May be of emotional origin or may be caused by drugs, and may occur in any of the five senses.

HEBEPHRENIA. A type of schizophrenia characterized by silly and childish behavior and shallow, inappropriate emotions.

HOMEOSTASIS. A tendency to uniformity or stability in the normal body states.

HYDROTHERAPY. The use of water in treating disease.

HYPERTENSION. Abnormally high tension, especially high blood pressure.

HYPNOSIS. A state of partial impairment of conscious awareness in which the subject is readily susceptible to suggestion and direction from the hypnotist.

HYPOCHONDRIA. A neurotic condition in which a person displays a persistent and exaggerated concern over bodily and emotional health, and complains of illnesses which cannot be verified by physical examination.

HYSTERIA. A neurotic illness resulting from emotional conflict and generally characterized by immaturity, impulsiveness, attention-seeking, dependency, and the use of the defense mechanisms of conversion and dissociation. Classically manifested by dramatic physical symptoms involving the voluntary muscles or the organs of special senses.

ID. In Freudian theory that part of the personality structure in which the unconscious instinctual drives take their origin and in which repressed materials, e.g. complexes, are harbored.

IDEAS OF REFERENCE. Incorrect interpretation of casual incidents and external events as having direct reference to oneself. May reach sufficient intensity to constitute delusions.

IDENTIFICATION. A mental mechanism, operating unconsciously, by which an individual endeavors to pattern himself after another. Identification plays a major role in the development of one's personality and, specifically, of one's superego. When done consciously, this is called imitation.

INCORPORATION. A primitive mental "mechanism," operating unconsciously, in which a person is symbolically "ingested," assimilated, and imitated.

INHIBITION. A spontaneous and unconscious mental blocking off or turning aside of the expression of an instinctual drive.

INTROJECTION. A mental mechanism, operating unconsciously, whereby loved or hated external objects are taken within oneself symbolically. The converse of *projection*. The process of introjection may serve as a defense against conscious recognition of intolerable hostile impulses. For example, in severe depression, the individual may unconsciously direct unacceptable hatred or aggression toward himself, i.e. towards the introjected object within himself.

INVOLUTIONAL PSYCHOSIS. A psychotic reaction taking place during the involutional period, climacteric (male) or menopause (female), characterized most commonly by depression and occasionally by paranoid thinking. The course of the illness tends to be prolonged; symptoms may include guilt feelings, anxiety, agitation, delusional ideas, insomnia, and preoccupation with the body.

LABILITY. A condition of rapidly shifting emotion.

LIBIDO. The psychic drive or energy usually associated with the sexual instinct. (Sexual is used here in the broad sense to include pleasure and love-object seeking.) Also used broadly to connote the psychic energy associated with instincts in general.

MANIA. A mental illness marked by heightened excitability, acceleration of thought, speech, and bodily motion, and by elation or grandiosity of mood.

MANIC-DEPRESSIVE PSYCHOSIS. A major emotional illness marked by severe mood swings (elation-depression) and a tendency to remission and recurrence.

> *Depressed type.* Characterized by depression of mood with retardation and inhibition of thinking and physical activity.

> *Manic type.* Characterized by elation, with overtalkativeness, extremely rapid ideation, and increased motor activity.

MELANCHOLY. Pathologic dejection and sadness, usually of psychotic depth.

MENTAL MECHANISM. *See* DEFENSE MECHANISM.

METABOLIC. Pertaining to physical and chemical processes by which the living organism is produced and maintained; processes by which energy is made.

MIND. The sum of all the activities termed psychological and their seat or subject. Includes activities such as thinking, willing, wanting, feeling, and perceiving as well as their products: concepts, images, urges, etc. Not limited to conscious operations.

MUSCULATURE. The muscular apparatus of the body, or any part of it.

NARCISSISM (also NARCISM). Self-love. In a broader sense it indicates a degree of self-interest and self-absorption which is characteristic of childhood but pathologic when found to the same degree in adults.

NARCOANALYSIS. A form of psychotherapy in which the patient's repressed problems are brought into consciousness under the influence of drugs.

NARCOSYNTHESIS. Similar to narcoanalysis but with emphasis on the reconstructive processes which follow up the emergence of repressed materials under the influence of drugs.

NEOLOGISM. In psychiatry, a new word or condensed combination of several words coined by a patient to express a highly complex meaning related to his conflicts; not readily understood by others; common in schizophrenia.

NEUROLOGY. The branch of medical science devoted to the anatomy, physiology, and pathology of the nervous system.

NEUROSES. Emotional maladaptations due to unresolved unconscious conflicts. One of the two major categories of emotional illness, the other being the *psychoses*. A neurosis is usually less severe than a psychosis, with minimal loss of contact with reality. Thinking and judgment may be impaired. A neurotic illness represents the attempted resolution of unconscious emotional conflicts in a manner that handicaps the effectiveness of a person in living. Types of neuroses are usually classified according to the particular symptoms which predominate.

NOSOLOGY. Medical science of the classification of diseases.

OBSESSIVE-COMPULSIVE. Pertaining to a neurotic condition characterized by reaction patterns associated with the intrusion of insistent repetitive and unwanted ideas or of repetitive unwelcome impulses to perform certain acts. Such individuals may feel compelled to carry out certain ritualistic acts such as handwashing, etc.

ORIENTATION. Awareness of oneself in relation to time, place, or person.

PARANOIA. A rare psychiatric disorder, characterized by an intricate and logical system of persecutory or grandiose delusions.

PARANOID. An adjective derived from the noun "paranoia." Ordinarily used to describe either grandiose or persecutory delusions.

PATHOGENIC. Productive of disease.

PEDOPHILIA. A morbid interest in children.

PERSONALITY. The sum of qualities which distinguish and characterize a person.

PHOBIA. A persistent, obsessive, unrealistic fear of an external object or situation, such as fear of dirt, high places, etc. This fear is thought to be displaced to an external object from some internal conflict.

POST-PARTUM PSYCHOSIS. A psychosis following childbirth.

PRIMARY GAIN. Term used in connection with neurotic symptoms. The internal psychological gain which accrues to an individual as a result of his symptoms. Primary gain refers to the element of unconscious gratification provided by the compromise (symptom). *See also* SECONDARY GAIN.

PSYCHE. The mind as distinguished from the soul or body.

PSYCHIATRY. A medical art and science which deals with the origin, prevention, diagnosis, and treatment of mental illness and asocial behavior. It includes also special fields such as mental retardation, psychosomatic medicine, etc.

PSYCHOANALYSIS. A psychologic theory of human development and behavior, originally described by Sigmund Freud. Also a method of research and treatment. It utilizes free association and dream analysis and traces emotional symptoms and behavior to repressed instinctual drives in the unconscious.

PSYCHOGENESIS. Production or causation of a symptom or illness by mental and psychic factors as opposed to organic ones.

PSYCHONOXIOUS. Not wholesome psychically; pernicious.

PSYCHOPATHIC. Antisocial or amoral behavior. Usually manifested by impulsive or irresponsible actions accompanied by minimal presence or complete absence of guilt.

PSYCHOSIS. A severe emotional illness in which there is a departure from normal patterns of thinking, feeling, or acting. A major category of mental illness.

PSYCHOSOMATIC. A term used to indicate the inseparable interaction of psyche (mind) with soma (body). Used to denote illnesses in which symptoms are predominantly physical but which have emotional connotations.

PSYCHOTHERAPY. A type of treatment based on verbal communication with patients, as distinguished from the use of drugs, surgery, etc.

RATIONALIZATION. In psychiatry a mental mechanism operating unconsciously in which the individual attempts to justify, or make consciously tolerable by plausible means, feelings, behavior, and motives which would otherwise be intolerable.

REACTION FORMATION. A mental mechanism operating unconsciously wherein attitudes and behavior are adopted which are the opposite of impulses which the individual disowns either consciously or unconsciously. An example would be a scrupulous overattention to something which an individual would rather neglect.

REGRESSION. The readoption, actually or symbolically, of behavior which was characteristic of a much earlier age, e.g. temper tantrums in an adult.

REMISSION. Abatement of symptoms of an illness. Does not necessarily indicate a cure.

REPRESSION. A mental mechanism operating unconsciously, known as the precursor of all mental mechanisms, in which there is involuntary relegation of unbearable ideas into the unconscious from whence, while they are not subject to voluntary recall, they may emerge in disguised forms through the utilization of one of the various mental mechanisms.

RESISTANCE. In psychiatry the psychologic defenses the individual uses to avoid bringing painful repressed material into awareness in order to avoid the attendant anxiety.

RETARDATION. Slowing down of mental and physical activity, seen often in depressive illnesses; also a synonym for mental deficiency.

SADISM. Pleasure derived from inflicting physical or psychological pain on others. Sexual significance of these wishes may be conscious or unconscious.

SCHIZOPHRENIA. A severe emotional disorder of psychotic depth marked ordinarily by a retreat from reality with delusion formations, hallucinations, emotional disharmony, and regressive behavior. Formerly called dementia praecox.

SECONDARY GAIN. The external gain which is derived from any illness, e.g. attention, service, money, insurance, etc.

SENESCENCE. From senesco (be aged); characteristic of old age. Usually refers to normal aging.

SENSORIUM. Roughly approximates consciousness. Includes the special sensory perceptive powers and their central correlation and integration in the brain.

SOCIAL REMISSION. Abatement of symptoms sufficient to permit a patient to return to a previous social status. Not necessarily a cure. *See also* REMISSION.

SOCIOPATHIC. A person whose behavior is predominantly antisocial or amoral; akin to psychopathic—a more recent term.

SOMATIC. Relating to the soma (body).

SUPEREGO. In Freudian theory that part of the mind which has unconsciously identified itself with important and esteemed persons from early life, particularly parents. The supposed or actual wishes of these persons are taken over as part of one's standards to form a guide for behavior. They may remain anachronistic and overpunitive in some neurotic persons.

SYMBOLIZATION. A mental mechanism operating unconsciously in which a person forms an abstract representation of a particular object, idea, or constellation thereof. The symbol carries in more or less disguised form the emotional feelings vested in the initial object or ideas.

SYNDROMES. A group of symptoms which, taken together, may indicate a recognized illness.

THERAPEUTIC. Curative; pertaining to the art of healing.

TRANSFERENCE. The unconscious attachment to others of feelings and attitudes which were originally associated with important figures (parents, siblings, etc.) in one's early life. The psychiatrist utilizes this transference as a therapeutic tool to help the patient understand his emotional problems and their origin.

TRAUMA. Injury, either physical or psychological.

UNCONSCIOUS. In Freudian theory that part of the mind or mental functioning, the content of which is only rarely subject to awareness. A repository for data which has never been conscious or which may have been conscious briefly and was then repressed.

VOYEURISM. Sexually motivated and often compulsive interest in watching or looking at others, especially the undressed form. Most often found in males. Peeping Tom is the prototype.

Imprimi potest: Very Reverend W. D. Marrin, O.P.
                 Provincial

Nihil obstat: Very Reverend Nicholas F. Halligan, O.P.
               Diocesan Censor Deputatus

Imprimatur:✠Richard Cardinal Cushing
           Archbishop of Boston

November 7, 1962

INDEX

IMAGE BOOKS

Image Books constitute a quality library of Catholic writings, broad in human interest and deep in Christian insight. They will include classical Christian writings, devotion, philosophy, education and history; biographies, novels and poetry; and books on contemporary social problems. They represent a planned program of making available to the widest possible audience the finest Catholic literature in attractive, paper-bound, inexpensive editions. They have been selected with these criteria in mind: that they must in every instance be well written, inspiring to the spirit, and of lasting value to the general audience who will purchase them.

The majority of Image Books will consist of reprints made possible through the cooperation of the publishers of the original editions. Occasionally certain much-needed volumes which are not available will also be initiated for this series.

A descriptive catalogue of the Image Books already published may be obtained by writing directly to the publisher. Comments and suggestions from those interested in the series are welcomed by the publisher. I 3